Improving the Child's Speech

Improving the
Child's Speech

SECOND EDITION

Virgil A. Anderson
Hayes A. Newby

New York   Oxford University Press   1973

Preface to the First Edition

This is primarily a book for the classroom teacher, although it will also prove useful to parents, child-guidance workers, physicians, and others who are concerned with the development and training of children. The majority of individuals who use this book will probably not continue their studies in this field to become specialists in speech correction. Rather, the book is primarily designed for the general teacher, the parent, and others who are interested in children's welfare and who would like to know more about some of the common speech problems of children and what to do for them.

Every effort has been made to prepare a book that would be as practical as possible. The content has been kept simple and the language is non-technical. Ample illustrative material has been included and emphasis has been placed upon practical techniques of diagnosis, prevention, and training as applied to the more common speech problems exhibited by children in the home and school environments. Although the chief emphasis in the book is upon the speech guidance of the younger child, much of the information is equally applicable to older children and even adults in some cases. Speech education as well as re-education has been stressed. Material has been included that can be used to facilitate and improve the speech development of all children, and to prevent the growth of undesirable speech habits and the appearance of more serious speech disorders.

A major objective of this work has been to include both an adequate discussion of fundamental principles, pertinent theory, and general procedures and a sufficient amount and variety of specific techniques, drill materials, and practical suggestions to enable the teacher and parent to deal effectively with such speech problems as it is wise or feasible for them to handle. This plan has been followed on the assumption that an individual who is interested in a child's welfare wants to know something constructive and tangible that he can do to help the child with his problems. It is hoped that the specific procedures explained in this book are sufficiently clear and workable to enable teachers and parents to apply them successfully even though they may have had no previous training in speech education or speech correction.

It is recognized, however, that there are certain hazards inherent in a work of this kind when it becomes either too general and theoretical, on the one hand, or too restricted and specific, on the other. If it remains too general, it is likely to appear vague and confusing to the teacher, who may lack the special experience and training necessary to apply it successfully. On the other hand, if it is too detailed and specific, there is the danger that it may not be sufficiently flexible to be adapted to the many varying problems and situations encountered by teachers in general throughout the country. There is danger, too, of oversimplifying what is often complex and involved.

The author has attempted to steer what he hopes will be a safe course between the two extremes and has included as much as possible of both. In many instances the reader is supplied with the essential materials to work with and is told how to use them. An entire chapter (Chapter XII) is devoted to practical suggestions for implementing the theory and methods explained in earlier chapters and for integrating this training with the regular school curriculum. This chapter especially has been written for the teacher who says, 'Yes, I should like to help my children with their speech problems, but I just don't see how and when I can work it in.' It is hoped that here she will find the answer to her seeming dilemma; she should consult Chapter XII frequently while covering some of the earlier chapters, especially Chapters V, VI, and VII.

The teacher is reminded that the procedures explained in Chapter XII are merely suggestions of what can be done in a given situation. They will doubtless need to be modified somewhat to fit a different situation. They are intended primarily to stimulate the teacher to think of many more similar techniques that she can work out and apply 'on her own.'

Since a wealth of routine corrective exercises and drill materials is readily available in a large number of good books, it seemed a waste of time and space to duplicate too many of them in the present work. Therefore, where additional material is needed beyond what is supplied herein, the teacher is referred to these outside sources, many of which have been listed in the selective references included at the end of each chapter, with the exception of Chapter ɪ. Only those references which the author felt would be readily available to the teacher or parent have been listed and, to facilitate their use, actual pages or chapters in the books have been given in many instances.

Not only has great stress been placed upon the desirability of arming the classroom teacher and the parent with as much information as possible about the simpler speech problems of children, but the author has also attempted to make clear the limitations of superficial training in dealing with serious disorders of such a vital and complicated activity as speech. It is hoped that part of the discipline the reader will get from this book is to learn what not to do in certain situations and where to turn for outside help with those problems that are too serious to be handled by one with a limited background in this field.

Because of the confusion that often results when speech sounds are represented by conventional spelling, the author decided to use phonetic symbols, believing that their accuracy and precision in the identification and representation of sounds would more than offset the slight task of learning to recognize them. Moreover, in many instances the phonetic symbols are supplemented by alphabet letters or key words which help identify the sound or sounds referred to. A complete table of the symbols used, together with identifying key words, will be found as a part of the articulation tests in Chapter ɪɪɪ. All phonetic symbols have been enclosed in brackets, thus [s]. When the symbol is reproduced in italics, as *s*, it is the alphabet symbol that is referred to, rather than the speech sound itself.

The author gratefully acknowledges his indebtedness to his colleague Dr. Hayes A. Newby, who read the entire manuscript and used portions of it experimentally in teaching a course in speech correction for the classroom teacher. From this associa-

tion with the book in embryonic form came a number of constructive suggestions which were incorporated into the final
revision. Dr. Newby is also the author of Chapter xi, which
deals with the problems of the hard-of-hearing child in the
classroom and in the home.

The author is also deeply indebted to Mrs. Ruth Montgom-
ery Jackson, Consultant in Speech Education to the Palo Alto
Unified School System. Mrs. Jackson, who has also had extensive experience as a classroom teacher, read the manuscript and
suggested several modifications to make it more adaptable to
the classroom situation. She also contributed Chapter xii, which
offers many practical suggestions for correlating speech training with a number of subject-matter areas of the regular school
curriculum.

The author wishes to express further appreciation to Dr. Mary
W. Huber, Director of the Speech Clinic, Los Angeles State
College, for her assistance with several phases of the manuscript, but especially for her help in the preparation of Chapter
vii, and to Miss Elvena Miller, Supervisor of Speech Correction
in the Seattle Public Schools, and Dr. Darrel J. Mase, Co-ordi-
nator of the Florida Center of Clinical Services at the University of Florida, for their constructive criticisms following a
careful reading of the entire manuscript during the formative
stages. The author also wishes to thank Dr. Lucie Lawson, Director of the Speech Clinic in Franklin Hospital, San Francisco,
for the many helpful suggestions that came from her reading
of Chapter iv, and several of his colleagues in the Stanford
School of Education for their guidance in the organization of
Chapter i. He is also grateful to Dr. Robert C. McNaught of
the Stanford University School of Medicine for his assistance
in the preparation of Chapter xi.

Last, but by no means least, the author expresses his grati-
tude to his daughter Jeannette for her assistance in the preparation of the drawings illustrating the speech sounds in the
articulation test in Chapter iii, and to his wife Martha for her
forbearance, constant encouragement, and editorial assistance
in the reading of the manuscript.

Stanford University   V. A. A.
April 1953

Preface to the Second Edition

Improving the Child's Speech was originally written primarily for the classroom teacher or the future classroom teacher, although it was also meant to be useful to parents, child-guidance workers, physicians, and others who are concerned with the development and training of children. While information on subsequent use of the book indicates that its principal application has indeed been as a text for courses in speech improvement and correction for classroom teachers, it has also often proved useful as a text for basic, general, or beginning courses in speech correction for general students and for individuals planning or contemplating a career in the field of speech pathology and audiology. In any case, it appears that the original focus of the book was correctly chosen—directed to non-professional persons with little or no background in the field, but who are interested in children's welfare and would like to know more about some of their speech, hearing, and language problems and what to do for them.

With this focus in mind, every effort has been made to prepare a book that would be as practical as possible. The content has been kept simple and the language is non-technical. Ample illustrative material has been included, and emphasis has been placed upon practical aspects of diagnosis, prevention, and remediation as applied to the more common speech and language problems exhibited by children in the home and school environments. Although the chief emphasis in the book is upon the speech and language guidance of the younger child, much of the information is equally applicable to older children and even adults in some cases. Speech education as well as re-education has been stressed. Material has been included that can be used to facilitate and improve the speech and language development of all children, and to prevent the growth of undesirable speech habits and the appearance of more serious communication disorders.

A major objective of this work has been to include both an adequate discussion of fundamental principles, pertinent theory, and general procedures and a sufficient amount and variety of specific techniques, drill materials, and practical suggestions to enable the teacher, and others, to deal effectively with such speech problems as it is wise or feasible for them to handle. This plan has been followed on the assumption that an individual who is interested in a child's welfare wants to know something constructive and tangible that he can do to help the child with his problems. It is hoped that many of the specific procedures explained in this book are sufficiently clear and workable to enable teachers and parents to apply them successfully even though they may have had no previous training in speech education or speech correction.

It is recognized, however, that there are certain hazards inherent in a work of this kind when it becomes either too general and theoretical, on the one hand, or too restricted and specific, on the other. If it remains too general, it is likely to appear vague and confusing to the reader, who may lack the special experience and training necessary to apply it successfully. On the other hand, if it is too detailed and specific, there is the danger that it may not be sufficiently flexible to be adapted to the many varying problems and situations encountered by teachers in general throughout the country. There is danger, too, of oversimplifying what is often complex and involved.

The authors have attempted to steer what they hope will be a safe course between the two extremes. In many instances the reader is supplied with the essential materials to work with and is told how to use them. An entire chapter (Chapter xii) is devoted to practical suggestions for implementing the theory and methods explained in earlier chapters and for integrating this training with the regular school curriculum. This chapter especially has been written for the teacher who says, 'Yes, I should like to help my children with their speech and language problems, but I just don't see how and when I can work it in.' It is hoped that here she will find the answer to her seeming dilemma; she should consult Chapter xii frequently while covering some of the earlier chapters, especially Chapters iii, iv, and v.

The teacher is reminded that the procedures explained in Chapter xii are merely suggestions of what can be done in a given situation. They will doubtless need to be modified somewhat to fit a different situation. They are intended primarily to stimulate the teacher to think of many more similar techniques that she can work out and apply 'on her own.'

Since a wealth of routine corrective exercises and drill materials is readily available in a large number of good books, it seemed a waste of time and space to duplicate too many of them in the present work. Therefore, where additional material is needed beyond what is supplied herein, the teacher is referred to these outside sources, many of which have been listed in the selective references included at the end of each chapter, with the exception of Chapter i. Only those references which the authors felt would be readily available to the teacher or parent have been listed and, to facilitate their use, actual pages or chapters in the books have been given in many instances.

Not only has great stress been placed upon the desirability of arming the classroom teacher and the parent with as much information as possible about the simpler speech problems of children, but the authors have also attempted to make clear the limitations of superficial training in dealing with serious disorders of such a vital and complicated activity as speech. It is hoped that part of the discipline the reader will get from this book is to learn what not to do in certain situations and where to turn for outside help with those problems that are too serious to be handled by one with a limited background in this field.

Because of the confusion that often results when speech sounds are represented by conventional spelling, the authors decided to use phonetic symbols, believing that their accuracy and precision in the identification and representation of sounds would more than offset the slight task of learning to recognize them. Moreover, in many instances the phonetic symbols are supplemented by alphabet letters or key words which help identify the sound or sounds referred to. On the suggestion of a number of individuals who were familiar with the original edition, the section on phonetics has been substantially expanded in this revision, with a fuller explanation of speech sounds and their behavior in spoken language and the addition of exercise material in the use of the phonetic alphabet.

The material on phonetics together with a complete table of the symbols used, with identifying key words, will be found as a part of the articulation tests in Chapter II. All phonetic symbols have been enclosed in brackets, thus [s]. When the symbol is reproduced in italics, as *s*, it is the alphabet letter that is referred to rather than the speech sound.

In addition to the expanded treatment of phonetics, this revision features a far greater emphasis on language—its development, disorders, and facilitation—than was included in the original edition. Much more attention has also been given to the importance of providing improvement in oral communication for all children, not just for those who exhibit a deficiency. In addition, there has, of course, been a general up-dating of theories, techniques, and references to keep the book current in this changing, rapidly expanding field.

The authors wish at this point to thank the many individuals who so kindly offered suggestions and recommendations, often quite detailed, many of which were profitably incorporated into this revision. They believe that such contributions materially helped to make the present edition more complete, more stimulating, and more generally effective than the original.

April 1973   VIRGIL A. ANDERSON
                                                      HAYES A. NEWBY

Contents

Figures

Improving the Child's Speech

Speech Improvement as an Educational Problem

Three significant developments characterize the present-day school to make it different from the traditional, or 'old-fashioned' school system.

The Whole Education of the Child

The first of these is the growing conviction that the school must assume a responsibility for the welfare of the child that extends considerably beyond mere intellectual development or the imparting of facts and skills that contribute to what we have conceived of as literacy. The areas into which the public schools have extended their influence and training include physical health, particularly as it may relate to diet, rest, and recreation; mental well-being and emotional balance; social consciousness, or the child's awareness of his social heritage; and a process that can be referred to as socialization—the fostering of points of view and patterns of behavior that enable the individual to function effectively as a member of the social group and to derive maximum profit from that association. Beyond these rather basic aspects of the child's development, the school has also often gone into supplementary or peripheral areas, such as training in safety through demonstrations, projects, and special courses; the encouragement of thrift through the establishment of such procedures as 'bank day'; and the development of attitudes and habits of honesty, helpfulness, and patriotism.

This emergence of the school into areas that once would have been considered entirely outside its province has resulted in part, no doubt, from the disintegration of the family as a self-contained and self-sufficient unit in which most of the physical, personal, and social needs of the child were supplied. Today the family is a more loosely organized and, in some respects, a more impotent institution than it was previously, with the result that many of its former duties and responsibilities have been delegated to outside agencies, one of the most important of which has been the public schools.

The Education of the Whole Child

Of more import and significance to the teacher of today, however, is another development in educational philosophy and practice, which also partially explains why the school has become so many-sided and far-reaching in its influence on the child's development. This has had to do with the growth of a concept that might be referred to as 'the whole child.' The tenets of modern psychology and the findings of experimental research point to the conclusion that the child develops as a whole, and that it is impossible to isolate completely the individual factors involved in his growth and either ignore or control them specifically, beyond a certain point. Intellectual, physical, emotional, and social development are, to a very large degree, interdependent and interrelated. A child who is constantly upset and tense as a result of unfavorable home conditions, for example, cannot be expected to function effectively at school. Studies in physiological psychology have amply demonstrated that the emotional state of the individual has a direct effect upon his performance even in so-called purely intellectual activities. Therefore, it is being unrealistic to assume that a handicap such as a hearing loss or a speech disorder can be ignored on the grounds that it is not of immediate concern to the teacher whose business supposedly is the mental training of the child. In reality, such a handicap should be of vital concern to the teacher and to the school, because it may well explain why the child is retarded in his studies, is socially immature, or is definitely a behavior problem. The proper procedure involves finding the basic cause of the difficulty and eliminating it, whatever it may be and wherever it may be found.

The modern teacher in a modern school is one who takes as her responsibility the fullest development of the boy or girl as a person. She cannot afford to confine herself to the teaching of subjects, or even subject matter. Rather, she is teaching *children*, and she must ever bear in mind that the child's whole personality and his total equipment are involved in every phase of his learning process as well as in his general development.

The Recognition of Individual Differences

The third important development in modern educational philosophy and practice is the recognition of individual differences, and the willingness to adjust teaching methods and curriculum to fit these differences. Research has demonstrated conclusively that children have different abilities and that these abilities tend to be relatively specific. The child is usually not all good or all bad, but he tends to be good in some activities, not so good in others. Modern education seeks out the child's potential abilities so that it may develop them, for every child should feel that there is something which he can do well.

There is more to this problem of individual differences, however, than merely finding the child's strong points. Children exhibit individual disabilities, as well as abilities, and these must also be taken into account if the child is to develop to his full potential. The modern school should, and does, make an effort to discover and alleviate these disabilities, especially those having to do with basic skills involved in the other learning processes, such as communication.

These modern trends in educational theory and practice have greatly altered not only the training of the teacher but her duties and responsibilities as well. She has become a dispenser of milk and orange juice, a collector of pennies and nickels for 'bank day,' a counselor and adviser to her pupils on subjects ranging from a difficult problem in arithmetic to questions of manners and morals, and frequently it has become necessary for her to go into the home to confer with the parents in order to get at the basis of the child's problem. To prepare herself for this many-sided task, the modern teacher has taken courses in child psychology and child guidance, in measurement and behavior modification, and in school counseling, in addition to the traditional preparation in pedagogy and the various subject-matter areas. The school's further concern for the child's more serious disabilities is reflected in such services and provisions as the visiting teacher, the school nurse, the psychiatric-social worker, and the special classes in language stimulation, remedial arithmetic, and remedial reading.

Special Education for Special Needs: Speech

One outgrowth of this interest in the child's individual needs came from an appreciation of the vital role oral communication plays in his educational and personal development. A logical result was not only an increased emphasis on oral language experience in the classroom, but also the addition of speech and hearing specialists to the school staff and the setting up of special programs in speech, hearing, and language for those children with obvious deficiencies in their use of oral communication. The movement, which had its inception in the early nineteen-twenties, has grown and spread steadily throughout the nation until today a substantial portion of the states have provisions in their departments of education for the certification and employment of special teachers and clinicians in speech, hearing, and language development and the setting up of special classes for handicapped pupils variously referred to as the educationally handicapped, the neurologically handicapped, or those with childhood aphasia. Whatever they are called, all of these classes reveal a high incidence of reading and oral language deficiencies. Generally these programs are the responsibility of the division of special education, which also includes the training of the deaf, blind, mentally retarded, and physically handicapped. In many states general funds, often augmented by federal assistance, are provided for these services, with the result that the local school districts receive substantial outside aid for the training of their handicapped children.

There is every indication that this trend toward providing specialized services for the child with a communication handicap will continue and at an accelerated rate. This is shown in the number of states, counties, and cities that have instituted programs, not only to help the handicapped child through special services, but also to prepare the classroom teachers to assist with this work through specific courses in their professional preparation as well as programs of in-service training. The trend is also shown in the increasing demand for specialists in speech, hearing, and language, a demand that exceeds the present available supply. Prevention is also being stressed through the present emphasis on oral language in the language arts curriculum of many elementary school systems.

This trend toward specialized help for the child with a communication handicap is as it should be. There is little question that the ultimate salvation of the child with a serious speech, hearing, or language problem rests with the specialist. It is not conceivable that the average classroom teacher will ever be able to acquire a sufficient background in these relatively complicated and technical fields to enable her to deal satisfactorily with the more serious types of communication disorders found among the public school population. The specialist we must have, but the specialist alone is not enough.

In the first place, the problem as a whole is too extensive. The American Speech and Hearing Association Committee on the Mid-century White House Conference on Children and Youth reports, 'Children with speech disorders make up one of our largest groups of seriously handicapped youngsters.'[1] The Committee estimated that there were 2,000,000 speech-defective children in the United States between the ages of 5 and 21, or 5 per cent of the assumed population within this age range. The results of actual surveys corroborate the Conference Committee's own admission that these figures are presented as the lowest defensible estimates. Moreover, not only has there been a population increase in the intervening years, but the percentage of communication disorders rises when consideration is limited to children of school age. There have been many speech surveys conducted in recent years, the most careful and extensive of which come out with approximately 10 per cent of the school population suffering from some form of communicative handicap. This would mean approximately 5 million such children in the United States—over 40,000 in a large city, and some 750 in a medium small city of 30,000 population.

It is inconceivable that within the foreseeable future a sufficient number of specialists in speech, language, and hearing will be available to take care of this large number of children who need help. At best there will be only enough to handle the more serious problems. Some other method must be found for dealing with the remainder of these cases.

Despite the encouraging advances made in the education of the handicapped throughout the country as a whole, there are still important areas where no specialized services in speech, language, and hearing are available through the public school system. No provision for this work has been made in the educational programs in these areas, no specialists in communication problems are available, and there would be no money to pay the specialists if they were available. Even in many of the states, counties, and cities where programs for the communicatively handicapped have been in existence for some time and are well established, a serious problem of understaffing exists.

1. ASHA Committee on the Midcentury White House Conference, 'Speech Disorders and Speech Correction,' *The Journal of Speech and Hearing Disorders*, June 1952, pp. 129–37.

Case loads are often in excess of recommended maximums and many handicapped children are either denied any professional help at all or are enrolled in programs that are far from adequate to meet their needs.

Faced with the problem of overcrowding and understaffing, the speech and hearing specialist has been forced to choose one of two solutions, both of which are bad. First, she can attempt to give some help to all of those children within her district who need it, thus spreading her time and energies so thin that not even the most serious cases receive sufficient help to do them much good. The best that can be done under these conditions is to give each child but a few minutes of special help each week, and that usually in groups. One does not need to be familiar with the exacting nature of the field of special education to realize how inadequate such a program is.

The second solution, still undesirable but in several respects to be preferred to the first, involves a hard-headed policy of selecting for special help only those children who need it most and who seem most likely to profit from it. There are many pitfalls involved in this procedure, as can be seen at once. While it is thus possible to give those with serious problems more time and attention, many other children with disorders that will still be a handicap to them in later life must be refused help altogether. There are possibilities for all sorts of trouble in such a course of action—when, for example, Johnnie's mother complains that Johnnie isn't getting any help with his speech problem, while Jimmie is getting help and his speech isn't as bad as Johnnie's. The clinician who chooses this solution to her problem will be required to justify and defend the basis of her choice of certain cases and exclusion of others, not only to Johnnie's mother but to the superintendent and principal as well, not to mention her own conscience and professional integrity.

A broader approach to the problem of understaffing, designed to extend the services of the specialist, has recently received considerable attention. This involves the employment of trained

non-professionals as speech aides or communication aides, as
they are called, to serve as supportive personnel to the speech,
hearing, and language clinician. Individuals selected for this
role have included mothers of children with communicative
disorders, undergraduate and graduate students in college or
university training programs, and in some instances any person
who gives promise of successfully responding to the basic
preparation required of these non-professional supportive personnel. Duties, under strict responsibility and supervision of a
professional, have included, in addition to clerical work, assistance with less complicated forms of speech, language, and
hearing therapy.

Communication Training in the Classroom

Among the individuals best prepared and best situated to render
valuable assistance to the child with a speech, language, or
hearing problem is, of course, the classroom teacher. Even if
there were enough clinicians to give specialized help to the
large number of children needing it, this in itself is not enough;
the teacher still has a vital role to play. It is difficult and, to a
degree, futile to attempt to teach a skill or an ability in a situation apart from that in which the skill eventually is to be used.
The clinician sees the child individually or in a special group
only for a short time each week, or twice each week, as her
schedule permits. It may not be too difficult to bring the child
to the point where he can speak, or otherwise perform, quite
normally while he is in this carefully controlled and restricted
environment. This is no guarantee, however, that he will use
his newly acquired communication skills when he returns to the
classroom or goes home after school, at least without some
encouragement and supervision beyond what the specialist is
able to give him herself in the short time she is with him. The
person best qualified and most strategically situated to assist
the child in this 'carry-over' of his good communication habits
into real-life situations is the classroom teacher, since she is
with the child during a large portion of his day and can thus

control and supervise many of his activities in which communication is involved. She will be much better prepared for this responsibility of assisting the speech clinician if she has sufficient background herself in the theory and practice of speech training and retraining to appreciate something of the nature of the problems involved.

The responsibilities of the classroom teacher must extend beyond merely assisting the specialist, however, if maximum results are to be obtained. She must be prepared to do a great deal of constructive speech teaching herself in connection with the normal curricular and extra-curricular activities in which speech plays a part, or can be made to play a part. It must be remembered that speech, as a basic function of the individual, cannot be separated from his other activities; his speech training must be an integral part of his normal and everyday uses of oral communication. If the training isn't thus integrated, it will remain in his thinking as a sort of extra 'frill' or just another something to be learned in school, and he will be unwilling or unable to use his speech skills constructively in normal situations in which they function as the means to an end. Thus, the classroom teacher enjoys a position of strategic importance with respect to the speech education of all her pupils and thereby acquires a responsibility for their speech welfare—a responsibility that cannot be wholly or successfully delegated, even to the special speech clinician.

The Function and Importance of Oral Communication

The charge has been made that the classroom teacher is already overworked—that, as a result of the broadening concept of education's responsibility to the child, miscellaneous duties and tasks have been heaped upon her. There undoubtedly is considerable truth in this contention; certainly the teacher's job today is far more complex than it was a generation ago. However, the solution is not as simple or obvious as is implied in the admonition, frequently heard, to 'cut out the frills and get down to fundamentals.' What are the 'frills'? What are the 'fundamentals'? Answers to these questions depend on the philosophy of education and the concept of its objectives held by the individual supplying the answers. Is the purpose of education merely to develop literacy, to foster a kind of intellectual functioning that might be referred to as 'book-learning' without regard to what the individual becomes as a person, how well he may be able to take his place in a free society, or how effectively he will be able to utilize that literacy and book-learning? If so, then it could well be argued that many of the activities of the present-day public school are indeed 'frills.'

Most thinking individuals, however, are unwilling to accept this restricted definition of education. There have been numerous authoritative statements of educational objectives, and almost all of them contain references to such functions and abilities as earning a living, adjusting to and co-operating with others, and practicing good citizenship. Such a concept certainly goes far beyond the traditional three R's, or even what have come to be the accepted classroom academic subjects. We are forced to extend our thinking beyond subjects, and even subject matter, to the child himself—the 'whole child' with all of his abilities and disabilities, his needs and his drives, and the environmental factors affecting him. All of these forces not only function to condition the educational process while the individual is in school but they will also materially influence his success in earning a living, adjusting to others, and becoming a good citizen after he has left school.

How do speech and hearing fit into this larger concept? It is widely held, and with considerable justification, that speech constitutes man's chief medium of social adaptation and control. But so far how much attention has been given to oral communication in our schools? The importance of written communication—reading and writing—has long been recognized by our educational system. The child begins to work on these skills soon after entering the first grade, and there is some form of instruction in either or both of them every year of schooling thereafter, up to and including, in many instances, the first year of college. As a matter of fact, no other subject in the entire public-school curriculum receives as much time and attention as English, but the instruction is, to a large extent, on the written side—composition, grammar, spelling, and reading. And there is ample justification for this emphasis on English.

But what of *oral* communication, of being able to say effectively what you have to say, as well as being able to write it; of being able to listen critically and understand what you hear, as well as being able to read? Surely, in these days of the radio and television, the 'open' council and board meetings, the telephone, the business conference, and the convention, the potency and importance of the spoken word need not be underlined to be appreciated. After all, a man can hire a secretary to do his writing for him, even to the point of correcting his spelling and bracing up his wobbly sentences, but eventually he must speak for himself. And to a measurable degree, his success or his failure, his ability to win others' confidence and cooperation, and the impression he makes as a person will depend on how effectively he can meet the many speech situations with which he is confronted daily.

In the classroom it is through his understanding of spoken language that the child gets much of his knowledge, especially during his earlier years, and through this understanding he is able to co-operate with others and function as a successful pupil in the learning situation. It is through his speech skill that he is able to demonstrate his knowledge to the teacher and use it properly in his general development. It is also largely through the child's oral expression that the teacher forms her judgments of his learning progress, his motivation, his adjustment to his home and to his fellows, his strengths and weaknesses as a person, and even his physical health and vitality. And, of course, his adequacy or inadequacy in speech may profoundly affect not only his attitudes toward others and his relations with them but his attitudes toward himself as well. A speech deficiency can become a potent factor, as is too often demonstrated, in contributing to a person's feelings of inferiority, of being different, of not belonging.

The Responsibility of the School and the Classroom Teacher

A serious defect of speech, such as stuttering, cleft palate, or a severe articulatory disorder, may affect the individual in a very concrete and far-reaching way. Many of the major professions, for example, medicine, law, teaching, business administration, and salesmanship, are very difficult to enter or succeed in for an individual seriously handicapped by a speech disorder. Further concrete evidence of how a speech deficiency can function to handicap an individual is supplied by studies disclosing that stutterers in general are often retarded in school, even though as a group they are the equal in intelligence of normal speakers. As pointed out earlier, it is quite in line with modern educational theory and practice that communication-handicapped individuals should be given help through the public schools, and today there is a growing realization of this responsibility on the part of public-school administrators, teacher-training institutions, and individual classroom teachers themselves. Recently one of the authors was asked to conduct a section program on speech at a teachers' institute for elementary- and secondary-school teachers coming largely from small towns and rural areas. Since the program was scheduled in competition with a number of other special-interest group meetings, it was assumed that the section on speech would be of interest only to the small number of speech clinicians who were known to be employed in that area. Contrary to expectations, however, the room overflowed with classroom teachers eager to learn something of what they had discovered to be an important problem in their classrooms. During the intermission teachers crowded around the speaker with such questions as 'I have a little boy in my class who talks like this (demonstrating graphically); what should I do for him?' It was evident that the speech welfare of their pupils was of genuine concern to these teachers, and they were eager to learn how they might function more effectively in helping the children with their problems.

Over the nation a significant number of teacher-training institutions are requiring of all candidates for a teaching credential a course in speech education and re-education as a regular part of their professional preparation, especially at the elementary level. Many of the schools that do not actually make such a course mandatory at least offer it. Several of the larger cities and a number of the counties in states where speech and hearing activities are well established have initiated more or less comprehensive programs of in-service training for their classroom teachers to equip them to meet more adequately the problems presented by the speech and hearing deficiencies of their pupils and to enable them to instruct all the children in better oral communication.

These are encouraging developments. There are both logical and practical reasons why this responsibility should be assumed by the public schools. In the first place, if this training is not obtainable there, where is the child to get it? College and university speech and hearing clinics are too widely scattered and generally inaccessible to the average parent seeking such help for his child. In some of the larger cities there are private clinics and private clinicians, but they do not solve the problem for the rank and file of children scattered throughout the country. Moreover, the processes of establishing proper oral communication and eliminating deficiencies are for the most part processes of education, or re-education, following the same fundamental principles of learning as those that underlie all of the child's educational development. Also, since oral communication is involved as a basic tool in the child's progress in his other school subjects and since speech education must be an integral part of the child's daily classroom experiences if it is to have any lasting benefit, it becomes obvious that the public school cannot easily escape its fundamental responsibility for the speech development of its charges. It is the logical and practical instrumentality through which this important aspect of the child's training should be accomplished.

The Potentialities and Preparation
of the Classroom Teacher

Just how serious are the problems of establishing proper oral communication and remedying deficiencies among the children of school age throughout the country? When viewed from (a) the task of providing constructive training in oral communication for all pupils, (b) the large number of children handicapped by speech, hearing, and language deficiencies, (c) the harmful influence these deficiencies may have on the child's intellectual and social development, and (d) the relatively large number who are receiving little, if any, help with their problems, the situation is indeed serious. On the other hand, from the point of view of what could be done for these children with the enlightened co-operation of the classroom teacher throughout the school life of the child, the problem, while still serious, presents a bright and hopeful prospect of satisfactory alleviation.

Most communication disorders found among the school population are not particularly complicated or deep-seated and a large proportion of them respond readily to intelligent handling, especially if dealt with in time. Only about 15 per cent of the disorders have any structural basis, and only about 25 per cent could be called involved, complicated, or difficult to correct. In other words, the majority are of the bad-habit type, resulting from imitation of poor models, or induced generally by carelessness, laziness, or indifference. The implications are obvious —in most cases of communication disorders found among school children there is nothing 'wrong' with the speech mechanism, as is so often popularly believed when speech production is defective. Many of these disorders are preventable if teachers stressed good habits of oral communication, especially in the early grades, and many of those already established are correctable if (a) they are discovered in time and (b) the proper methods are used. Thus, bad speech habits can be prevented or changed for the better; what has been poorly learned can be improved through relearning.

Therefore, it is possible and practical to give the classroom teacher sufficient background in the principles and techniques of speech education and re-education to enable her to prevent many of the communication problems that might otherwise develop and to cope adequately with a substantial number of those she encounters routinely in the course of her daily teaching. Beyond that, such training should make clear to her her limitations as a communication specialist and should teach her where to turn for help when she discovers a problem she is not equipped to handle herself.

Objectives of Training

More specifically, adequate preparation in speech re-education for the classroom teacher should accomplish the following objectives:

1. Impress the teacher with the importance of providing her pupils with a good model in her own speech, which, if not superior, should at least be free from defects.
2. Acquaint her with the processes and factors involved in the child's 'natural' speech and language development so that she will be prepared to facilitate that development and assist the child in establishing good habits of speech while he is young.
3. Teach her to recognize and evaluate speech and hearing disabilities when she encounters them and instruct her where to turn for assistance with those problems she is not capable of handling herself.
4. Equip her to alleviate the simpler types of speech difficulties that can be adequately dealt with in a classroom situation with a minimum of technical knowledge and skill.

5. Train her to co-operate more effectively with the speech clinician, if there is one in her school or school system. Such co-operation implies:

   a. Some understanding of the methods and techniques being employed by the speech specialist.
   b. The provision of opportunities for supervised classroom experiences that will contribute to the child's speech growth and development and will insure adequate 'carry-over' into real-life speech situations of those skills taught in the special speech sessions.
   c. Furnishing the therapist with intelligent, periodic reports on the child's progress in overcoming his speech problem in the classroom.
   d. Maintaining in the child a high degree of motivation and morale in relation to the special speech therapy by showing enthusiasm and offering words of encouragement.

6. Impress her with the importance of oral communication and acquaint her with the relation of speech and speech defects to the personality development and behavior patterns of the child, to his progress in reading, and to his achievement in the rest of his school subjects.

This program may sound rather formidable to the classroom teacher or prospective teacher as she thinks soberly of her manifold duties and responsibilities in connection with an already overcrowded curriculum. And indeed it would be formidable if it were something apart from or in addition to all of the rest she is supposed to teach. Fortunately, most, if not all, of the speech education and re-education she would be expected to handle can be effectively integrated with the activities that form the present curriculum, especially at the elementary level, and more especially as the elementary curriculum is concerned with language arts. In this connection, Bennett quotes from the results of a conference on communicative disorders sponsored by the United States Office of Education, 'Public school speech and hearing programs were perceived as being most effective when integrally related to the total educational program . . . and carried on as basic educational activities.' [2] Such a concept surely involves the classroom teacher in a very important way.

As the speech-training materials are presented in the following chapters, many possibilities will be suggested to the teacher for accomplishing this integration. Moreover, an entire chapter is devoted to concrete and specific suggestions for making speech training and speech correction a functional and integral part of the regular school curriculum, to which it rightly belongs.

2. Clayton L. Bennett, 'Communications Disorders in the Public Schools,' in Lee E. Travis, ed., *Handbook of Speech Pathology and Audiology*, Appleton-Century-Crofts, New York, 1971, p. 973.

II

Recognizing Speech Disabilities

With the exception of the more obvious types of speech disorders, such as cleft palate and stuttering, the definition of a speech disability is not absolute but relative. Speech is seldom so good that it could not be improved, yet in the majority of instances it falls into a classification we designate as 'normal.' It is only when it deviates sufficiently from this norm to call adverse attention to itself generally, or to fail seriously in its role of oral communication, that we label it defective.

Let us consider in more detail some of the implications of this concept of defective speech. In the first place, the norm upon which this definition is based is relative. What would be considered normal in one section of the country may be regarded as an example of defective speech in another area. What passes unnoticed in the speech of individuals from one level of society may call adverse attention to itself in another cultural environment. For example, the 'nasal drawl' characteristic of certain parts of our country is considered quite normal and acceptable in those areas but may become conspicuous in other areas where such a quality is uncommon. Again, we do not expect the same standard of speech to prevail on the street corner as we expect to hear at a formal reception or from the teacher in the classroom, nor do we expect the child of five to speak as well as a ten- or twelve-year-old. Hence 'normal speech' is what is to be expected from the environment in which it is used, taking into account the speaker's age and general background.

It must be concluded, therefore, that whether a given sample of speech deviates sufficiently from the norm to be conspicuous and, hence, to be defective is, in the end, a matter of judgment on the part of the person who hears it, provided intelligibility is not seriously affected. A person may be unaware of the lisp or defective voice quality of his friend because he has grown used to it, and he may be oblivious to his own speech problems partly for the same reason. An individual may not label oral inactivity or nasality as defective because his standards are sufficiently low and his concept of 'normal' speech so broad that such deviations do not impress him as being conspicuous or distracting. In contrast, the trained speech specialist may have set her standards so high that the slightest deviation or deficiency is labeled a defect. Somewhere between these two extremes will be found the dividing line between speech which, while still not 'perfect,' may be considered 'normal,' and that which a significant number of individuals in the environment will find unpleasant, conspicuous, or unintelligible. This tenuous line of demarcation the teacher should attempt to discover for herself and use as the basis for her classification of speech into 'normal' and 'defective.'

Why is the element of conspicuousness so important in our concept of defective speech? In the first place, it must be remembered that speech is but a means to an end; it is not for display but for communication. Any quality about it, therefore, which tends to call attention to the speech itself detracts to that extent from the effectiveness of the communication, since the hearer is dividing his attention between the manner of communication and what is being communicated. The more unobtrusive the speech itself is, the better is the listener able to give his complete attention to what is being said. Such characteristics and concomitants of speech, therefore, as peculiarities of pronunciation, facial grimaces or tics, unusual qualities of voice, and abnormalities of rhythm or tempo can, and do, become distracting to the hearer and thus hinder the speaker in his attempt to communicate his 'meaning.'

Moreover, any element of conspicuousness in an individual's speech may have serious repercussions on his personality and social adjustment. Such peculiarities have the effect of setting him apart as being abnormal, inferior, or 'different' from others. This can be a most unfavorable factor in an individual's development, especially during the early years when conformity with the peer group in all matters of attitude, appearance, and behavior is the *sine qua non*, not only for acceptance into the group, but also for the individual's self-respect and feeling of personal well-being. During this critical period, especially, any peculiarity that marks a person as being different from his fellows may well provide the subsoil for the growth of feelings of inferiority, shyness, and self-consciousness, and withdrawal or regressive tendencies that may permanently warp the personality.

The possibility of a deleterious effect of a speech handicap upon the personality must not be underestimated. Serious stutterers, for example, have been known to become so sensitive about their speech and the supposed attitude of others toward it that they were unwilling to change it, even to improve it, because they could not face the prospect of having still more attention directed their way when their friends noticed the improvement and perchance commented on it. This is, indeed, a sad state of mind for an individual to develop, but such attitudes are a real problem with which the teacher must often deal in her efforts to alleviate the effects of handicaps that loom large in the thinking of the individuals who suffer from them. The element of conspicuousness, therefore, plays an important part in our definition of defective speech.

Types of Speech Disorders

In how many ways can speech be defective? There are a number of bases upon which different classifications of speech disorders can be built, but perhaps the most practical and useful basis is that of symptomatology—the way the speech sounds. Considered from the point of view of the more obvious symptoms or characteristics, all speech problems can be classified under one or more of the four types: (1) phonatory, or voice disorders; (2) articulatory, or pronunciation and enunciation disorders; (3) linguistic, or language disorders; (4) disorders of speech rhythm.

In evaluating the speech of individuals or in conducting speech surveys, the following check-list form will be found useful. It lists the more common and obvious speech characteristics that should be watched for under each of the four categories mentioned in the previous paragraph, plus a fifth category covering general observations on the speech performance as a whole. The form will be more useful as a basis for speech placement or referral if a rating is suggested for each item that is checked. For example, the examiner can use 1 for slight, 2 for considerable, and 3 for severe. Perhaps it is unnecessary to remind the teacher that an adequate description of a speech problem will usually involve checking more than one item, since there is an inter-relationship among and between these various factors of speech and voice production. A voice that is nasal, for example, may be too high in pitch and may exhibit oral inactivity in the articulation as well. The stutterer's rate may be too fast, et cetera.

It is not expected at this early stage that the terms used will be fully meaningful to the teacher. They are defined later in this chapter and discussed in more detail in later sections of this book.

Speech Analysis Rating Chart

PHONATORY DISORDERS

A. *Quality:*
1. Nasal _____
2. Denasal _____
3. Breathy (aspirate) _____
4. Hoarse-husky _____
5. Strained-strident _____
6. Harsh-guttural _____
7. Falsetto (juvenile voice) _____
8. Weak-thin _____
9. Tremorous _____

B. *Pitch:*
1. General level high (above average) _____
2. General level low (below average) _____
3. Monopitch _____
4. Pitch spasmodic, uncontrolled _____

C. *Intensity:*
1. Too weak _____
2. Too loud _____
3. Spasmodic, uncontrolled _____

ARTICULATORY DISORDERS

A. *Speech sounds:*
1. Omitted _____
2. Substituted _____
3. Added _____
4. Distorted _____

B. *Oral inactivity* (indistinct articulation) _____
C. *Slow, labored speech* _____
D. *Rapid, slurring* _____
E. *Articulation below age level* _____
F. *Foreign dialect* _____
G. *Regional dialect* _____

LANGUAGE DISORDERS

   A. *Speechlessness* _____

   B. *Speech confusion, search for words* _____

   C. *Cannot understand words* _____

   D. *Cannot write words* _____

   E. *Reading below grade or age level* _____

DISORDERS OF RHYTHM

   A. *Abnormal repetition of sounds* _____

   B. *Abnormal repetition of words* _____

   C. *Speech blocks* _____

   D. *Abnormal hesitations* _____

   E. *Cluttering, irregular rhythm* _____

GENERAL OBSERVATIONS

   A. *Tics, facial grimaces* _____

   B. *Excessive stage fright* _____

   C. *Unusual posture or bodily movement* _____

   D. *Abnormally shy, unresponsive* _____

   E. *Belligerent, negativistic* _____

   F. *Obvious organic defects* (cleft lip, etc.) _____

Phonatory Disorders

Strictly speaking, phonatory disorders are those that have their origin in some malfunctioning of the sound-producing mechanism—the larynx or the breathing mechanism which supplies the motive power. As a matter of convenience in classification, however, some of the symptoms listed under quality and intensity in the check-list above may also be related to articulation and especially resonance. This is most likely to be true of nasality, denasality, stridency, and a weak-thin quality. In this discussion, therefore, the term *phonatory disorders* is understood to embrace all of those disorders of *voice*, as opposed to those involving principally articulation and language. Hence, all quality disorders are included under phonatory.

Disorders of Quality

Of all aspects of voice and speech production, quality is the least objective and the most difficult to identify and standardize. As a result, one finds in the literature relating to voice production literally hundreds of terms, many of them quite fanciful, that have been used by various writers at various times to describe good and bad qualities of the voice. Many of these terms are purely subjective, having an identifiable meaning only for the individual who used them. In this category would be included such descriptive adjectives as *dull, flat, coarse, squeaky, reedy,* and *gravelly.* Even some of the terms designating quality disorders included in the present analysis chart are difficult, if not impossible, to verify objectively. Perhaps a brief description of each one will help identify it for the examiner.

1. *Nasality* Nasality can usually be identified quite readily, although, for reasons discussed at the beginning of this chapter, opinions may differ about its extent or seriousness. Nasality shows up as excessive nasal resonance on sounds, particularly vowels, that should be predominantly oral in production and quality, and sometimes oral consonants are nasally emitted also. The individual with this voice quality disorder may be said to be 'talking through his nose.' Nasality will be discussed in detail in Chapter VII.

2. *Denasality* In some respects this is the opposite of the condition described above. Here there is insufficient nasal resonance of the sounds that should be nasally emitted, namely, the [m], [n], and *ng* [ŋ] (as in *sing*) sounds. The individual talks as if he had a clothespin clamped over his nose, and the whole voice sounds stopped-up. It is often referred to as 'adenoid' or 'cold-in-the-head' speech. In extreme cases the [m] resembles [b], the [n] sounds like [d], and the *ng* [ŋ] tends to become [g], so that the expression 'good morning' turns into 'good bawdig.'

3. *Breathiness* This quality, which results from improper alignment of the vocal folds where their edges come together, can be
identified by the presence of unvocalized breath in the vocal
tone. It will be particularly noticeable on vowel sounds following voiceless consonants, such as [h] in *hit,* [t] in *tap,* [f] in *five,*
and *th* [θ] in *thin.* A breathy tone may also be a weak tone,
since some of the motive power of the voice is being wasted.

4. *Hoarse-husky* No effort is made here to distinguish between
these two closely related terms. When a person talks as if he
had laryngitis or had yelled all afternoon at a football game,
his voice is hoarse or husky, with hoarse being the more commonly used term. In pronounced cases vocalization is obviously
difficult for the speaker, and it may be painful as well, or even
impossible, in which case a person 'loses' his voice.

5. *Strained-strident* Such voices have a piercing quality and
they are often described as metallic. The pitch is frequently
high and there may be evidence of 'nasal twang,' as well as excessive muscular tension in and around the neck and throat.
This voice is likely to be loud rather than soft.

6. *Harsh-guttural* This unpleasant quality, which superficially
resembles hoarseness, but without any breathy component, is
more likely to be found among adults than among children.
Pitch is likely to be lower than normal and this harsh, throaty
quality may become more noticeable as the voice trails off in
pitch on the last word or syllable of a phrase or sentence. The
term 'raspy' might also apply.

7. *Falsetto (juvenile voice)* This defect is more likely to be
found among boys than among girls and results from failure of
the voice to 'change' properly at puberty. The pitch will be
considerably higher than it should be, and the thin, falsetto
quality is often combined with a roughness or hoarseness. The
voice may 'break' occasionally, or sound as if it were going to.

8. W*eak, thin,* and *tremorous*   The first two of these terms are highly subjective and refer to a disorder that involves intensity perhaps more than quality. The pitch will be high, the voice lacking in vitality and carrying power, and the effect as a whole may be described as infantile in many instances. If the voice is tremorous, there will be a quaver in the tone. The causes of tremor are likely to be neurological or emotional.

Disorders of Pitch

Since pitch is a relatively objective attribute of voice, deviations from the norm are not difficult to recognize in most instances. Indications that the general pitch level used by the individual may be too high, considering age and sex, include (1) strained or strident quality; (2) thin, falsetto, or infantile quality; and (3) signs of muscular tension around the throat and face. The habitual pitch level may be too low if the voice (1) has a throaty, harsh quality; (2) lacks intensity; or (3) is characterized by a limited range of falling inflections. The pitch variations may be confined within a narrow range—a condition sometimes referred to as monopitch—or the pitch changes may appear spasmodic and uncontrolled.

Disorders of Intensity

The most common disorder of intensity, especially among children, is inadequate carrying power—the voice is simply too weak to be heard easily. This condition is likely to be associated with excessive shyness, in which case the voice may be quite adequate when the child is on the playground or at home but may drop to a weak and unintelligible mumble when he is called upon to recite in class. A voice that is habitually too loud suggests personality factors also, but of the opposite type from those just mentioned. Both conditions, however, may also result from a hearing loss. Spasmodic or uncontrolled variations in intensity usually have a neurological basis.

Articulatory Disorders

Articulation has to do with the formation of speech sounds and involves two processes primarily: (1) Forming sounds *clearly*, often referred to as enunciation, and (2) producing sounds *correctly* according to some standard, a process commonly called pronunciation. The first deals with a general characteristic of an individual's speech closely related to intelligibility. If a person's enunciation is faulty, words and sounds may be so poorly formed that his speech becomes difficult to understand. The familiar 'mushy,' mumbling type of speech illustrates one common form of articulatory deficiency involving enunciation.

There are two chief aspects of pronunciation: (1) the placing of the accent on the proper syllable within the word—that is whether one says 'DE tail' or 'de TAIL' for *detail*—and (2) the choice of the particular vowel or consonant that is to be used in a given instance. For example, the word *data* may be heard as 'DAY ta,' 'DA ta,' or even 'DAH ta,' depending on which vowel the speaker chooses to use in the first syllable. However, it is with problems of improper enunciation, commonly referred to as articulatory disorders, that we are primarily concerned.

Articulatory Disorders Involving Specific Sounds

Sounds may be omitted from a word, which is what happens when *ice cream* becomes something resembling 'ie eem.' Certain incorrect sounds are substituted for the proper ones when the child says 'fum' for *thumb* or 'wamp' for *lamp*. Individual sounds are frequently produced incorrectly, as when [s] is lisped, or [l] becomes 'muffled.' It is obvious that some of these problems are more common or more serious than others.

Oral Inactivity

A large number of articulatory problems can be labeled as oral inactivity, a term designating relatively unintelligible speech, usually the result of carelessness or poor speech habits. In general, the speech of individuals exhibiting oral inactivity is either of the slow, sluggish type, in which case the speaker may be described as 'lip-lazy' and 'tongue-lazy,' or the speech may be characterized by a rapid, slurring, often irregular tempo sometimes described as 'hitting the high spots.' In both types many speech sounds are either omitted or are imperfectly formed, speech becomes unclear and distorted, and intelligibility is reduced.

Articulation Below Age Level

When the pattern of sounds omitted, substituted, or defective in other ways resembles the typical speech of the young child, it is often referred to as 'baby talk.' Such substitutions and omissions as 'fwee' for *three* and 'tee tah' for *streetcar* are typical of this pattern. If the defective articulation is also accompanied by a deficient vocabulary and an immature form of grammatical structure, the problem may be one of retarded speech or language development. Forms of delayed speech vary from no speech at all to only minor manifestations of retardation.

Foreign and Regional Dialect

A child who has been exposed to a foreign-language background may exhibit in his speech certain sound substitutions and distortions. Dialectal influences may show up, not only in articulatory deviations but also in grammatical structure and idiomatic usage as well as in stress and intonational patterns. Marked differences in pronunciation are also characteristic of various regions in the United States, and these may be reflected in the speech of the child who has been exposed to their influence.

Language Disorders

Language disorders are those that involve the formulation, expression, or understanding of language in any of its four aspects —reading, writing, speaking, or understanding what is spoken. Such deficiencies are ordinarily classified as forms of aphasia, usually traceable to an injury or maldevelopment in the association areas of the brain. However, there are many cases of reading deficiencies and speech inadequacies that resemble aphasia very closely but in which it is impossible to find evidence of any neurological involvement. For convenience, these are often referred to as examples of 'functional' aphasia, or merely speech or language retardation.

Symptoms of a language problem would include any one or any combination of the following: inability to read, or marked retardation in reading; deficiency in comprehension of spoken language; serious difficulty in the expression of ideas in either speech or writing. If true aphasia is present, a disability in any one of these categories is almost always accompanied by some loss in the others as well. The above symptoms are not to be confused with mere 'slowness' in reading or with the labored, hesitant, inadequate manner in which many individuals express themselves in either speech or writing. The difference is largely one of degree—aphasia being the more severe as well as more generally involving all aspects of language. Fortunately for the teacher, aphasia is relatively rare, although the simpler functional disorders of speech and reading retardation are quite common.

Disorders of Rhythm

The most common, and most severe, disturbance of speech rhythm is stuttering, sometimes called stammering. This serious speech disorder is characterized by two general categories of speech symptoms: (1) abnormal repetitions of speech sounds or of words—the familiar 'c-c-c-cat' type of stuttering—and (2) tonic spasms, or speech blocks, during which the individual is unable to utter a sound although he may be trying desperately to get something out. These speech manifestations may be accompanied by numerous accessory activities, such as the use of 'starters' in introducing a phrase or sentence, marked tenseness of the body, broken, irregular speech rhythm, and facial grimaces, tics, and other bodily movements. As in the case of aphasia, the symptoms of true stuttering should not be confused with the shyness, hesitations, and irregular rhythm patterns often found in children who speak 'normally.'

Relative Incidence of Speech Defects

It may be of some value to the teacher to know approximately how many of each type of speech defect she may expect to find in any given school population. In Chapter 1 reference was made to the Mid-century White House Conference on Children and Youth, which estimated an admittedly conservative 5 per cent of the country's population between the ages of 5 and 21 as presenting a speech or hearing handicap. It was also pointed out that more exact and more recent surveys indicated that the total of these handicapped children was closer to 10 per cent than the estimated 5 per cent, especially among those in the elementary grades. The Mid-century Conference Report also cited the following percentages of various types of speech problems among this handicapped population:

TYPE OF IMPAIRMENT	PER CENT
Functional Articulatory	60
Stuttering	14
Voice Problems	4
Cleft Palate Speech	2
Cerebral Palsy Speech	4
Retarded Speech Development	6
Impaired Hearing (with speech disorder)	10

Some observations regarding these data are worth noting. In the first place, it must be remembered that the total percentage will be found to be considerably higher among the kindergarten and first three or four elementary grades than among older children. This is especially true of certain types of articulatory problems, of stuttering to some extent, of delayed speech and language, and certain voice problems. Looking at the breakdown from another point of view, we discover that from two-thirds to three-fourths of the total disabilities are articulatory in nature, considering that a portion of defects resulting from cleft palate, cerebral palsy, retarded speech development, and impaired hearing also involve articulation. This means that they are basically mechanical and are, on the whole, much easier to correct than the more obscure types of disorders. Moreover, an overwhelming percentage of the articulatory problems, as well as a portion of some of the other disabilities, is functional in nature. That is, these problems have no discoverable structural or other organic basis. Many of them are of the imitative or bad-habit type; the child's speech is as it is simply because he learned to talk that way and no one has taught him anything different.

The possibilities for improvement, therefore, are indeed great in the major portion of speech-defect cases, although it must be observed that some of the less common disorders are at the same time the most disabling and most severe—for example, stuttering, hard-of-hearing speech, and speech disorders resulting from paralysis. It is not to be expected, however, that the parent or classroom teacher will be able to take care of these more serious problems alone. Here she will need the help of the specialized speech therapist. Fortunately, many of the speech problems encountered in the classroom, especially among the lower grades, are not severe and can be handled without too much specialized skill and knowledge. This should not be taken to mean, however, that the classroom teacher or parent is an adequate substitute for a trained speech clinician where one is available. The informed parent or teacher should reinforce and supplement the work of the specialist, or, where such is not available, do the best she can with what knowledge she has and within the limitations set forth in various portions of this book.

The American Speech Sounds

One of the first concepts that the parent or teacher must grasp if she is to be successful in helping children with their speech problems is the distinction between a speech sound and a letter of the alphabet; the two are often quite different. While written language is recorded in alphabet symbols which we call letters, spoken language consists of words made up of combinations of phonetic units, or speech sounds, more exactly labeled phonemes. If the spelling of modern English were phonetic, as it was during the early period of its development, there would be a close correspondence between letters and sounds, each letter symbolizing only one sound and always the same sound.

A few examples will demonstrate how far modern English spelling has departed from the actual sounds it is supposed to represent. The word *ought* consists of five letters, but only two sounds—the vowel sound as in *ball* [bɔl] and a *t* [ɔt]. The same spelling, *ough*, produces six different sounds and combinations of sounds in *through* [θru], *though* [ðo], *trough* [trɔf], *bought* [bɔt], *bough* [baʊ], and *enough* [ɪnʌf]. On the other hand, the same vowel sound *ee* [i] is spelled in nine different ways in the words *feet, feat, be, people, receive, key, believe, quay,* and *machine*. Consider the different ways in which the letter *a* is pronounced in *man* [mæn], *say* [se], *barn* [barn], *hall* [hɔl], *human* [hjumən], and *any* [ɛnɪ]. It is thus futile, and misleading, to talk about the *a* sound, for example, unless some key word is used to identify it, for if it is the '*a* sound' in *ball* that is referred to, it isn't *a* [e] at all, but rather *aw* [ɔ].

One of the reasons for such confusion becomes plain when we realize that we have some 45 sounds in English speech but only 26 letters with which to represent them. Furthermore, of these 26 letters, three—*q, c,* and *x*—are useless, since they always duplicate sounds also represented by other letters; for example, *q* is usually *kw*, as in *quick* [kwɪk], *c* is *s* or *k*, or entirely silent as in *back* [bæk].

The teacher, therefore, in testing and appraising the speech of her pupils, must learn to think and listen in terms of speech sounds, since nobody talks in alphabet letters. It can be seen immediately that at least an elementary knowledge of phonetics (the study of speech sounds) is a most valuable asset to the teacher. The most important tool of phonetics is the phonetic alphabet, in which one symbol is used to represent one sound that is always the same. It will be to the advantage of the teacher to use this system of sound identification and representation when she is analyzing speech; it is the easiest and surest method of recording what is actually heard, as well as the most effective means of becoming conscious of speech sounds as separate and distinct entities.

The Phonetic Alphabet

A simplified form of the phonetic alphabet is included immediately below. The phonetic symbol is given in the first column. This is followed by a key word that illustrates the use of that sound. The third column contains words illustrating several other spellings for the same sound. As we have already noticed, some of the sounds are regularly spelled in as many as eight or ten different ways, but only the most representative examples are included in this list.

Phonetic Symbols for American Speech Sounds

CONSONANTS

Symbol	Key Word	Representative Spellings
[p]	*p*ig [pɪg]	a*pp*le [æpl̩], ca*p*e [kep]
[b]	*b*ig [bɪg]	e*bb* [ɛb], tri*b*e [traɪb]
[t]	*t*op [tɑp]	a*tt*end [ətɛnd], *Th*omas [tɑməs]
[d]	*d*ay [de]	la*dd*er [lædɚ], bla*d*e [bled]
[k]	*k*ey [ki]	li*qu*or [lɪkɚ], *c*an [kæn], a*cc*ount [əkɑʊnt]
[g]	*g*o [go]	*gu*est [gɛst], *gh*ost [gost], e*gg* [ɛg]
[h]	*h*e [hi]	*wh*o [hu]

CONSONANTS

Symbol	Key Word	Representative Spellings
[f]	*f*ee [fi]	rou*gh* [rʌf], *ph*onetic [fənɛtɪk], pu*ff* [pʌf]
[v]	*v*ine [vaɪn]	o*f* [ʌv], do*v*e [dʌv]
[θ]	*th*in [θɪn]	(spelled only with *th*)
[ð]	*th*en [ðɛn]	(spelled only with *th*)
[s]	*s*ent [sɛnt]	*c*ent [sɛnt], le*ss*on [lɛsən], nie*c*e [nis], gee*s*e [gis]
[z]	*z*oo [zu]	hi*s* [hɪz], bu*zz* [bʌz], free*z*e [friz]
[ʃ]	*sh*ip [ʃɪp]	*s*ure [ʃʊr], na*ti*on [neʃən], fi*ss*ure [fɪʃɚ]
[ʒ]	a*z*ure [æʒɚ]	mea*s*ure [mɛʒɚ], gara*g*e [gərɑʒ]
[tʃ]	*ch*ip [tʃɪp]	crea*tu*re [kritʃɚ], wa*tch* [watʃ]
[dʒ]	*j*oy [dʒɔɪ]	*g*entle [dʒɛntl̩], sol*di*er [soldʒɚ], he*dge* [hɛdʒ]
[m]	*m*e [mi]	gra*mm*ar [græmɚ], sole*m*n [sɑləm], li*mb* [lɪm]
[n]	*n*ap [næp]	*kn*ee [ni], *gn*aw [nɔ], pe*nn*y [pɛnɪ]
[ŋ]	si*ng* [sɪŋ]	si*n*k [sɪŋk]
[l]	*l*amp [læmp]	E*ll*a [ɛlə], who*l*e [hol]
[r]	*r*un [rʌn]	a*rr*ive [əraɪv], *wr*eck [rɛk]
[j]	*y*ou [ju]	*u*nite [junaɪt], on*i*on [ʌnjən]
[w]	*w*on [wʌn]	ang*u*ish [æŋgwɪʃ]
[hw]	*wh*en [hwɛn]	(always spelled with *wh*)

VOWELS

Symbol	Key Word	Representative Spellings
[i]	*s*ee [si]	*sea* [si], recei*ve* [rɪsiv], beli*e*ve [bɪliv]
[ɪ]	s*i*t [sɪt]	b*u*sy [bɪzɪ], pr*e*tty [prɪtɪ], h*ea*r [hɪr], b*ui*ld [bɪld]
[e]	*a*ge [edʒ]	br*ea*k [brek], th*ey* [ðe], h*ai*l [hel], s*ay* [se]
[ɛ]	m*e*t [mɛt]	br*ea*d [brɛd], f*ai*r [fɛr], *a*ny [ɛnɪ]
[æ]	c*a*sh [kæʃ]	(customarily spelled with *a*)
[ɑ]	f*a*ther [fɑðɚ]	h*o*nest [ɑnəst] (as pronounced in certain areas)

VOWELS

Symbol	Key Word	Representative Spellings
[ɔ]	*all* [ɔl]	*ought* [ɔt], *taught* [tɔt], *law* [lɔ], *broad* [brɔd]
[o]	*go* [go]	*boat* [bot], *soul* [sol], *low* [lo], *hoe* [ho]
[ʊ]	*look* [lʊk]	*full* [fʊl], *should* [ʃʊd]
[u]	*moon* [mun]	*group* [grup], *grew* [gru], *true* [tru]
[ʌ]	*cut* [kʌt]	*love* [lʌv], *trouble* [trʌbl̩], *flood* [flʌd]
[ɝ]	*bird* [bɝd]	*her* [hɝ], *word* [wɝd], *fur* [fɝ], *heard* [hɝd] (General American pronunciation)
[ɜ]	*bird* [bɜd]	*her* [hɜ], *word* [wɜd], *fur* [fɜ], *heard* [hɜd] (Southern and Eastern Pronunciation)
[ɚ]	*ever* [ɛvɚ]	*actor* [æktɚ], *liar* [laɪɚ], *murmur* [mɝmɚ] (General American pronunciation)
[ə]	*ever* [ɛvə]	*actor* [æktə], *liar* [laɪə], *murmur* [mɜmə] (Southern and Eastern pronunciation)
[ə]	*above* [əbʌv]	*connect* [kənɛkt], *acid* [æsəd], *suppose* [səpoz]

DIPHTHONGS

Symbol	Key Word	Representative Spellings
[aɪ]	*ride* [raɪd]	*lie* [laɪ], *buy* [baɪ], *dye* [daɪ]
[aʊ]	*how* [haʊ]	*flour* [flaʊr]
[ɔɪ]	*voice* [vɔɪs]	*boy* [bɔɪ]
[ju]	*cute* [kjut]	*union* [junjən], *few* [fju]

Exercises for Ear Training and Use of the Phonetic Alphabet

A few observations regarding the make-up of the phonetic alphabet may be in order at this point. In the first place, it will be observed that many of the symbols for consonants are the same as those of conventional spelling. The only new symbols are for sounds that are not adequately or correctly represented by alphabet letters. For example, the initial sound in the word *thin* [θɪn] is spelled *th,* but there is neither [t] nor [h] in this sound, so we need a new symbol, [θ]. Moreover, the same two letters are used for a different sound in *then* [ðɛn], which is formed in the mouth the same as the other *th* [θ], but this time a voice element is added, the same as in [d] when contrasted with [t]. Do you hear the difference between the initial sound in *den* [dɛn], when contrasted with *ten* [tɛn]? Try the same thing with *thin* [θɪn] and *then* [ðɛn]. Study the new symbols in the consonant list and compare them with the conventional spelling in the examples given, and you will see that in each case the alphabet symbols are either inadequate or misleading. For example, in speech there is no [s] or [h] in *ship* [ʃɪp], no [n] or [g] in *sing* [sɪŋ], and the *wh* in *when* is actually pronounced backward with the *h* first—[hwɛn]. Try the word alound in 'slow motion' and you will hear the [hw] beginning, unless you pronounce *wh* as [w], as many people do.

The vowels present more new symbols for the simple reason that we have only six alphabet letters—*a, e, i, o, u,* and *y*—to represent some fifteen vowel sounds and four additional diphthongs. But note that the phonetic symbols generally have the same sounds as the letters do in most foreign languages. That is, the letter *i* is pronounced as *ee, e* as *a, u* as *oo, a* as *ah,* et cetera. Special study and attention should be given the use of the symbol [ə] for several reasons: (1) it can be spelled in many different ways; (2) since it is an unstressed sound (a weak form of the vowel in *up* [ʌp]), it is often difficult to identify; and (3) it is one of the most common sounds in English speech. Special attention should also be given to the stressed form of the vowel sound in *bird* [bɝd]. Compare it with the weak, unstressed form of the same sound as heard in the final syllable of *ever* [ɛvɚ] as pronounced in the speech of those who speak the General American dialect.

One further word about the sound [ɝ]—although it is always spelled with an *r* following a vowel as in *fur* [fɝ], *fir* [fɝ], *her* [hɜ˞], et cetera, or more than one vowel as in *heard* [hɜ˞d], there is actually only one sound involved, the prolonged sound of *r* itself, an in *err*. The accompanying vowel sounds are never heard as such. Somewhat the same situation exists with respect to the unstressed form of [ɜ˞], the weak vowel [ə˞]. This is also spelled in a variety of ways, as in *actor* [æktə˞], *better* [bɛtə˞], *mustard* [mʌstə˞d], *surprise* [sə˞praɪz], and *glamour* [glæmə˞]. Although spelled differently, all of these words contain the simple, unstressed vowel [ə˞]. The foregoing examples were all taken from General American speech. If you were brought up in certain sections of the East or South, you would use a different vowel, [ɜ], for the stressed position, and the unstressed vowel [ə] for the unstressed position. Thus, *murmur* would be pronounced [mɜmə]. The vowel [ɜ] is also heard in British speech.

The first step in learning to use the phonetic alphabet, as in any form of speech education or re-education, is to learn to think in terms of speech sounds rather than written alphabet letters. The way a word sounds often bears little relationship to the way it looks. For example, the word *suns* ends with the letter *s*, but in speech this final sound is actually a *z*—[sʌnz]. Try it aloud; do you hear the [z] at the end? The same is true of *his* [hɪz], and *is* [ɪz]. Try these aloud, too, and you will hear the [z] at the end. However, *this* which looks similar to *his* does actually end in [s]. Compare the two and you will see. The words *ripped* [rɪpt] and *rigged* [rɪgd] both end with the letter *d*, but it is obvious that when they are pronounced the final sound is not the same. Try it.

Likewise we need to become aware of what we know when we stop to think about it—that there is no [k] in *knot* [nɑt], no [n] in *sink* [sɪŋk], no [p] or [h] in *phonics* [fɑnɪks], no [t] or [h] in *they* [ðe], and, of course, no [b] in *thumb* [θʌm]. We need to remember also that *taught*, which has six letters, has only three sounds, [tɔt], and that the *eigh* in *height* [haɪt], the *ie* in *lie* [laɪ], the *ye* in *lye* [laɪ], the *y* in *by* [baɪ], and *uy* in *buy* [baɪ] all spell the same sound—the diphthong [aɪ].

Furthermore, we do not pronounce two *s's* in *miss* [mɪs] or
two *t's* in *bottle* [batl] simply because they happen to be spelled
that way.

One further problem in spoken language needs to be explored
briefly—the relationship of stress to the pronunciation of individual sounds or combinations of sounds. For example, the
word *man* is normally pronounced [mæn], but in the word
postman the [æ] changes to [ə] and the word becomes [post-
mən], simply because the second syllable becomes unstressed—
it is more quickly and lightly spoken. How do you pronounce
the word *papa?* Do you stress the first syllable and say [papə],
or the second syllable and say [pəpa]? Note that the [a] changes
to [ə] when it becomes unstressed. The same thing happens to
the *e* in *garment* [garmənt], the *i's* in *university* [junəvɝsətɪ],
the *o* in *converse* [kənvɝs], and the *u* in *unless* [ənlɛs]. As
stated previously, the [ə] is a very common sound in speech.

Very much the same thing happens when words get together
in the stream of speech, where individual words act like syllables
within a word. Take the simple statement, 'I see the cat.' This
looks like four separate words put together—[aɪ si ði kæt]—
which is the way a second grader might read it. We know that
is not the way it sounds when spoken in normal speech, which
is more like [aɪ si ðə kæt]. Unstressing the *the* changes the
vowel to the unstressed [ə]. The same thing happens to many
other short connective words in the run of speech, such as
from, of, an, and, but, and *was.* These examples illustrate the
value of learning to listen to the sounds in the stream of speech
as they are actually spoken. And the phonetic alphabet enables
us to record what we hear.

1. Study carefully the examples included below. Look at the
printed word, pronounce it carefully aloud to see whether you
can hear each of the sounds in it. Then compare what you
hear with the phonetic transcription of that word. Do you see
the correspondence between the sound and the symbol in each
case? Compare with the key to the phonetic alphabet given
earlier.

heat	[hit]	true	[tru]
long	[lɔŋ]	should	[ʃʊd]
think	[θɪŋk]	beauty	[bjutɪ]
around	[əraʊnd]	measure	[mɛʒɚ]
where	[hwɛr]	call	[kɔl]
city	[sɪtɪ]	jump	[dʒʌmp]
heard	[hɝd]	are	[ɑr]
Salem	[seləm]	quote	[kwot]
fleece	[flis]	mother	[mʌðɚ]
she	[ʃi]	honor	[ɑnɚ]
house	[haʊs]	freshman	[frɛʃmən]
they	[ðe]	advertise	[ædvɚtaɪz]
chimes	[tʃaɪmz]	can't	[kænt]

2. Transcribe the following simple words, using phonetic symbols. Refer freely to the key included earlier as well as to the examples just given. Pronounce each word aloud several times slowly and carefully, although you must avoid distorting any of the sounds in doing so. Listen for the sounds and put down each one as you hear it. Ignore the conventional spelling.

hill	school	money	books
get	bag	piece	calm
stop	salt	rug	agree
lazy	point	around	right
booth	these	vista	better
nurse	wish	yarn	chest
white	June	long	dance
bank	trees	leaped	quick

3. Most of the words in Exercise 2 were made up of single syllables. Incidentally, can you pick out those with more than one syllable? The words in the following list contain two or more syllables. You may find these more difficult to analyze for their component sounds because the problem of stress or accent is involved in the pronunciation of most polysyllabic words, and, as we have seen, a change of stress may produce a change of sound. Proceed as you did above, listening carefully

as you pronounce the word aloud, trying to catch each separate sound. Try to pronounce the word naturally in relation to individual sounds, even though you put it into 'slow motion' to make analysis easier. Remember that every unstressed vowel that sounds like a short, weak form of the vowel in *up* [ʌp] is transcribed as [ə], regardless of how it is spelled. Remember, too, that the weak form of [ɝ], as we hear in the final syllable of *letter* [lɛtɚ], is transcribed as [ɚ] if your pronunciation pattern conforms to General American, but [ə] if your speech is Eastern or Southern American, in which case the word would be [lɛtə]. *Perverse* would be pronounced as [pəvɜs] instead of [pɚvɜs]. Do you hear the difference?

suppose	supper	football	autocrat
gasoline	isolate	special	feature
meadow	evoke	dictate	dogmatic
enough	phonetics	friendly	surpass
further	kingdom	quality	occasion
frequently	similar	champion	cabbage

4. Now, let us try some phrases and simple sentences similar to the following examples: *around the block* [əraʊnd ðə blɑk], *out of luck* [aʊt əv lʌk], *from time to time* [frəm taɪm tə taɪm], *in and about* [ɪn ənd əbaʊt], *the boy went to see a circus* [ðə bɔɪ wɛnt tə si ə sɝkəs]. You will note that the weak, unstressed [ə] occurs very frequently in these examples, as it will in the natural flow of speech. Just listen for the individual sounds and transcribe them as you hear them spoken naturally by yourself or some one else in the following examples:

a. bread and butter
   down the street
   for better or for worse
   sink or swim
   from here and there
   on top of the world

b. The boy stood on the burning deck
c. Birds of a feather flock together
d. He was trying to catch a fish
e. This is the house that Jack built

f. What was that you brought home from the store?

g. Mary had a little lamb,
   Its fleece was white as snow.
   And everywhere that Mary went
   The lamb was sure to go.

h. Twinkle, twinkle little star,
   How I wonder what you are;
   Up, above the world so high,
   Like a diamond in the sky.

5. Now, let us reverse the process. Can you 'translate' the following sentences into speech?

a. [wɪθ fənɛtɪks, æz wɪð mɛnɪ ʌðɚ θɪŋgz, præktɪs meks pɚfɪkt]

b. [dɪd ju hæv mʌtʃ dɪfəkʌltɪ wɪð ðə privɪəs əsaɪnmənt?]

c. [ə mɪnəməm kors ɪn fənɛtɪks juʒʊlɪ læsts ə fʊl səmɛstɚ]

d. [hwɛn wɚkɪŋ wɪθ spitʃ dɪsɔrdɚz, ə trend ɪr ɪz ɪsɛnʃəl]

e. [fənɛtɪks ɪz fʌn hwɛn ju gen ə lɪtl̩ fəsɪlətɪ wɪð ət]

f. [sɛvrəl wɚdz ɪn ðɪz sɛntənsɪz kən bi prənaʊnst ɪn mor ðən·wʌn we, kænt ðe?]

g. [ðə wɚdz ɪn ðɪz ɛksɚsaɪzɪz ɑr trænskraɪbd əkɔrdɪŋ tu ði ɔθɚz on prənʌnsieʃən. jurz me dɪfɚ sʌmhwɑt]

h. [lɛts kənklud wɪð ən izɪ wʌn]

6. Perhaps the following exercise will provide you with some practice in discriminative listening. Take a look at the list of words below. Following each word in phonetic transcription are two different pronunciations. Pronounce each example, 'translating' the phonetic symbols as faithfully as you can. Which pronunciation would you say was the more acceptable in each case?

poor	[pʊr]	[por]
Mary	[mɛrɪ]	[merɪ]
fellow	[fɛlo]	[fɛlə]
fog	[fɑg]	[fɔg]
door	[dor]	[dɔr]
stomach	[stʌmɪk]	[stʌmək]
new	[nju]	[nu]

because	[bɪkɔz]	[bɪkʌz]
when	[hwɛn]	[wɛn]
luxury	[lʌgʒərɪ]	[lʌkʃərɪ]
adult	[ədʌlt]	[ædʌlt]
room	[rum]	[rʊm]
candidate	[kænədet]	[kændədet]
probably	[prabəblɪ]	[prablɪ]
quantity	[kwantətɪ]	[kwanətɪ]
hundred	[hʌndɚd]	[hʌndrəd]
February	[fɛbruɛrɪ]	[fɛbjʊɛrɪ]
creek	[krik]	[krɪk]
grimace	[grɪməs]	[grɪmes]
coupon	[kupan]	[kjupan]
harass	[hærəs]	[həræs]
penalize	[pɛnəlaɪz]	[pinəlaɪz]
tremor	[trimɚ]	[trɛmɚ]
zoology	[zoalədʒɪ]	[zualədʒɪ]
usually	[juʒəlɪ]	[juʒʊəlɪ]

Locating the Child with Speech Disabilities

In many instances no formal survey or special speech tests are necessary to reveal the particular children who have disabilities in the oral use of language. Through recitations and other forms of classroom activities the teacher has usually had an opportunity to observe the speech performance of each pupil on numerous occasions. If she is sufficiently speech conscious to know what to listen for, she will have located the children who are in need of speech help without their having been aware that they were under observation. Or if she is fortunate enough to have the services of a speech clinician, the names of her pupils with speech or hearing problems will be furnished to her.

Survey Tests

In other cases it will be more convenient or more desirable to run through an entire class, or perhaps several classes, with a rapid, screening-type survey test that will (1) disclose those children with speech problems and (2) provide the teacher with an opportunity to record in some detail the exact nature of the disability, provided it is not too complicated. For this purpose a reading test is usually employed with those children who are sufficiently advanced in reading to manage it. With a test such as those that follow, the teacher can run through an average-size class in a very short time by having each child read in turn while she takes notes on his performance. While the tests are designed primarily to disclose errors of articulation, observations can also be made on the child's voice, speech rhythm, and symbolization, so far as his reading is concerned, at least.

1. *Test for older children* The following paragraph contains all of the sounds of the English language. All consonants appear in each of the three positions—initial, medial, and final—in which they are regularly found in English. The consonants most commonly found to be defective, such as [l], [r], and [s], are repeated a number of times. All of the vowels and diphthongs occur at least once, and many of them are used in at least two of the three positions. It is recommended for use with older children and more advanced readers.

It is usually rather easy to reach the Virginia Theater. Board car number fifty-six somewhere along Churchill Street and ride to the highway. Transfer there to the Mississippi bus. When you arrive at Judge Avenue, begin walking toward the business zone. You will pass a gift shop displaying little children's playthings that often look so clever you will wish yourself young again: such things as books and toys, and, behind the counter, a playroom with an elegant red rug and smooth, shining mirrors. Beyond this shop are the National Bank and the Globe Garage. Turn south at the next corner; the theater is to your left.

2. *Test for younger children* The following speech test also contains all of the English speech sounds, distributed in a manner similar to that found in the preceding selection. The chief

difference is that, because of its more elementary nature, the following test is more suitable for pupils in the intermediate grades.

We have a club of six boys and girls who are full of real pep. Each Thursday we visit the beach. Ruth, Roy, and I meet at Lily's house at noon. Her father and uncle drive us to Judge Avenue, where everyone takes a taxi to the seashore. I enjoy running about upon the smooth, yellow sand in the fresh air, and dashing into the foaming waves. All this is healthy exercise, and I soon become somewhat hungry. We usually ask to eat our lunches in the shade of the big church behind South Garage. If we have time, we often walk to the zoo, which is just beyond Orange Street.

Articulation Tests for Individual Sounds

If the teacher or speech clinician wishes more exact information about just which sounds are defective and in what way they are improperly formed, omitted, or substituted, then a test somewhat more complete and analytical than the foregoing must be employed. Such a test should be arranged so that only one sound is under observation at any one time, and the examiner listens only for that sound. It is desirable, although not always necessary, to test each sound in each of the three positions—initial, medial, and final. If there is time to test for only one position, then the initial is to be preferred; if the sound is found to be defective or missing at the beginning of the word, it is almost certain to be defective in the other two positions as well, although perhaps not so conspicuously. Since the converse is not always true, however, a test using only the initial position must be regarded as less thorough than the other type.

1. *Test for non-readers*   There is no rapid or simple test that can be used with non-readers or with children in the lower grades where reading is still laborious. In the case of such individuals the speech must be judged from spontaneous samples arising out of the child's normal activities in which speech plays a part, or it must be elicited in response to requests to name

objects or identify pictures. A list of suitable pictures or objects is included under each sound in the test immediately following. In addition, pictures that illustrate the first word in each group have been provided. In most instances this one picture will suffice as a stimulus for each sound, but where additional checks are desired on certain sounds, attractive illustrations, often in full color, can be found in the advertising sections of popular magazines. These can be used to supplement the pictures given here, or readily available objects, such as books, pencils, lamps, et cetera, can also be employed.

Only consonants have been included in the test for non-readers, because vowels are least likely to be defective in the speech of the child. The sound should always be tried first in the initial position, examples of which have been included for most sounds. Additional examples of the sound as used in the medial and final positions have also been included for many of the sounds. The teacher should avoid pronouncing the word for the child, and where the simple request 'What is that?' fails to secure the desired response from the child, a more indirect method may be necessary, in which reference is made to the story-telling aspects of the picture, for example, or in which the procedure is turned into a game.

Speech Test for Non-Readers

Sound	Suggested Pictures or Objects Which Illustrate the Sound
1. [p]	pig, pie, pencil, apple, puppy, cap
2. [b]	bubble, bear, boat, boy, baby, tub
3. [t]	table, toes, kitty, bottle, hat
4. [d]	duck, dog, doll, candy, Indian, bread
5. [k]	ice cream cone, cup, kitten, chicken, cake
6. [g]	gun, girl, goat, wagon, tiger, egg
7. [f]	fish, finger, elephant, telephone, leaf
8. [v]	vacuum cleaner, valentine, stove, television

	Suggested Pictures or Objects
Sound	*Which Illustrate the Sound*
9. [θ] *th*	thumb, three, birthday cake, toothbrush, bath
10. [ð] *th*	feather, father, mother
11. [s]	Santa Claus, sleep, spoon, bicycle, horse
12. [z]	zebra, zoo, bees, nose, eyes
13. [ʃ] *sh*	shoe, sheep, shovel, washing, goldfish
14. [ʒ] *zh*	not necessary to test; if [ʃ] is defective, [ʒ] will in all likelihood be defective also
15. [tʃ] *ch*	chair, chicken, chin, pitcher, watch
16. [dʒ] *j*	jump, giant, soldier, engine, bridge
17. [m]	monkey, man, Christmas tree, hammer, comb
18. [n]	knife, nest, nose, running, banana, spoon
19. [ŋ] *ng*	swing, drink, monkey, finger
20. [l]	lion, lamp, balloon, yellow, ball
21. [r]	roller skate, rabbit, radio, tree, orange
22. [j] *y*	yarn, yellow, onion
23. [w]	window, wagon, watch, spider web, bow-wow
24. [h]	house, hat, horse, hand
25. [hw] *wh*	wheel, white, whistle, pin wheel

Picture Articulation Test for Non-Readers

[p] pig

[b] bubble

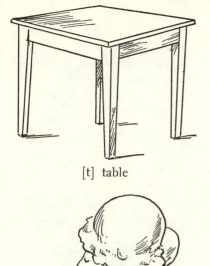

[t] table

[d] duck

[k] ice cream cone

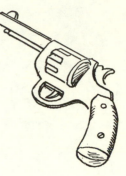

[g] gun

[f] fish

[v] vacuum cleaner

th [θ] thumb

th [ð] feather

[s] Santa Claus

[z] zebra

sh [ʃ] shoe

[h] house

ch [tʃ] chair

j [dʒ] jump

[m] monkey

[n] knife

ng [ŋ] swing

[l] lion

[r] roller skate   *y* [j] yarn

[w] window   *wh* [hw] wheel

2. *Test using sentences—Short form* The following ten sentences contain all of the important consonants, vowels, and diphthongs commonly found in American speech with which the teacher need be concerned. Consonants are tested in the initial position only, with the exception of *zh* [ʒ] and *ng* [ŋ].

CONSONANTS

1. Pat bought two dark colored geese.	*Plosives:*	[p], [b], [t], [d], [k], [g]
2. Thank them for voting.	*Fricatives:*	*th* [θ], *th* [ð], [f], [v]
3. She usually studied zoology.	*Fricatives:*	*sh* [ʃ], *zh* [ʒ], [s], [z]
4. He chased Jack.	*Aspirate:*	[h]; Affricates: *ch* [tʃ], *j* [dʒ]
5. When will you leave, Ruth?	*Glides:*	*wh* [hw], [w], *y* [j], [l], [r]

VOWELS AND DIPHTHONGS

6. Move nothing.	*Nasals:*	[m], [n], *ng* [ŋ]
7. He will pay them back	*Front vowels:*	*ee* [i], short *i* [ɪ], long *a* [e], short *e* [ɛ], short *a* [æ]
8. Who would go call father	*Back vowels:*	*oo* [u], short *oo* [ʊ], *oh* [o], *aw* [ɔ], *ah* [ɑ]
9. Above murder	*Middle vowels:*	short *u* unstressed [ə], short *u* stressed [ʌ], *er* stressed [ɝ], *er* unstressed [ɚ]
10. Boys like you now	*Diphthongs:*	*oi* [ɔɪ], long *i* [aɪ], long *u* [ju], *ow* [aʊ]

3. *Test using sentences—Longer form*   Each of the sentences in the following list is designed to test just one sound. As the pupil reads each sentence, the teacher should listen only for the one sound that the sentence is designed to illustrate. Most of the sounds, especially the consonants, appear in all of the three positions—initial, medial, and final. A complete analysis of the child's speech should include: (1) What sounds are defective? (2) How are they defective? and (3) In what positions do the defects occur? The key to this test will be found immediately following the test.

CONSONANTS

1. Pay me for the apples you want to keep.
2. Bob hurt his elbow and broke a rib.
3. Tom had wanted to buy a new coat.
4. Dan put the ladder back in the shed.
5. Can you keep my books in your locker until I get back?
6. Give me the biggest dog.
7. Harry had a happy childhood.
8. Four men went out after breakfast to look for the wolf.
9. Very few people ever saw the cave.
10. Thelma has a birthday next month.
11. This old leather has worn very smooth.

12. Susie went skating with her sister and slipped on the ice.
13. Zella and her cousin went out to feed the hens.
14. Shirley's father went down to the seashore to fish.
15. He came late as usual.
16. Charles was asked by his teacher to make a speech.
17. Jack put the pigeon back in its cage.
18. More men are needed during the summer to work on the farm.
19. Near the window sat a little kitten.
20. The young man was singing a song.
21. Last week violets were growing all over that hill.
22. Robert ran around the car.
23. Yesterday I saw a million butterflies.
24. Walk twelve miles along this highway.
25. White daisies were blooming everywhere.

VOWELS AND DIPHTHONGS

26. Eat some meat and drink this tea.
27. Indians came to visit the city.
28. Eight boys came to play.
29. Eddie kept the pencil in his desk.
30. Andy sang every evening in camp.
31. Are you learning to drive your father's car?
32. All boys should be taught to obey the law.
33. Open the window a moment before you go.
34. Put the book on the table.
35. Ruth wants to play school every afternoon.
36. Under the truck he found the gun.
37. Early in the morning the bird would sing to her.
38. Father goes fishing every summer.
39. About eleven boys agreed that it was a good idea.
40. I like blackberry pie.
41. Out of the field and down the road came the cow.
42. Roy has a big voice but he is a little boy.
43. You should meet the new pupil whose name is Hugh.

Key to the Articulation Test

CONSONANTS

1. [p]   *p*ay, a*pp*les, kee*p*
2. [b]   *B*ob, el*b*ow, ri*b*
3. [t]   *T*om, wan*t*ed, coa*t*
4. [d]   *D*an, la*dd*er, she*d*
5. [k]   *c*an, boo*k*s, lo*ck*er, ba*ck*
6. [g]   *g*ive, bi*gg*est, do*g*
7. [h]   *H*arry, *h*ad, *h*appy, child*h*ood
8. [f]   *f*our, a*f*ter, break*f*ast, wol*f*
9. [v]   *v*ery, e*v*er, ca*v*e
10. [θ] *th*   *Th*elma, bir*th*day, mon*th*
11. [ð] *th*   *th*is, lea*th*er, smoo*th*
12. [s]   *S*usie, *s*kating, *s*ister, *s*lipped, ice
13. [z]   *Z*ella, cou*s*in, hen*s*
14. [ʃ] *sh*   *Sh*irley's, sea*sh*ore, fi*sh*
15. [ʒ] *zh*   u*s*ual
16. [tʃ] *ch*   *Ch*arles, tea*ch*er, spee*ch*
17. [dʒ] *j*   *J*ack, pi*g*eon, ca*g*e
18. [m]   *m*ore, *m*en, su*mm*er, far*m*
19. [n]   *n*ear, wi*n*dow, kitte*n*
20. [ŋ] *ng*   you*ng*, si*ng*ing, so*ng*
21. [l]   *l*ast, vio*l*ets, a*ll*, hi*ll*
22. [r]   *R*obert, *r*an, a*r*ound, ca*r*
23. [j] *y*   *y*esterday, mill*i*on
24. [w]   *w*alk, t*w*elve, high*w*ay
25. [hw] *wh*   *wh*ite, every*wh*ere

VOWELS AND DIPHTHONGS

26. [i] *ee*   *ea*t, m*ea*t, t*ea*
27. [ɪ] *ĭ*   *I*ndians, v*i*sit, cit*y*
28. [e] *ā*   *ei*ght, c*a*me, pl*ay*
29. [ɛ] *ĕ*   *E*ddie, k*e*pt, p*e*ncil, d*e*sk
30. [æ] *ă*   *A*ndy, s*a*ng, c*a*mp
31. [ɑ] *ah*   *a*re, f*a*ther's c*a*r
32. [ɔ] *aw*   *a*ll, t*au*ght, l*aw*
33. [o] *o*   *o*pen, m*o*ment, g*o*
34. [ʊ] *ŏŏ*   p*u*t, b*oo*k
35. [u] *ōō*   R*u*th, sch*oo*l, aftern*oo*n
36. [ʌ] *ŭ*   *u*nder, tr*u*ck, g*u*n
37. [ɝ], [ɜ] *er*   *ear*ly, b*ir*d, h*er*

38. [ɝ], [ə] *er* fath*er*, summ*er*
39. [ə] *a*bout, *a*greed, ide*a*
40. [aɪ] *ī* *I*, l*i*ke, p*ie*
41. [aʊ] *ow* *ou*t, d*ow*n, c*ow*
42. [ɔɪ] *oi* R*oy*, v*oi*ce, b*oy*
43. [ju] *ū* *you*, p*u*pil, H*u*gh

General Observations on Testing

It will be observed that the foregoing tests are most useful in detecting disabilities of articulation. Fortunately they can also be used to provide an opportunity for observing the pupil's voice and speech characteristics in general. While the pupil is reading the sentences or paragraphs, the teacher can also check on the loudness, pitch, and quality of his voice, the rhythm and tempo of his speech, and his general behavior while performing. More detailed instructions will be included in subsequent chapters with regard to the recognition and diagnosis of the more common types of specific speech disabilities.

It might be well to remind the teacher at this point, however, that a test limited to a reading performance may be inadequate as a means of disclosing all of the habitual characteristics of an individual's voice and speech as they would normally be seen and heard in a natural speech situation. Children frequently do not read with the same pitch and intensity of voice, the same tempo and rhythm pattern, or even the same intonation and general quality of voice as they use when talking naturally. Therefore, certain disabilities may be more, or less, obvious in reading than in speaking, depending on the nature of the problem. Stutterers, for example, may learn to read aloud with scarcely a trace of difficulty but may be virtually speechless when they attempt to respond in a normal speech situation. In the case of other individuals the converse may be true.

If, for any reason, the teacher has not had previous opportunity to observe the child's performance through daily work and recitation in the classroom, the more formalized articulation tests should be supplemented with a minimum amount, at least, of spontaneous speech. Suitable spontaneous responses can usually be elicited by the use of such stimulus questions as 'What pets do you have at home?' 'What do you like best to do when you go home from school?' 'What did you do last Sunday?' or 'What sport do you like best, and why?' With the average child, any question such as those suggested will serve to open up a subject for a brief, informal chat, provided the examiner displays a suitable degree of interest in the subject and is reasonably facile with appropriate 'come-on' questions to keep the conversation going. The amount of time involved can be kept to a minimum. This performance can either precede or follow the more formal speech test, the personality of the child and the general circumstances of the situation determining which will likely be the more efficacious.

References

Ammons, R., and H. Ammons, *Full-Range Picture Vocabulary Test*, Psychological Test Specialists, Missoula, Mont., 1948.

Carrell, James, and Wm. R. Tiffany, *Phonetics: Application to Speech Improvement*, McGraw-Hill Book Company, New York, 1960.

Dunn, L., *Peabody Picture Vocabulary Test*, American Guidance Service, Minneapolis, Minn., 1965.

Leutenegger, Ralph R., *The Sounds of American English*, Scott, Foresman, Chicago, 1963.

Templin, Mildred, and Frederic Darley, *The Templin-Darley Test of Articulation*, Bureau of Educational Research and Service, University of Iowa, Iowa City, Iowa, 1960.

Thomas, Charles K., *An Introduction to the Phonetics of American English*, 2nd. ed., Ronald Press, New York, 1958.

Travis, Lee Edward, ed., *Handbook of Speech Pathology and Audiology*, Appleton-Century-Crofts, New York, 1971, Chaps. 24, 25.

Van Riper, Charles, *Speech Correction: Principles and Methods*, 4th ed., Prentice-Hall, Englewood Cliffs, N. J., 1963, Chap. 2.

Wise, Claude M., *Applied Phonetics*, Prentice-Hall, Englewood Cliffs, N. J., 1957, Part I.

(For more extensive tests involving speech and language, consult the References following Chapter IV.)

III

Development of Speech and Language

Many theories have been advanced from time to time to explain how man first learned to speak. Since the whole problem is shrouded in the mists of antiquity and speculation, the answer may never be found. Social psychologists are agreed, however, that even though we may not know *how* man learned to talk, we can be fairly certain that we know *why* he learned. He needed some means of communication by which he could exert a measure of control over his environment, particularly his social environment. Speech and, later, other forms of language such as writing, supplied that need most effectively and thus became the most potent force in effecting social organization and control, as it also became the instrument through which man's intelligence could make itself manifest. For, as man's thinking ability developed, it was necessary that he have something to think with; language symbols thus became the tools, or media, of his mental functioning. In fact, the two, thought and speech, are so closely interrelated that it cannot be said which preceded the other in man's development. They undoubtedly emerged together—there is evidence to indicate that they are little more than two sides of the same thing.

In our preoccupation with the many problems of education we are sometimes prone to forget the vital role that language, predominantly oral in the case of the child, plays in his social and intellectual development. In this connection Allport, who was vitally interested in the relation of language to the social interaction of human beings, states, 'Making and responding to language stimuli, oral and written, has become deeply rooted in our most vital interests. . . Education is the socialization and training of the individual through language symbols' [1]—an observation which is as true today as it was then. Despite its obvious importance, we have often been guilty of taking speech, and language, for granted and have likewise been insensitive to the significance of speech and language handicaps, without realizing what they can do to hamper the individual's social and educational progress. We have too often forgotten the dual role of speech as the tool of thought and the medium of communication.

In any consideration of oral and written language and its place in the educational process two important factors which condition its development and functioning must ever be borne in mind: (a) language is wholly a product of the individual's social environment, and (b) it is not innate or 'instinctive' but rather a learned process which each child must acquire anew. In these respects it differs from such 'natural' functions as walking, eating, or crying. While the individual would naturally get about, eat, and cry in the normal course of his development, he would never speak unless he were taught to, or perhaps more properly, he learned to, as a child. Speech is thus a derivative of the child's social heritage; as such it has been called an 'overlaid function,' because it makes use of organs and mechanisms of the body intended by nature to serve basic, biological needs. Strictly speaking, there are no speech organs as such in the human animal. The larynx, for example, of first importance in speech, was originally developed as a valve to prevent foreign

1. Floyd H. Allport, *Social Psychology*, Houghton Mifflin, Boston, 1924, p. 197.

matter from entering the trachea. The lungs, which furnish the motive power for voice production, as their primary function ventilate the blood by supplying it with oxygen and carry off waste products that arise from the process of metabolism. The mouth is primarily concerned with the intake and mastication of food. Speech, therefore, is an activity developed by man and superimposed upon these basic biological mechanisms. It is no more a natural activity for him than is dancing or singing, probably not as much. The principal difference is that speech has come to have a much deeper social significance and intellectual involvement.

The most important implication from these considerations is this: since speech is a learned activity, it follows that it can be poorly learned. The process of learning to talk is largely one of imitation; the child comes to use the kind of speech he hears. The model thus set is frequently faulty. This factor plus all of the others that commonly function in a learning situation—motivation, readiness, emotional stability, and the sensory and motor abilities that go to make up what we call aptitude—all exert some influence on the child's speech to facilitate or retard its development, or cause it to become maldeveloped. Thus it can be seen why a substantial percentage of the speech defects found among school children are traceable to causes no more serious than poor speech habits. Also, it can be appreciated why there is definite hope for many of these problems, for undesirable habits can be modified or eliminated and more desirable ones developed in their place.

The Development of Speech in the Child

Perhaps the nature and essential function of speech will be understood better if a brief outline is given of the child's progress in learning to speak, and if some account is taken of the various factors that influence this development. It is fairly common practice among authorities to divide this development into certain stages or episodes, which are at best only approximate, representing merely the general average from which there are marked deviations in individual instances. Nor are the steps separate and distinct; it is often difficult to tell when a child has progressed from one into another, partly because of typical over-lapping of one stage with another. The concept of stages of progress is a useful one, however, if its limitations are also kept in mind.

Pre-lingual or Crying Stage

During the first month or so of the child's life his general behavior and the use of voice are wholly emotional. The infant's crying during this period is simply a part of his total, undifferentiated response to stimuli coming largely from within his own organism. It is as natural and as meaningless as the thrashing of his arms and legs. It is an automatic, reflexive response which in no sense of the word could be called speech, for at this stage there is no attempt at communication or control of the environment. There is probably little, if any, awareness that an environment exists.

After approximately the end of the first month, however, some differentiation in the child's crying becomes discernible, and the mother can often tell from the sound he makes whether he is hungry, suffering from pain or other physical discomfort, becoming sleepy, or merely taking his daily exercise. The crying is still a part of a total bodily response, but it is growing to be more differentiated as a reflection of more specific emotional and feeling states. In other words, the child is now able to react in a more specific way to specific stimuli or patterns of stimuli. It should be understood, however, that this behavior is still not speech, because the child does not as yet cry in a certain manner with the knowledge that this type of expression will bring forth a desired specific response. It is still reflexive vocalization, but the specialization of response does reflect the process of maturation that is taking place within the child's nervous system. More direct and specific nerve pathways are being established between sensory end-organs, or receptors, and the muscles and glands that are capable of producing a response that is appropriate to stimuli received by those receptors. The differentiated laryngeal activity is simply a part of that more specialized response.

The process of conditioning soon begins to operate at this stage to impart a degree of significance to these varying modes of pre-lingual expression. Contemporary learning theory holds that behavior is influenced by the consequences it generates. In other words, behavior followed by a pleasant response tends to be perpetuated or 'reinforced,' while behavior that produces a painful or unpleasant response to the person or organism involved tends to decrease or disappear. As an example, the child reflexively cries in a certain way; through experience and observation the parent has learned that this particular type of cry indicates that the child is hungry, and the adult satisfies the child by feeding him. It does not take even a very young baby long to discover he can get desirable attention from certain kinds of vocalization, and we thus have the genesis of what could be called a crude kind of speech—vocal expression is used to effect a measure of control over the environment. Baby cries to be picked up and we say he is 'spoiled,' which is only another way of saying he has learned how to get results.

Behavior thus far, however, is on a wholly emotional level and neither the expressive action nor the response is particularly specific. In these respects early vocalization is closely comparable to the speech behavior of animals. Crude though it is, a similar form of laryngeal expression continues to function throughout adult life in the tonal and pitch qualities of the voice and in such pre-lingual and pre-symbolic types of expression as outcries, interjections, and swearing.

While it has been said that during this first period the child cries when he is unhappy and remains silent otherwise, observers have reported apparently happy sounds being produced as well. This gurgling or cooing, referred to as comfort sounds, differs from the babbling to be discussed in the following section primarily with respect to the degree of articulation or resemblance to actual environmental speech sounds in the child's phonation. Cooing is more laryngeal than articulatory but it still may represent something of a transitional link with the following so-called babbling period, which is basically articulatory.

Random Articulation, or Babbling
Subsequent to the stage of crying just discussed and overlapping it comes a period of random articulation or vocal play, often referred to as babbling. In babbling are the roots of articulate speech. While it is true that during the crying state a number of the vowel sounds appear, and a few of the consonants as well, it is not until babbling begins that we hear the variety and combinations of vowels and consonants that will later form the basis of the child's oral language pattern. This stage of development usually begins near the middle of the first six months of the child's life. One significant difference between this and the previous stage should be taken into account—while both types of vocalization are primarily emotional, crying is an expression of a compulsive, unpleasant feeling state, but babbling is indicative of a pleasant mood.

This distinction should be kept in mind when considering the factors that influence the development of speech in the child. Pleasant states of mind facilitate that development, while unpleasant ones retard it, for whenever the unpleasant states become dominant, the child will stop babbling and start to cry. Therefore it can be said that, other things being equal, the happy child will learn to speak faster than the unhappy child, since more of his time will be spent in vocal play.

During this period of vocal experimentation the child will spontaneously produce not only the speech sounds that will ultimately comprise his language pattern but a large number of 'extra' ones as well. These will disappear later when the child begins to restrict his sound production to those speech sounds that become fixed during the echolalia stage of his develop-

ment, discussed further on. Every effort should be made to encourage babbling in the child, for this is his first step toward
true articulate speech.

Siegel cites several experiments which show that vocal output
during this stage can be increased and intensified by the application of an appropriate social stimulus in response to the vocalization. In one typical experiment a group of three-month-old infants demonstrated a significant increase in vocal output when
a female adult leaned over the crib following each vocalization
smiling broadly and encouraging the child with endearing word
play, in contrast to the periods when she leaned over silently and
with an expressionless face.[2] The implication here is for the
mother to enjoy this period of her child's speech development
and participate in it along with the baby by obvious pleasurable
reactions and a great deal of vocal play herself.

Lallation—The Ear-Voice Reflex

Sometime during the babbling period, usually near the end of
the first six months of the child's life, his nervous system will
have matured sufficiently, especially that part having to do with
the discrimination of auditory impressions, to set up a circular
response or feedback between the infant's vocal mechanism and
his ear, and back to his vocal mechanism again. During babbling
the child pronounces a sound or a syllable from which he derives
not only pleasure but an auditory stimulus as well. Through the
formation of a response pattern, the stimulus of hearing the
sound is sufficient to set the vocal mechanism into operation to
produce the sound again, which in turn again stimulates the
ear, which again in turn stimulates the speech mechanism. Thus
a type of circular reflex is set up that can, and frequently does,
proceed virtually *ad infinitum*—all of which explains why the
child gets started saying *da-da-da-da*, for example, and goes on
for hours apparently unable to stop. There is also evidence to

2. Gerald M. Siegel, 'Vocal Conditioning in Infants,' *Journal of Speech
and Hearing Disorders*, February 1969, pp. 3–19.

indicate that the child finds the whole process a most enjoyable one.

This stage in the child's speech development is a significant one for a number of reasons. For one thing, it is the first time that hearing enters significantly into the process and becomes definitely associated with sound production. The congenitally deaf child will continue through at least a part of the babbling period, but his speech development ends there; he does not progress into lallation because hearing is necessary for the establishment of the circular reflexes. Lallation is also significant, as Young points out,[3] because during this period other important phases of the child's neurological maturation are also taking place, especially in the motor pathways having to do with control of the vocal mechanism.

Echolalia—The Effect of Linguistic Environment

After the circular response is well enough established so that the child's hearing his own voice is sufficient to set off the mechanism to produce the same sound again, it is a simple step to transfer the auditory stimulus to a second person. Now the child repeats sounds he hears someone else make, provided they bear a reasonable resemblance to those he has already learned to make by himself. Because the child's auditory discrimination is inferior to that of adults, he will probably hear some resemblance in almost any sound that another person is likely to make. He will then attempt to repeat the sound, or something like it, and the repetition will stimulate him to produce it again; thus the familiar ear-voice reflex is set into operation.

The importance of this stage in the child's speech development can hardly be overestimated because, for the first time, he has become aware, neurologically speaking, of the sounds and sound patterns in his environment. These he will retain because he now responds to them when he hears them; the others which he does not hear around him he will gradually lose from his

3. Kimball Young, *Personality and Problems of Adjustment*, Appleton-Century-Crofts, New York, 1952, p. 140.

'repertoire.' It is during this period, then, that the special sound pattern of the child's native language becomes fixed, as it were, and it is with these sounds, later refined and produced more exactly, that his adult speech will be built. This, briefly, is the role so-called imitation plays in the speech learning of the child, but it is imitation only in a restricted sense, for the child is actually only producing the sounds he has earlier learned how to make by himself. However, its function must not be minimized; it does serve to establish the basic sound pattern of the child's adult speech by providing the standard according to which the crude, random sounds the child has stumbled upon in his vocal play are refined and modified. This period of imitation usually begins toward the end of the first year and lasts more or less indefinitely.

Many attempts have been made to explain in more detail by just what processes and through what steps the effects of 'imitation' operate to 'program' the child to acquire the specific speech sound system of his environmental language, be it English, Chinese, Russian, or what have you. Some years ago Mowrer[4] proposed an explanation of language learning which he called the autism theory, in which he cited the close relationship of love and dependence normally existing between mother and child. Sounds and, later, words uttered by the mother in the presence of the child produce a nice, comforting feeling in the child, who tries to re-create the warmth and comfort of the mother's presence by attempting to repeat the sounds and words he has heard her say. In other words, these are 'mother' sounds, and imitating them involves a predominantly favorable feedback to the child. The implications in this theory for early speech and language facilitation are obvious.

Other explanations of speech development typically involve certain aspects of what has become known as operant conditioning, an example of which was cited by Siegel in a previous sec-

4. O. H. Mowrer, 'Hearing and Speaking: An Analysis of Language Learning,' *Journal of Speech and Hearing Disorders*, May 1958, pp. 143–52.

tion on babbling. According to this viewpoint, those sounds and words which are selectively reinforced by obvious pleasure and encouragement on the part of an adult, usually the mother, are the ones that will become established in the child's speech and language development. After the babbling stage, these reinforced sounds and words are, of course, those most similar to actual speech. Again, the implications are obvious.

Articulate Utterance

As soon as the child has reached the stage at which he will repeat, or attempt to repeat, sounds and words that he hears others make, it is an easy step to the acquiring of true, articulate speech. Meanings become attached to sounds and words through a relatively simple process of association, or conditioning, in which the word and the object for which the word stands appear together. For example, the mother shows the child a ball, at the same time pronouncing the word *ball*. Through the more or less automatic mechanism of echolalia, the child repeats something probably approximating *baw*. Some type of reward will in most instances follow this remarkable performance; the mother will smile, praise the child profusely, and he will be given the ball to play with. After a few experiences like this, the child soon learns that *baw* 'stands for' a round, brightly colored object that can be handled, mouthed, and thrown on the floor. Soon the mere sight of the object is sufficient to evoke the verbal response without any vocal prompting from the mother. The next step is reached when the child says *baw* without the object's being present, meaning 'Where is the ball?' or 'I want the ball.' If, as usually happens, in response to this verbalization the ball is immediately produced and presented to the child by the happy parent, we can truly say that the child has learned to talk because he is now using words deliberately and purposefully with the intention of exerting a measure of control over his environment. This big event occurs, on the average, at the age of about fourteen or fifteen months for girls and fifteen or sixteen months for boys, although many children will say a few recognizable words by one year of age, or even earlier in some cases.

In this way the child's first naming habits develop. His first words are often only crude approximations of adult words, but to him they are meaningful, and usually equally so to the adults in his environment. It should also be observed that the meanings associated with the words in the child's mind are likewise approximate and vague. For example, the word *baw* may be used to designate not only a ball but any object faintly resembling the particular ball of the child's acquaintance, such as an orange, a chunk of modeling clay, or even a brightly colored picture block. Later he will learn that only round things are 'balls'; cubical things are 'blocks.' He will also discover that 'balls' are not good to eat—as oranges are—and later that some balls are big, others small; some are hard, others are soft. In this way the child develops the concepts for which words stand, or, as we more often call them, meanings. These meanings continue to become more specific and more complex as the child's experience expands.

In addition to name words, the child quickly adds action words to his vocabulary, as meanings become attached to such verbs and verb forms as 'come,' 'go bye-bye,' and 'eat' through association of the word with the corresponding action. Descriptive and qualifying words—adjectives and adverbs—come later in the child's language development, and words showing relationship such as conjunctions and prepositions, make their appearance last.

The first words used by the child may refer simply to one object, or class of objects, or to one type of action. Or they may be used with the meaning of a whole sentence in mind. *Da-dy* or *da-da* may be used to indicate 'Where is Daddy?'; 'I want Daddy'; 'Daddy take me'; or some other more or less complete idea. This is referred to as the one-word sentence. Later the child will combine a noun and a verb, as 'Baby go' or 'Daddy come.' More complicated sentences do not ordinarily appear before the beginning of the third year.

Factors Influencing the Development of Speech and Language[5]

Maturation

While it is incorrect to say that speech is a product of maturation, because maturation alone is incapable of producing speech in the child, it is still a very important factor in determining the age at which speech begins, as well as the rate and quality of its development. The child is ready to learn to talk only when his speech organs and nerve centers have matured to a certain point. It will be observed that several of the items to be discussed in the following paragraphs are closely related to maturation. It should also be remembered that there is marked variation among individual children in the degree of maturity to which they have attained at any given age and for any given specific ability or characteristic.

Intelligence

The close relation between speech and language, on the one hand, and intelligence, on the other, has long been recognized, and periodically confirmed by the many studies that have been done on this subject, of which McCarthy's much-cited investigation is an example. She found a consistent and positive relation between size of vocabulary and mental age at each level from 18 months to 78 months.[6] In addition to vocabulary, other aspects of language such as sentence length and complexity also are believed to be related to intelligence. Nor does this relationship reflect merely the heavy dependence of most intelligence tests upon the language function; similar results have been obtained with non-language tests. In brief, it can be said that, other factors being equal (which they seldom are), the child

---

5. Many of the factors discussed briefly in the paragraphs that follow will be dealt with in more detail in the next chapter.
6. Dorothea McCarthy, *Language Development in the Pre-School Child*, University of Minnesota Press, Minneapolis, 1930, p. 121.

with superior intelligence will usually begin to talk at an earlier age, and the quantity and quality of his vocabulary, as well as his general facility with language, will surpass that of his less gifted brother at any given age level. The importance of speech and language in the educational process and the close relation of speech to the thought functions of the individual have already been discussed earlier in this chapter.

Health

Good health facilitates the development of speech for a number of reasons. For one thing, the healthy child has more energy and he will devote more of his time to those types of activities that will hasten the development of the muscles and nerve pathways which make speech possible. Then, too, the healthy child is more likely to be a happy child who will engage vigorously in the vocal-play activities that are so necessary to carry his speech progress through important stages of its development. Moreover, the child with good health is more alert, his senses are keener and his powers of attention superior, and his scope of activity and hence his range of speech-stimulating experiences will be greater than would be the case if the child were not well.

Hearing

Adequate hearing is absolutely essential to the 'natural' development of normal speech. If the child is congenitally deaf, he will never develop any oral speech without specialized instruction. If the hearing is defective while the child is learning to talk, not only will his comprehension be impaired but his speech pattern will almost certainly reflect the influences of the hearing handicap. Hearing deficiencies among young children are much more prevalent than is generally believed. From sampling tests, as well as from hearing surveys, it is estimated that 5 per cent of the elementary-school population suffer from some form of hearing impairment, and that 1 per cent have serious hearing defects which warrant medical attention as well as other forms of special handling.

In order to appreciate the relation of hearing to the speech development of the young child, something of the role it plays in his speech-learning process must be understood. In the first place, the ability to produce a certain speech sound at will is contingent upon the ability to hear that sound. It was shown earlier how hearing makes possible the echolalia stage in the child's speech development, and how he responds with the sound in his own repertoire that corresponds most closely with the sound spoken to him by someone else. Therefore, if the influence of other factors is disregarded, the fidelity and precision of the child's speech sounds will be determined, and limited, by the precision of his hearing.

There is more to this problem of hearing than the mere development of gross auditory acuity, however. For the purposes of understanding and producing speech sounds, it is not enough that the child be able to hear sounds; he must be able to hear *differences* between and among complex sounds which vary with respect to individual pitch, quality, and intensity characteristics. For example, he must learn that *sun* and *fun* are two quite different words and that a *cat* is not a *cap*.

Even though his hearing may be defective and his discrimination poor, the child can often hear enough of the pattern of speech to understand what is said to him. He hears a sufficient number of the sounds to enable him to perceive a recognizable and meaningful pattern of language, although it may be considerably distorted. He may be quite deceptively normal in his responses to what he hears, but his own speech will reflect the distortions caused by his hearing deficiency—for, as we have learned, the child comes to speak the speech he hears about him. Hearing and hearing problems will be discussed in detail in Chapter xi.

Motor Development

It must be remembered that, although the controls of speech are sensory, that is, auditory, visual, tactile, and kinesthetic, the production of speech is a neuromuscular process and, as such, is as dependent upon motor skills as is any other mechanical ability. In other words, the child's speech may be poor because he is 'clumsy' with his speech organs, in the same way that he may be awkward in his play because he is clumsy with his hands and feet. While it has been shown that motor skill, especially that involving the smaller muscles and finer co-ordinations of the body, develops with maturation, there is still considerable variation among individuals at any given age level. This variation is especially marked during the early months and years of a child's life, as shown by the wide range of ages at which different children sit up, learn to walk, feed themselves, dress themselves, and perform other comparable motor activities. Undoubtedly similar factors help explain why some children begin to talk by the end of the first year, while others speak very little, if at all, at the age of two. As a matter of fact, those children with retarded or defective articulation have been found to be generally inferior in motor development and skill to those children of the same age with normal speech.[7] There is some evidence to indicate that this relationship can be found even among adults.[8] Therefore we must conclude that the motor development of the child is an important factor in determining the age at which he will begin to talk, as well as the rate of his speech learning and the quality of his articulation at any given period.

Sex

Virtually all of the studies comparing the speech and language development of boys and girls report a consistent and sometimes significant advantage in favor of the girls when chronological age and intelligence are kept constant. Girls usually begin to talk at an earlier age than boys, and at any given age their

7. Edna Jenkins and Frances E. Lohr, 'Severe Articulation Disorders and Motor Abilities,' *Journal of Speech and Hearing Disorders*, August 1964, pp. 286–92.
8. Robert Albright, 'The Motor Abilities of Speakers with Good and Poor Articulation,' *Speech Monographs*, 15, 1948, pp. 164–72.

speech will be more advanced, more free from defects, and their vocabulary will be larger. Virtually all types of speech defects, even those having a structural basis, show a higher incidence among males than among females. The most dramatic illustration of this tendency is to be found among stutterers, where we find from four to five times as many males as females.

No completely adequate explanation of this sex difference in speech development and speech excellence has ever been offered. Taking into account the previously discussed role of motor skills in speech, undoubtedly part of the explanation can be found in the earlier and more rapid physical maturation of girls. There seems little doubt that additional factors, some of which remain as yet obscure, are also involved.

Environmental Factors

Here are to be found some of the most potent forces of all in conditioning the speech and language development of the child. All other factors may be positive, but if the environment is sufficiently unfavorable, speech development may be greatly delayed or otherwise seriously interfered with. Among the possible environmental factors involved, the following are singled out as being of special importance:

1. *Motivation* As was pointed out earlier, the child develops speech in order to make his wants known and to control his environment toward a satisfaction of those wants. Speech thus becomes useful and necessary to him. If, however, his wants are anticipated by an over-solicitous parent, and a simple gesture or a primitive grunt is all that is required to get results, then there is not much incentive to go to the trouble of learning and using speech. Such a situation appears to prevail in a significant number of cases of retarded speech among children who are well past the age at which they should be talking in a normal manner.

2. *Opportunities for experience* The child has learned to talk when he begins to use words purposefully with a knowledge of

what the word means and the response he can expect from its use. These meanings for which words stand, or of which words are symbols, are acquired by the child as a result of his experience. For example, the child learns the meaning, or meanings, of the word 'ball' through his experience with the object itself in handling it, bouncing it, seeing it, and trying to eat it. At first, all balls are red, or soft, or whatever his original ball happens to be, and all similar objects are 'balls.' Later as his experience becomes more extensive, he learns about tennis balls, footballs, basketballs, golf balls, and the ball of fire we call the sun. The word has come to *mean* more to him as a result of his enlarged experience. Thus we can see that the acquisition of vocabulary is related to experience, for with new experiences come new words to describe or symbolize those experiences.

It is important, therefore, that the child's environment be such as to permit and provide a wide variety of rich experiences in the form of things to see, to do, to hear, and to play with. Any factor in his environment that tends to restrict his range of movement and activity or deprive him of experience with objects and situations will contribute to his speech and language retardation.

3. *Socio-economic status of the home* Partly for reasons discussed in the preceding paragraphs, it is evident that the cultural level of the environment to which the child is exposed will influence his linguistic development. Most of the studies that have compared the speech and language progress of children from markedly different social and occupational groups have disclosed that children who come from the middle and upper socio-economic classes tend to surpass those of the lower groups in degree of linguistic development.[9] This is not surprising nor difficult to understand. Children from the upper strata of society are exposed to an environment that provides opportunities for

9. Jane B. Raph, 'Language Development in Socially Disadvantaged Children,' in Paul C. Burns and Leo M. Schell, eds., *Elementary School Language Arts; Selected Readings*, Rand McNally, Chicago, 1969, pp. 83–95.

richer and more varied experiences, both verbal and non-verbal, than are available to the children whose lives are more circumscribed, monotonous, or barren because of social and economic limitations.

4. *Speech stimulation* From the time the infant is first brought home from the hospital, if not before, the average mother talks to him as if he were perfectly capable of understanding every word she speaks. While this procedure contributes little to the child's speech development during the first few months, it pays dividends later when the child enters the echolalia stage of his language growth, and such practice becomes increasingly important after the child begins to use his first words. During this period it is necessary that the right kind and proper amount of speech stimulation be present in the child's environment if he is to develop fully his potentialities.

The speech models set for him should be on a slightly higher plane than he himself is able to attain at the time. It is obvious that parental baby-talk, for example, will scarcely furnish a standard conducive to the child's speech progress. On the other hand, long words, complicated sentences, and involved phrasing will only confuse the child instead of helping him. He will not have a sufficient memory span to encompass the long words and complicated sentences, nor would he have the motor skill to pronounce them if he could perceive them. On the whole, however, it has been shown that children who associate mostly with adults are the most advanced in their speech and language development.

Too much speech stimulation can also be bad. The child who is constantly bombarded by overeager parents to 'say this' or tell 'what is that?' may well develop negativistic tendencies and respond by shutting up and saying nothing. Although speech stimulation can be overdone, the child is also likely to be handicapped in his development if there is no one around to talk to him. The child who lives in an institution or who has been reared by people who neglect or ignore him is likely to be retarded in his language development, as, indeed, in many of his other activities.

5. *Bilingual environment* Reports on the effect of a bilingual environment on the child's speech development are somewhat conflicting. It has been assumed that the child who is exposed to more than one language during the time he is learning to talk may be retarded as compared with the child who hears only one language spoken in the home. While a number of studies tend to support this assumption,[10] the problem, as Eisenson points out, is more involved than many of the researchers have taken into account and no definitive conclusion can be drawn on the basis of information available at present. It cannot be denied, however, that under certain circumstances a bilingual environment can be a problem for the child in his speech and language development. More will be said about this in the following chapter on speech and language delay.

Emotional Factors
The truism that the child learns best when he is happy has a special significance when applied to the language-learning process because, as we have seen, speech develops out of the child's vocal play activities—his babbling, gurgling, and cooing. The unhappy child will spend more of his time crying; emotional shocks may delay his speech development or inhibit it even after it has begun. Other types of maladjustment in the form of frustrations, emotional immaturity, feelings of insecurity and inferiority, and general instability may, and often do, seriously interfere with the child's later speech learning. Some of these problems will be presented in more detail in Chapters IV and IX. In general it can be said that factors which contribute to the child's happiness, his emotional maturation, and his emotional stability will facilitate his speech learning. Negative or disin-

10. Jon Eisenson, J. Jeffery Auer, and John V. Irwin, *The Psychology of Communication*, Meredith Publishing Company, Appleton-Century-Crofts, New York, 1963, pp. 222, 223.

tegrative emotional states and personality characteristics may seriously disrupt the process.

Characteristics of the Speech- and Language-Learning Process

As we view the developmental steps and processes through which the child progresses in acquiring speech and language skills, certain general characteristics or principles become evident.

From the Emotional to the Intellectual

As we have seen, the child's vocalization is at first on a wholly emotional level. The crying is merely a part of his general, random, all-over bodily response to the stimulation from his environment. Later as neuro-motor maturation takes place, the first signs of articulation appear in babbling and progress through to articulate speech, which is primarily intellectual in nature in the sense that it is used symbolically and with the deliberate purpose of controlling the environment to the satisfaction and advantage of the user. In this way a pattern of speech and language is established; this pattern forms an interesting and useful basis for the study of adult speech.

The intellectual elements of language are the words we use, the skill with which we choose them, and the way in which we put them together as we express ourselves. This is articulated symbolization, a form of communication to which only man, of all the animals, has been able to attain. While our words supposedly express our thoughts, our feelings are revealed through the voice—its quality, its intensity, the rate at which we speak, and the ways in which we vary the basic pitch level and the pitch patterns of our utterance. Such expressive vocal qualities are said to convey the deeper meanings of our speech, a concept that has provoked such proverbial sayings as 'Your voice will give you away.'

At this point it might be useful to attempt to make a working distinction between voice and speech. Voice can be said to be the raw material, produced by vibration of the vocal folds, out of which a large part of speech is made. That is, when vocal tone is shaped and modulated into what we call the speech sounds—the vowels and consonants—by the resonance and articulatory mechanisms of the throat and mouth, we have a recognizable, conventionalized sound pattern referred to as speech. This process of modulation by which speech sounds are formed is known as articulation. Thus it is seen that while we can have voice without speech, as is illustrated in crying, exclamations, and a large part of animal vocalizations, we cannot ordinarily have speech without voice, except in the case of whispering, unless we broaden the concept of speech to include other forms of communication such as pantomime and sign language.

Development of Individual Speech Sounds

One index of speech maturation that has attracted considerable attention over the years is the age at which the child customarily learns to pronounce the various speech sounds correctly. Investigators agree that vowels are among the first sounds to appear, since they are more gross and require less articulation than the more precise consonants. Most of the work, therefore, has been done on consonants. Sander[11] reviews the schedules that various researchers have proposed for the development of consonants and discusses the problems involved in assigning age levels for the individual sounds. He suggests the following composite schedule, giving the various percentages of children at that age level discovered to be correctly articulating each sound in the initial position in a word (final position for [ŋ] and medial for [ʒ]). This represents customary production or use; many of the sounds have been spoken correctly in many words at earlier ages.

11. Eric K. Sander, 'When Are Speech Sounds Learned?' *Journal of Speech and Hearing Disorders*, February 1972, pp. 55–63.

AGE	CONSONANT SOUND AND PERCENTAGE
Under 2	[h] (87), [m] (87), [n] (100), [w] (79), [b] (93), [p] (87)
2	[t] (80), [k] (66), [g] (57), [ŋ] (60), [d] (87)
3	[f] (88), [j] (70), [s] (70), [r] (58), [l] (67)
4	[tʃ] (72), [ʃ] (75), [dʒ] (85), [z] (62), [v] (51)
5	[θ] (67), [ð] (62)
6	[ʒ] (72)

First of all, as Sander points out, there is a wide age range at which each of these individual sounds appears. For example, although 70 per cent of children three years of age were producing [s] correctly in the initial position, up to 10 per cent of all children had failed to acquire this sound even at age eight. A similar situation was found in regard to [z], [v], [ð], and [ʒ]. Likewise a possible 10 per cent were not producing [tʃ], [ʃ], [dʒ], and [θ] correctly at age seven, and a like proportion were lacking a proper [t], [ŋ], [r], and [l] at age six.[12] These are the sounds, then, that a substantial number of children in kindergarten, first, and second grades will likely need special help in acquiring.

A look at some of these sounds appearing late in the speech of certain children, such as [s], [v], [tʃ], [θ], [l], and [r], reveals that in general they require a much more complicated and precise adjustment of the articulators—tongue, lips, and teeth especially—than a number of the earlier-appearing ones, such as [m], [w], [p], and [b]. Additionally, some of the late-appearing sounds in certain children are of very weak intensity, such as [s], [θ], [ʃ], [tʃ], and [t], and others bear some acoustical resemblance to each other, such as [f]/[θ], [θ]/[s], and [w]/[r] (all common substitutions in children). These factors are doubtless important in explaining why some children are later than others in acquiring or perfecting certain sounds in their speech.

With respect to the developmental pattern of individual speech sounds, studies indicate that the sound passes through the following typical sequence in the speech, not only of the

12. Ibid. p. 62.

child exhibiting delayed speech, but often also of the child whose speech is developing normally:

1. Omission of the sound; [kaɪ] for *sky*, for example.
2. Substitution of another sound, usually one acoustically similar, as [wʌn] for *run*.
3. Distortion of the 'correct' sound; not quite right.
4. Final achievement of the proper sound.

We observe here, especially in the two final stages, a process of refinement, probably both sensory and motor, as the child 'corrects' himself and comes closer and closer to the desired model. Constancy of articulation, both from word to word and in different positions and phonetic contexts within a word, tends to increase with age.

We can assume, therefore, that certain selective factors may be operating to delay acquisition of certain sounds in children who are late in developing them. Among such factors, some of which are undoubtedly related to maturation, are specialized motor control, auditory acuity, and speech sound discrimination ability, all of which should be carefully checked in children with articulation deficiencies.

Age of Onset of Speech

Darley and Winitz, in a review of research studies relating to the age of appearance of the child's first word, comment on the wide variability among the different results and the problems involved in collecting valid data.[13] From more than a dozen studies examined, they found a reported age range for the first word from from 9–10 months to 18–19 months, reflecting not so much the populations studied, as the research methodologies used in collecting the data. They conclude that an acceptable average

13. Frederic L. Darley and Harris Winitz, 'Age of First Word: Review of the Research,' *Journal of Speech and Hearing Disorders*, August 1961, pp. 272–90.

age would be one year for the first word, and they add, 'Delay of appearance of first word beyond 18 months may indicate a serious physical, mental or hearing involvement.' [14]

It should be kept in mind that these data are for first words only and do not necessarily imply that the child has actually begun to talk at the ages given. A more likely average for the real beginning of speech, as defined earlier in this chapter, would be about fourteen months for girls and about a month later for boys. There is often wide variation in these ages in individual instances, many children talking at a somewhat earlier age and many not being able to speak at all until they are two or even older. As a matter of fact, the variability is so great that the beginning of speech can be delayed until the age of three before the child should be considered definitely abnormal in his speech development.

Hawk refers to a concept that is useful when one is considering the speech learning of the child. The age at which the child is most susceptible to the acquisition of spoken language she refers to as the period of speech readiness.[15] As was stated above, this varies considerably in individual cases, but on the average it occurs sometime between the end of the first year and the beginning of the third. It is important that maximum opportunity for communication and encouragement of speech be provided during this time, for, as Hawk states, 'With the coming of the second birthday, or around the twenty-fourth month, the most favorable period for speech development may have passed, so that speech subsequently develops much more slowly and with less facility when it is begun.' [16] It is important, therefore, to take advantage of the child's natural readiness for speech as determined by maturational and other factors, for it becomes increasingly difficult for the child, once this period has passed.

14. Ibid. p. 289.
15. Edna Hill Young and Sara Stinchfield Hawk, *Moto-Kinesthetic Speech Training*, Stanford University Press, Stanford, Calif., 1955, p. 127.
16. Ibid. p. 128.

Early Development of Oral Language

In earlier sections of this chapter we have referred to various periods or phases through which the child's pre-speech development is believed to progress. In an attempt to show that this is a continuing process and that the stages overlap and eventually blend into the child's environmental language pattern, Menyuk suggests the following schedule with approximate ages of each step in the process, which she refers to as a series of gross linguistic performances.[17]

AGE	VOCALIZATIONS
birth	Cry and other physiological sounds
1–2 months	Cooing as well as cry
3–6 months	Babbling sounds as well as cooing
9–14 months	First words as well as babbling
18–24 months	First sentences as well as words
3–4 years	Use of all basic syntactic structures
4–8 years	Correct articulation of all speech sounds in context

While Menyuk is concerned here with the expressive or motor aspects of language, it is generally conceded that reception precedes expression in all aspects of oral language development. That is, the child must be able to hear the sound and discriminate it from all other speech sounds before he can be expected to produce it. Evidence indicates that a similar relationship exists with respect to vocabulary and the grammatical aspects of language as well. That is, the child must know the *meaning* of a word when he hears it before he can be expected to use it in his own speech, and the same holds true for the structural aspects of language, such as tense, active-passive voice, sentence structure, et cetera.

Molyneaux, in discussing what she refers to as the 'decoding' or comprehension activities of the infant and young child observes,

17. Paula Menyuk, *The Development of Speech*, Bobbs-Merrill, Indianapolis, 1972, p. 10.

A crying one-month-old infant often 'quiets down' when he hears a voice. Around four months of age, he will actually turn his head to try to locate the source of the voice. Most seven- or eight-month-old babies will raise their arms when their mother reaches toward them and says 'up' or some such term. That same-age child will often look at 'daddy' when daddy is named. Many ten-month-olds can respond to 'Wave bye-bye'; by twelve months of age, they can give a toy on request when that request is accompanied by a gesture. During the second year, the normal child progresses to a point where he responds to simple commands, enjoys picture books and can point to pictures of familiar objects when he is asked to do so.[18]

Knowing the wide variability that exists from child to child at various age levels in the development of all aspects of language, it is always hazardous to attempt any age-related schedule of events in the language acquisition process. There is always the possibility that if a given child has not acquired a certain skill or ability at the age suggested, he will be considered seriously retarded. In reality, he may merely be at the lower end of the normal range for that ability at that age and should evoke no cause for concern. With these cautions and limitations in mind, the following composite schedule of various language and language-related activities during the first five years is presented as an aid in calling attention to certain typical steps in the communicative development of the average child. It should be noted that, in addition to language, it also reflects intellectual development and, to some extent, social maturation as well.

12 *months*   Uses one to four words, usually nouns (daddy, mama, milk, et cetera). Understands very simple instructions, especially if accompanied by meaningful gestures or intonation, for example, 'give me the ball.'

18 *months*   Uses 20 to 25 words, still mostly nouns. Some verbs beginning to appear; may be combined with

18. Dorothy Molyneaux, 'Childhood Language Development,' in Morris Val Jones, ed., *Language Development*, Charles C. Thomas, Springfield, Ill., 1972, p. 22.

nouns to form a basic linguistic unit, as 'daddy come,' 'milk gone,' et cetera. The one-word sentence is predominant; 'ball' [bɔ] meaning 'Where is the ball?' 'I want the ball,' et cetera. Negative protest frequent; 'no' very common word! Good deal of jargon. Mean length of response (MLR) 1.2 words.[19]

24 *months*   Squealing and screaming still prominent. Usually uses initial consonants. Can name some common objects or pictures shown him (ball, shoe, watch, cup, et cetera). Can use two prepositions (in, on, or under). Vocabulary 275–300 words. MLR 1.8 words.

36 *months*   Uses pronouns I, you, and me correctly. Uses plurals, past tense, comparatives. Knows three or four prepositions. Can distinguish such opposites as *big-little, fast-slow,* and *up-down.* Knows colors *red, brown,* and *blue.* Knows the chief parts of his body. Language construction is 50 per cent grammatically correct. Vocabulary 900 words. MLR 4.00 words.

48 *months*   Can name colors generally; can use four or five prepositions. Knows some numbers and can tell what familiar animals do or 'say' (cat, dog, cow, fish, et cetera). Names most common objects in pictures; can repeat three digits after hearing them. Knows tense of verbs (run, ran, will run) and number (is, are). Knows forms of simple pronouns (him, her, his, et cetera); can distinguish *when—where* and singular versus plural nouns. Vocabularyy 1500 words. MLR 5.4 words.

60 *months*   Uses many descriptive words accurately. Knows common opposites (hot-cold, big-little, long-short)

---

19. Average number of words used in each of 50 sentences or responses by the child in communication with an adult. Generally recognized as the one most valid measure of oral language development.

and can distinguish *alike-different, left-right,* and can comprehend *few.* Knows when to say 'please' and 'thank you.' Can count to 10 and can name two or three coins. Speech is fully intelligible, although likely to display some errors in formation and use of consonants. Vocabulary 2000 words. MLR 5.7 words.

While the schedule above is far from complete and choice of items seems often random, it does display important facets of developing comprehension and expression of oral communication. Note the inclusion of certain items involving a type of symbolization not ordinarily considered language, such as recognition of colors and the concept of numbers—*one* as opposed to *two; many* as opposed to *few; one, two, three, four,* et cetera. Also note the steady increase in size of vocabulary with age. For the years given, only the expressive vocabulary, or vocabulary of use, is shown. If the receptive vocabulary, or vocabulary of understanding, had been likewise included, it would have been substantially larger at each age level. For example, while the vocabulary of use at age six is estimated to consist of about 2500 words, the understanding vocabulary at that age has been found to be about 15,000 words.[20] This discrepancy will be found at any age throughout life. Since the vocabulary of use is based on the vocabulary of understanding which in turn arises from the experience of the child in language and language-related activities, it can be seen how important it is to further the young child's opportunities in these areas. More will be said about this in the following chapter.

While attention has been given to such aspects of language competence as size of vocabulary, mean length of response, et cetera, little has been said about other aspects of language structure. From the simple one-word naming response and later one-word sentence of the very young child, he later comes to

20. Mildred Templin, *Certain Language Skills in Children; Their Development and Interrelationship,* University of Minnesota Press, Minneapolis, 1957, p. 111.

understand and use ever longer and more complex sentences involving more sophisticated parts of speech as well as descriptive and qualifying phrases and clauses, all of which enable him to express himself more precisely and completely as he matures. Incidentally, attention is given to these aspects of language, at least in written form, through all the years of elementary and secondary school and, in some instances, through part of the college years as well. In many respects this development parallels that of other aspects of language.

Speech and Language Development as a Continuing Process

We must not make the mistake of considering the period covered thus far in this chapter—the first five or six years of the child's life—as being a terminal stage in his speech and language development. The oft-heard statement, 'My child has learned to talk,' might well be changed, as it sometimes is, to 'My child has begun to talk,' because the child's development in speech and language should normally be a continuing process, matching and reflecting his physical, social, and intellectual progress. If this highly desirable growth is to take place, it becomes the responsibility of the school to provide a series of carefully graded oral language experiences for the child extending up through the elementary grades and continuing as long as the child remains in school. At the present time we have far too many students entering high school or college, or even graduating from college, whose ability to express themselves either orally or in written form remains on a distressingly elementary level.

A number of plausible reasons could doubtless be given for this frequently criticized weakness in our educational process. In the first place, in many school systems there is no organized program for providing systematized training in all of the phases of communication—reading, writing, speaking, and listening. True, there are usually the traditional 'lessons' or courses in spelling, writing, grammar, and reading, but, if results are to be taken as any measure of success, it must be admitted that this approach is insufficient for several reasons. (1) It largely ignores one very important aspect of communication, the oral—possibly because of our traditional identification of reading and writing with literacy. Yet oral communication plays a far more important role in the development of the child through his early school years and is coming to play an increasingly vital role in the intellectual, social, and political activities of the adult. (2) Such aspects of language as have been taught—reading, writing, and grammar, for example—have too often been segmentalized and presented as separate disciplines with little regard for their inter-relationship or their importance to the process of communication as a whole. Too often the child has little or no concept of the value or ultimate utility of his exercises in grammar, the 'theme' he is required to grind out, or the reading lesson that has been assigned. The use of any one of these activities in connection with the others too often remains a mystery to him. (3) Instead of making the need for communication grow naturally out of the child's daily life and his other activities in school, language teaching has been attempted almost in a vacuum with too little motivation on the part of the student. Small wonder the pupils often find the writing of themes so onerous—they have nothing they wish to communicate.

Adequate speech and language training in the school involves, first of all, a change in the traditional concept of the nature and use of the basic communication skills referred to earlier—reading, writing, speaking, and listening. It must be recognized that these are all a part of the general communicative act and that no one part should be either isolated or ignored. Further, it must be recognized that the child's intellectual and social development should be accompanied by a growing ability to communicate the fruits of that development, to assimilate new material, and to profit from new experiences. This involves a carefully integrated program of language training, including speech and listening, that will parallel and reflect his general development through his formative years. This should be a part of, not separate from, his schoolwork and his other daily activities. Language and speech training should be involved in every aspect of his education. The oral recitation in hygiene or social studies is just as basic to the child's speech and language training as is the lesson in speech or the class in public speaking —in some respects more so because here there is present, or should be if the lesson has been properly handled, fundamental motivation in the form of a manifest need for and value in effective communication. Oral language training need not be, and should not be, a discipline apart from the child's total educational development, especially at the elementary level. Thus, all teachers are in part speech teachers, because speech, or at least some form of language, is being used both by the teacher in the act of teaching, and by the pupil in the process of learning and in the utilization of that learning through communication back to the teacher as well as to others in the immediate situation. Any disability on the part of either teacher or pupil can seriously interfere with this process.

Speech and Reading Problems

As further evidence of the close relationship of the elements of communication referred to above, a number of research studies have indicated that children with certain types of speech defects are more likely to exhibit reading disabilities than are normal speakers. Also, more speech problems have been found among deficient readers than among the school population as a whole. The nature of this relationship has not as yet been fully explored. Doubtless there are a number of factors common to both of these forms of language that operate to determine the individual's ability in both speaking and reading. It is encouraging to observe that reading disabilities, as well as speech disorders, are being recognized and dealt with in the schools, but it would be a mistake to consider them as wholly separate problems. Where both are deficient, training in the one activity must, in many cases, be accompanied by improvement in the other.

Betts has proposed the theory that, since the child's language maturation proceeds through the stages of first understanding speech, then speaking, and finally reading, any disability in one of these skills will impede progress in succeeding ones.[21] Considerable weight has been added to Betts's theory as a result of an investigation conducted by Jones, who demonstrated that speech training administered to third-grade school children materially and significantly improved their silent reading achievement.[22] More recently Sawyer cites a study in which practice in better speaking substantially improved the reading ability, both oral and silent, of a group of intermediate grade children. Training stressed general speech ability with attention to articulation, pronounciation (use of *git* for *get*, for example), and proper grammar and sentence structure.[23]

There is some reason to believe, therefore, that, educationally speaking, we may have been guilty of getting the cart before the horse in stressing the importance of written language without first making sure that the child possessed adequate ability in oral communication.

Speech Training vs. Re-training

It should be obvious from this discussion that the teacher in the kindergarten and the lower grades plays a strategic role in the oral language development of the child. Speech habits acquired in these formative years tend to persist and to become reinforced as the child grows older. Good speech becomes deeply rooted 'second nature' to the child; poor speech habits and speech disorders also become more difficult to modify or eradicate with the passing of the years, for, by the time the child

21. Emmett Betts, *Foundation of Reading Instruction*, American Book Company, New York, 1946, p. 6.
22. Morris Val Jones, 'The Effect of Speech Training on Silent Reading Achievement,' *Journal of Speech and Hearing Disorders*, September 1951, pp. 258–63.
23. Richard P. Sawyer, 'Better Speech for Better Reading,' *Elementary School Journal*, April 1965, pp. 359–65.

has arrived at the upper grades in elementary school or junior high school, the speech habit-pattern has become pretty firmly set. The speech teacher, or any teacher, is thus confronted with a two-fold problem: (1) to break up or modify the old, incorrect habit, and (2) to substitute and develop the new one in its place. These two tasks may well be merely two aspects of one process.

In the early years of school, therefore, prevention supersedes correction, and speech education is basic to speech re-education, which at best is merely an attempt to correct what is often the product of ignorance and mismanagement at an earlier stage. In those cases where the child comes to school with a speech disorder already in evidence, the problem is to correct it as soon as possible before the pattern becomes too strongly reinforced through use, and before the child develops any unfortunate attitudes and personality characteristics from his awareness of his inadequacies and of others' reactions to them. The longer the process of re-education is delayed, the more difficult is the task and the greater the danger that there may be lasting effects upon the personality of the child that cannot be easily eradicated.

(For References, see end of Chapter iv.)

IV

Delayed Speech and Language

The word 'speech' might well have been omitted from the title of this chapter, since we are dealing with what is basically a language disorder, and, of course, oral communication is only a facet of language. However, at the early age at which this disorder first manifests itself, the understanding and production of speech are the only aspects of language involved. Hence, this problem has often been referred to as delayed speech. Many other terms have also been associated with it, among them childhood aphasia, congenital aphasia, developmental aphasia, aphasoid, minimal brain damage or impairment or dysfunction, language disorder or disability, and it is quite likely, considering the critical role language plays in all learning activities, that children suffering from delayed speech or language have also been labeled as educationally handicapped or learning disabled. This multiplicity of labels is clear testimony to the confusion of authorities as to the cause, or causes, of this malady, as well as its essential nature and possible ramifications. The dilemma has led one authority to observe that the actual name may be unimportant; what is important is to know what we mean when we use the name.

Whatever we call it, one thing is certain—we are dealing here with one of the most important and most baffling problems to confront the parent, the classroom teacher, and the speech and hearing clinician. For example, in a survey of nearly 600 California speech and hearing specialists, the child with delayed speech or no speech at all was judged to constitute the second most prevalent and important problem they had to deal with, exceeded only by the child with non-organic articulatory disorders.[1] Although the problem is likely to be most critical in the young child and during kindergarten and the early grades, symptoms of speech and language retardation may be seen at any level through the elementary grades, especially as reading skills may be affected, and even into the high school years. Speech symptoms may range all the way from a complete absence of speech, through a kind of jargon that only the mother and perhaps a close sibling can understand, to minor examples of articulatory disorders and sound substitutions that follow the general pattern of baby-talk. Deficiencies in the comprehension of spoken language, ranging from mild to serious, are also generally found in this child.

The typical child of four or five who shows symptoms of being slow or disordered in his speech development will have a limited vocabulary composed largely of names for common objects and made up of words seriously distorted by sound changes, omissions, and substitutions. This meager and otherwise inadequate language may bear some resemblance to normal speech, in that the words are merely distortions of real words, or it may consist largely of strange combinations of sounds making up new words which the child has apparently invented himself—an idioglossia, as it is technically called. This makeshift language will usually be accompanied by a rather elaborate gesture system on which the child often appears to rely for communication more than on oral symbols. He may, upon occasion, make strenuous efforts to communicate and may demonstrate great impatience and exas-

1. Robert Gillen, ed., *The Voice, Monograph Supplement*, May 1963, California State University at Los Angeles, Los Angeles, p. 13.

peration when others fail to understand him. He is likely to be shy and reticent before strangers although he may exhibit the other extreme of garrulousness, jabbering away in his garbled language as if he were perfectly intelligible. He may understand what is said to him, although in individual instances some of these children give no evidence of responding in a meaningful way to their verbal environment.

What Is Delayed Speech and Language? Diagnostic Indications
It is not always easy to identify the symptoms that characterize delayed speech and language development as distinguished, for example, from a case of merely defective consonant articulation. The following diagnostic aids will be helpful:

1. The child with delayed speech will usually have started using words at a markedly later age than the average. While, as we saw in the preceding chapter, the average child will start to use words meaningfully at approximately fourteen or fifteen months of age, the child with disordered speech and language may be three to four years of age before he begins to talk. Or, in rarer instances, he may start to talk at or near the normal age and then stop mysteriously or appear to regress in his oral communication.

2. As one authority has pointed out, the developmental lag in those children who have language disorders is likely to be a general or total developmental lag, encompassing the child's motor, emotional, intellectual, and social evolvement.[2] Early histories are likely to disclose that the child was slow in sitting up, crawling, and walking, as well as in finer motor activities, such as feeding and dressing himself, in drawing with a crayon or pencil, and in the establishment of laterality, or handedness. The speech pattern may exhibit a general clumsiness and the rate may be too fast or too slow. The child may be poor at manipulating toys, playing ball, running, et cetera.

---

2. Lauretta Bender in Robert West, ed., *Childhood Aphasia*, California Society for Crippled Children and Adults, San Francisco, 1962, p. 25.

3. Special attention should be given to the sentence structure and other grammatical aspects of the child's oral communication. Grammar is usually greatly simplified, with many connectives, auxiliary verbs, prepositions, and other language elements showing relationships of words being omitted entirely. The child's vocabulary is likely to be meager and to consist of a larger proportion of nouns than is usual for his age, pertaining to concrete things that are for the most part present in the environment and directly related to his immediate needs and desires. As the child gets older, he will likely encounter difficulty with the other aspects of language—spelling, writing, and especially, reading.

4. Unlike the child with other types of speech disorders, the child with delayed speech and language is more likely to rely on gestures and 'acting out' in attempting to make his meaning clear. He may prefer a gesture to any attempt at speech whatsoever, if the circumstances are favorable to the use of sign language.

5. A great many sounds will be omitted, especially initial and final consonants. Many of the sounds that are retained will be distorted or other sounds will be substituted for them. The substitutions are likely to follow a rather definite pattern, sometimes referred to as baby-talk. In general, an easier sound—one that occurs early in the child's natural speech development—will be substituted for a sound that is normally learned later. For example, [f] will tend to be substituted for [θ], so that *thumb* will become *fum*; [r] will become [w], making *run* sound like *wun*; [l] is also likely to become [w], making *lamb* resemble *wam*; [t] may replace [k], changing *cake* into *tate* or more likely just [te], or the word may simply degenerate into something resembling the vowel [e], with both consonants missing.

6. Since language, in addition to its use for communication, also serves for control of one's own behavior, there are certain non-language characteristics that may provide additional help in identifying the child with the delayed speech and language

syndrome. So-called hyperactivity may be a distinguishing sign. Such children are restless, flitting about from one thing to another in a seemingly aimless fashion. They have a short attention span, have difficulty 'settling down,' and are easily distracted. They are characteristically impulsive and are likely to be subject to quick changes of mood, with a low frustration level. The child may also display general orientation defects, seemingly confused as to his whereabouts and having difficulty in identifying himself as part of the immediate environment. He is likely to exhibit difficulty in organizing and formulating his thoughts and, of course, is generally ineffective in expressing himself.

The characteristics described in the foregoing paragraphs are by no means invariable from child to child, all of which complicate the problem of identifying the child with speech and languge delay and distinguishing him from a simpler case of articulation disorder, for example. Of course, the surest and preferred procedure where time and adequate facilities are available, is to administer one or more of the several tests of language development availables, three of which are listed in the references at the end of this chapter. Where testing is not feasible, the teacher must rely on her own observations and judgment. A general principle to be followed here could be stated thus: if, upon entering kindergarten or the first grade, the child exhibits speech that is inadequate to serve his communicative needs in the school situation and if his speech deficiencies follow the general pattern as outlined above, then his problem may be identified as delayed speech that is sufficiently serious to require some special attention from the teacher or the speech specialist, if one is available. In the case of the pre-school child it can be said that if he has not started to talk by the time he is three years of age, he should be considered delayed in his speech development, and some special assistance should be provided. By the time the child is eight, all of the speech sounds should have been mastered.

Causes of Delayed Speech

As was seen in Chapter III, there are many factors that influence the speech development of the child, favorably or unfavorably, as the case may be. If the child gives evidence of being retarded in his speech, a serious effort should be made to locate the factor, or factors, causing that retardation, since in many cases mere alleviation of the cause is all the treatment needed. Moreover, all other efforts to help the child may prove relatively futile if the conditions that prevented him from developing normal speech and language in the first place are allowed to remain. Therefore, the first concern of the teacher or parent should be to find an answer to the question: why is this child retarded in his speech and language development? That answer should be found in one or more of the most common categories of causes to be discussed in the following paragraphs.

Structural Deficiencies
The first thought of the parent or other layman in the case of a child with delayed speech is that there must be something wrong with his speech mechanism, and a pediatrician or the family physician will in most instances be the first one to be consulted regarding the problem. Usually nothing will be found wrong with the child's speech organs. Speech is seldom delayed because of such an organic deficiency; it will develop as usual, although it may be seriously defective. An exception appears to be cleft lip and palate, where Morris found in a group of children with clefts significant retardation in communicative skills, in addition to the usual voice quality and articulation disorders. The deficiencies included vocabulary, length and complexity of responses, and amount of spontaneous speech.[3] This language handicap appears to persist, even though the cleft is closed

3. Hughlett L. Morris, 'Communication Skills of Children with Cleft Lips and Palates,' *Journal of Speech and Hearing Research*, March 1962, pp. 79–90.

surgically at an early age. Such children are late talkers and learn to speak in a slow cumbersome manner, often with faulty and inadequate grammar. With the exception of clefts, however, the teacher or parent should not generally expect to find the cause of delayed speech and language to be organic deficiency directly connected with the production of speech. There are many other much more likely causes to be investigated.

Mental Retardation

Mental retardation or mental deficiency is probably the most common cause of speech and language delay. As Brown states, 'Speech is a learned process, and if the child finds all learning difficult, he will find slow going also in acquiring the complex skills of speech.' [4] The relationship of speech to intelligence is sufficiently close to make any serious deficiency in intelligence almost certain to be reflected in speech retardation, the degree and amount of the one being roughly proportionate to the loss in the other. The child who is at all seriously retarded in intelligence will start to talk at a later age than the child of normal intelligence, his vocabulary will be more limited, his sentence structure clumsy and ungrammatical, voice quality hoarse and nasal, and his speech will exhibit more sound omissions, substitutions, and distortions. The pattern of sound changes will follow in general the type previously referred to as baby-talk. As a matter of fact, with the possible exception of number six, the numbered paragraphs in the early pages of this chapter present a very accurate picture of the general development, including speech and language, of the mentally deficient child.

Because of this close relationship between mental retardation and delayed speech and language, the teacher would do well to have the child's mental capabilities assessed by a qualified psychologist, especially if the child's background and behavior

4. Spencer F. Brown, 'Retarded Speech Development,' in Wendell Johnson, et al., *Speech Handicapped School Children*, 3rd ed., Harper and Row, New York, 1967, pp. 334–35.

fit the pattern herein presented and in the absence of any obvious cause of the speech problem. How is the teacher to interpret the results of the psychologist's appraisal? Since it is not likely that she will have in her classes any child whose intelligence falls into the lower class with IQ's under 50 and ordinarily referred to as the trainable mentally retarded (TMR), her concern will be with the less severely retarded, identified as the educable mentally retarded (EMR). The Bureau of Special Education in California has suggested an IQ range of 55 to 75 plus or minus 5 points for inclusion in this group.

Unfortunately only a relatively small percentage of EMR children are receiving any professional help with their communication problems, outside of that provided by the special teacher of these customarily segregated groups. Yet there is considerable evidence to indicate that EMR children can profit measurably by the proper kind of training presented with patience and understanding.[5] In any case, the teacher will find the suggestions included later in this chapter helpful in dealing with these children.

Short Auditory Memory Span

The term 'memory span' refers to the ability of an individual to retain and associate together for purposes of immediate reproduction a series of impressions, usually auditory or visual. For speech purposes, of course, the auditory span is of more importance than the visual. Individuals differ markedly in their ability to retain a series of auditory stimuli, such as speech sounds, digits, or syllables. Being able to repeat a seven-digit telephone number after hearing it once taxes the memory span of many individuals, while others can repeat readily a series of eight or ten numbers. Evidence indicates that memory span is a product of maturation, and in some children it develops more

5. Patricia Scofield, 'Oral Language for the Educable Mentally Retarded,' in Morris Val Jones, ed., *Language Development*, Charles C. Thomas, Springfield, Ill., 1972, pp. 106–28.

slowly than in others. Where memory span is delayed in maturing, speech development is also likely to be retarded.

Word Deafness

Some individuals present symptoms of a condition that does not appear to be true aphasia, nor is it directly related to deafness; but, largely for want of a better term, it has long been referred to as 'word deafness.' This term designates a condition of lowered sensitivity to auditory stimulation, at least in the form of oral language. Some individuals simply do not respond readily to what they hear; they are not auditory-minded. They may be visual-minded and they may be able to imitate and remember what they see, but what they hear does not make a very strong impression on them. Naturally, children with such a deficiency will be handicapped in the learning of speech, which, as we saw in Chapter III, is a process heavily dependent on auditory stimulation.

Word deafness is a condition that is not clearly understood. It may be related to some phase of intelligence, possibly having its basis in improperly developed association centers in the brain. In those cases where some dullness of auditory sensitivity is suspected, the teacher and parents would be well advised to stress the visual and kinesthetic approaches to speech training, relying somewhat less heavily on purely auditory factors. The child's attention should be called to the visual components of speech sounds and words, and he should be trained to perceive how it feels to produce the correct movements and positions with the speech organs. In this respect, the approach would be essentially similar to that followed in helping a child who has an actual hearing loss.

Brain Injury—Central Nervous System Impairment

1. *Aphasia* The condition resulting from brain injury most closely relating to language functioning is known as aphasia. Aphasia involves a loss or disturbance of the individual's ability

to associate words, or other symbols, with meaning—an inability to think in terms of symbols. True aphasia thus has an organic basis—injury to, or improper development of, certain association areas of the brain where connections are made between symbols, usually language symbols of some sort, and corresponding objects, ideas, and concepts—in other words, meanings. Language has lost its meaning for the aphasic; he cannot express himself in terms of words, nor can he understand what he sees on the printed page or what he hears. The common causes of aphasia in childhood are certain diseases that affect the brain, such as encephalitis or meningitis, or some physical trauma involving an injury to the brain or skull. The injury is most likely to occur at birth, or the damage may result from some condition that deprives the brain of oxygen for a period of time preceding, during, or immediately following birth.

Aphasia is quite difficult to diagnose properly and treat in the older child or adult; in the case of the younger child where the condition has developed before he learned to speak, the task becomes even more involved. Such children may have no speech at all, or very meager language ability, and they may present symptoms that are very difficult to distinguish from those characteristic of deafness or mental retardation. Under these conditions there is very little the teacher or parent can do for the child. In general, cases where aphasia is suspected had better be left in the hands of the physician, the psychologist, or the speech specialist.

2. *Minimal brain damage* The inclusion of the word 'aphasia' in so many of the several terms mentioned in the opening paragraph of this chapter is evidence of the close association of the general symptom-picture of true aphasia with the characteristics of what we have called delayed speech and language. Because so many of the children in this latter category exhibit no history of identifiable physical symptoms of actual or other neurological malfunction, yet behave like true aphasics, the concept of minimal brain damage, or dysfunction, has come into

general acceptance. It is true that in some cases intensive study and testing of these children do disclose what are called 'soft symptoms,' or suggestions, of actual brain dysfunction, but in many other instances the medical history is negative and no very reliable evidence of actual brain impairment can be found. But because the behavior patterns, plus psychological and language testing, so closely resemble true aphasia, the suspicion persists that a slight, unidentifiable brain injury may have been sustained. If so, then the speech and language disorder is the only recorded symptom of the condition. The general characteristics are those described in the opening paragraphs of this chapter.

3. *Cerebral palsy* Where some type of physical impairment results from injury to the brain, usually sustained at or soon after birth in the case of the child, the condition is called cerebral palsy. The identifying symptom is lack of control of the skeletal muscles of the body as evidenced by tension or stiffness; an uncontrolled rhythmic movement of such muscles as those of the arm, neck, et cetera; or a general disturbance of balance and basic coordination of the body. Severity of the physical handicap may range from a mild, general incoordination or slight articulation difficulty to complete disability rendering the patient unable to walk, feed himself, or otherwise care for his needs. Accompanying symptoms may also involve hearing or visual disturbances, aphasia, emotional disturbances, and mental retardation.

Because of these several possible handicaps, it is easy to see why a substantial portion of cerebral palsied children have a speech or language problem or both. It may be a mechanical problem, involving the muscles of articulation, making speech difficult, if not impossible to understand. Or language may primarily be affected, causing the child to be slow in developing speech and later experiencing difficulty with reading and the other facets of language. It can be seen also why the child's environment may well present a number of negative factors occasioned by his impaired mobility, restricted experiences, and possible extended illness and poor health.

If the child is at all seriously handicapped physically, he will likely be placed in a special school, or at least in a special class specifically equipped to deal with the several problems he presents. When there is less involvement, the teacher of the child will find the suggestions in this chapter useful for dealing with a language problem, and the material in the following chapter designed to assist with an articulatory disorder. A psychological and medical work-up is a must.

Impaired Hearing

The importance and function of hearing in the child's speech learning processes were discussed in some detail in Chapter III. There it was pointed out that the child who cannot hear will not ordinarily develop speech, and in those cases where hearing is imperfect, the speech will reflect sound distortions and omissions characteristic of the particular hearing loss involved. In other words, the child learns to speak the kind of speech he hears; if he hears it imperfectly, he will speak imperfectly. In every case of delayed speech some study should be made of the child's hearing, either by a standard audiometer test given by a hearing specialist if one is available, or by a simple speech-sound identification and discrimination test such as the one included in the Appendix. If any evidence of a hearing loss is uncovered, it would be well to recommend that the child be examined by a physician, preferably an otologist. More detailed suggestions about how to handle the child with a hearing loss in the classroom will be included in Chapter XI.

Retarded Motor Development

As was also pointed out in Chapter III, the maturational factors that make speech possible include the development of the muscles and nerves that enable the child to control the phonatory and articulatory organs responsible for the production of speech. If the child is slow in his motor and neurological development, his speech will likely be delayed or it may be imperfect when it does appear, just as he may be late in learning to walk or may be clumsy in handling his hands and feet. After all, speech involves a complicated series of rather precise adjustments of a number of different muscle groups, performed at a rate of speed determined for the most part by the natural tempo of the adult speech in the child's environment. Considerable development must take place before the child is able to negotiate these rapid shifts and adjustments. As West points out, the child would in all probability master speech more readily if it were a slower process.[6]

Some writers have called attention to the possible relation between motor maturation and the development of laterality in the child (the tendency to prefer the right, or left, hand in performance of unimanual activities), and the relation of both to the acquisition of language skills. Since both speech and right, or left, hand preference depend on the establishment of certain association areas in either the right or left hemisphere of the brain, it is believed that the two are interrelated in their development. West, for example, states, 'Children who are late in the acquisition of dextral skills are also late in the development of good language habits.'[7] Some suggestions for helping the child who presents evidence of retarded motor development will be given later in this chapter.

Emotional Maladjustment

The role played by emotional factors in predisposing the child to develop various types of speech defects or in precipitating speech problems will be discussed in some detail in Chapter IX. There it will be shown that one of the symptoms of various forms of emotional maladjustment, such as aggressive behavior, withdrawal tendencies, and aggressive, protest behavior, may be the entire absence of speech or a pronounced speech retarda-

6. Robert West and Merle Ansberry, *The Rehabilitation of Speech*, 4th ed., Harper and Row, New York, 1968, p. 40.
7. Ibid. pp. 41–42.

tion. Clinical experience indicates that the child with delayed speech is much more prone to display behavior problems of various kinds than is his contemporary who speaks normally. Whether these behavior symptoms are causes of, or effects of, the communications handicap is not always easy to determine in individual cases. There are many instances, however, where it is obvious that the speech deficiency is only a part of a larger symptom-picture of emotional maladjustment. As Harris states,

Language is fundamental to the normal intellectual, social, and emotional development of children. . . . There is no question but that there is a reciprocal relation among these several areas, and that what we call healthy personality development requires inter-communication of children with children as well as of children with adults.[8]

The underlying problem is not always as serious, however, as the term 'emotional maladjustment' would imply. The speech disturbance may merely reflect the child's reaction to improper methods used in teaching him to talk. Overeager parents who have bombarded the child with speech stimulation in their efforts to speed up his linguistic development may discover that a negative adaptation has taken place: the child may seemingly be no longer aware of the stimulation, or a definite negativism may prompt him to refuse to say anything at all. Moreover, any factor in the child's environment that operates to create tensions, repressions, or unhappiness will retard his speech learning, just as it will tend to influence adversely any other learning that he undertakes. The child learns best when he is happy, and speech, as we have seen, develops fastest during the child's periods of play, beginning with his pleasure-giving cooing and babbling.

In appraising the possibilities of a psychogenic basis for cases of delayed speech and language, the teacher should give special attention to any evidence from the child's speech history that a period of apparently normal speech development may have been

8. Dale B. Harris in Mildred Templin, *Certain Language Skills in Children,* op. cit. p. v.

interrupted to be followed by a regression or a cessation of language activities. A special study should be made of circumstances, both physiological and environmental, that appear to be associated, in time at least, with the speech deviation. For example, if a child's speech becomes progressively disturbed following an illness, it might be suspected that the illness may have caused a hearing loss that is beginning to manifest itself in a corresponding speech loss. On the other hand, the circumstances of the illness may have induced 'babying' of the child with the result that the disturbed speech may be a symptom of regression or an unusual bid for attention. If the speech aberration, however, coincides in time with some emotional trauma, such as a severe fright or a death in the family, then the teacher can more readily, and safely, arrive at a psychogenic diagnosis.

Infantile Autism

The occurrence of autism in children is, fortunately, a rare disease, but perhaps some mention of it should be included among the possible causes of speech and language absence or delay. The autistic child is one who lives in a world apart and who refuses to relate to the human world around him, including his own mother. His behavior can only be characterized as bizarre, erratic, and unpredictable, resembling more that of an intractable monkey than a human child. Such attributes as biting, rocking, staring, banging the head, hitting the ear with the hand, temper tantrums, strange eating habits, and general out-of-this-world aloofness are characteristic. Communication with this child is very difficult or, more commonly, impossible.

Speech activities include:

1. No speech at all, or crude animal-like noises including wild yelling, squealing, chirping, gurgling, clicking, et cetera, but all self-centered; no communication is intended.
2. There may be some precocious, but non-communicative, uses of language in which the child talks to himself, to the television set, or a non-existent person. There is no indication of

understanding speech or wishing others to understand him. He may repeat certain words and phrases endlessly.

No one knows what causes autism, nor have any attempts at language or other therapy met with much success. Obviously there is little the teacher can do with such a child except attempt to secure psychiatric help.

Adverse Environmental Factors

Among the environmental factors (discussed in Chapter III) important in influencing the speech and language development of the child are: (1) motivation, (2) opportunities for experience, (3) socio-economic status of the family, (4) the amount and kind of speech stimulation, and (5) bilingual influences. Without doubt, the most important of these is the socio-economic level of the home. For example, Burns and Schell state,

Socially disadvantaged children have more conspicious language and speech deficiencies than any other large identifiable population segment. Born into a quantitatively and qualitatively deficient family, they interact with equally deficient peers, receive little direction in expressing themselves coherently and lucidly, and fail to develop certain cognitive abilities common to and prized by the rest of our society.[9]

Virtually all of the studies of language acquisition and status have found identifiable and often significant retardation and other language disorders when children from the lower socio-economic groups were compared with children from middle and upper classes. Templin, for example, found consistent, usually significant, differences in favor of her upper groups in all of the five measures of language development employed in her study.[10] Doubtless a number of plausible explanations for the communicative advantage enjoyed by children from the middle and

9. Paul C. Burns and Leo M. Schell, *Elementary School Language Arts,* op. cit. p. 56.
10. Mildred C. Templin, *Certain Language Skills in Children,* op. cit.

upper classes will come to mind. Wyatt[11] suggests that these children customarily learn both the formal, more elaborate form of speaking with adults, as well as the more limited, informal style they use with contemporaries. Lower class children learn only the latter. Thus they have to 'translate' the formal language of the teacher, for example, into their own style to 'understand' it—make it personally meaningful to them. This not only slows them down, but something is also likely to be lost in the 'translation.'

There are also more specific factors in the child's environment that play an important role in facilitating or retarding his speech and language development. Molyneaux reports on a study that calls attention to some of these factors that appear to be more important than others in contributing to communicative retardation.[12] Molyneaux investigated two groups of kindergarten children differing greatly in linguistic development but matched with respect to a number of other factors. The most important items which appeared to distinguish the superior speakers from those linguistically retarded had to do with the quality of the speech models set for the children, the amount and type of speech stimulation provided, the available opportunities for experiences conducive to speech development, and the order and stability of the home situation generally.

It was discovered, for example, that children of advanced speech development tend to be 'only' children or the oldest child in the family, while those with delayed speech were in general the 'baby' of the family. Parents of the delayed speech group were inclined to be older at the time of the study than those of the advanced speech group. All of these factors indicate that the child with delayed speech arrives in a family in which there are already other children with whom he associates and who present

11. Gertrude Wyatt, *Language Learning and Communication Disorders in Children*, Free Press, New York, 1969, p. 255.
12. Dorothy Molyneaux, 'Childhood Language Development,' in Morris Val Jones, ed., *Language Development*, Charles C. Thomas, Springfield, Ill., 1972, pp. 20–23.

him with a poorer speech model than his more fortunate contemporary who happens to be an only child, or a first child who remains an only child for a period of time, and who consequently receives more time and attention from his younger parents who provide him with a superior speech model.

The study also disclosed a very significant difference between the two groups with respect to the amount of bedtime story reading, the prevalence of nursery-rhyme memorization, the tendency to find amusement and pleasure in looking at books and listening to children's records, and the prevalence of toys of the constructive type, such as alphabet blocks, blackboards or spelling boards, painting and drawing books, and building toys of various kinds. In other words, children with normal or superior speech tend to come from homes in which there is more speech activity, where such activity is motivated and made fun, and where the parents try to teach recognition of letters of the alphabet and awaken an interest in reading. An unfavorable environment, therefore, would be one in which the child is left to his own devices or in association with other children rather than with more mature individuals, and where fewer opportunities are offered him to learn language symbols and develop other habits of constructive thinking.

Further, it was discovered from the study that the children with retarded speech were considered by their mothers to be immature for their age and hence were inclined to be overprotected and denied opportunities for seeking new experiences and assuming responsibilities commensurate with their age level. Also, the mothers of this group expressed the opinion that their children were not as well behaved or as well adjusted as they should be, and confessed that they had no consistent or constructive policy for dealing with their children when they misbehaved. There was considerable evidence that the mothers of the children with delayed speech spent far less time with them than the mothers (and the fathers, too) of the normal and advanced-speech group, that they were inclined to be over-protective and to practice favoritism among their children, and that they felt helpless and baffled when problems involving the management and training of their children arose.

All in all, the results of this study, which are generally in line with clinical experience and observation, would indicate that children with normal or superior oral language tend to come from homes in which the parents, while not better educated, do appear to exercise more intelligence and good sense in the speech training of their children in particular and in over-all management and education generally than do parents of children who are likely to be retarded in their communicative development. The superior parents are more aware of their children's basic needs and are more interested specifically in activities involving the use of speech and language functions; they display more good sense in the selection of their children's toys and in organizing their leisure-time activities, many of which involve doing things with their children. These homes appeared to be more stable, on the whole, and the parents better able to adjust themselves to the maturational needs and problems presented to them by their growing children than was found to be the case in the other group.

What to Do for Delayed-Speech-and-Language Cases

While there is much that can be done directly to promote the linguistic development of the child with retarded speech, it is also true that some of the more important steps are fundamental and, to a degree, indirect, dealing as they must with the child's environment and his whole development generally. Often the latter course is the more important; it must not be forgotten that, given favorable environmental conditions, the child normally develops speech more or less automatically without any *special* training or attention. It should be the concern of the teacher to arrange things to approximate the normal situation as closely as possible in those instances where the child gives evidence of deviating from the usual course of speech development. The following specific procedures and general principles are offered as guides to anyone attempting to help such a child.

Diagnosis

The first question which the teacher should attempt to answer is 'Just *why* is this child retarded in his speech development?' The answer is not always easy to find, but that fact does not excuse her from trying, since, as we have seen, removal of the cause may be the most important, and perhaps only, step that will need to be taken. Suggestions have already been made for securing the assistance of outside specialists in getting general health, hearing, and intelligence examinations. The teacher must first make sure that she has a child to work with who is free of other special disabilities. The possible causal factors that may be uncovered as a result of these examinations must be left in the hands of these same specialists for such rehabilitation as may be possible. Whatever the teacher may safely undertake to do for the mentally or physically disabled child must be done with the advice and guidance of the proper authority.

Diagnostic indications that the child may be retarded in his motor or neurological development include a general clumsiness and lack of co-ordination as shown in the way in which the child walks, runs, sits, stands (poor posture may be a positive symptom here), and handles himself generally. Ability in finer, more specific co-ordinations is indicated by the child's skill in playing various games, such as catching and throwing a ball, by his facility with a pencil or crayon in writing and drawing, and by the use of his fingers in manipulating toys or using tools. The teacher may discover that the child was late in learning to walk, and the mother may be able to furnish other evidence of the child's motor immaturity from his behavior at home at various age levels. The teacher may also observe that the child has no marked hand preference, performing certain activities with the right hand and then switching over to the left as convenience or fancy dictates with no apparent loss, or gain, of manual skill.

In her appraisal of the environment and in her search for possible emotional and psychological factors, the teacher is referred to the discussions of the speech development of the normal child, his fundamental drives and needs, and the symptoms of emotional maladjustment in children included in previous and subsequent chapters.

The teacher should not be discouraged or too surprised, however, if her most diligent efforts are rewarded with no tangible or logical explanation of the cause of the child's speech problem. Delayed speech cases are often among the most difficult to explain, some of them apparently defying diagnosis. There may be several reasons for this seeming mystery. It may be that the causes are too involved and too obscure to be easily discovered. After all, when factors related to an individual's environmental background, his personality, and his adjustment to his environment are being considered, the significance of any one factor, or any isolated group of factors, must be appraised in relation to the total situation. For example, several of the children with delayed speech examined in the Stanford Speech and Hearing Clinic were found to have moderately low intelligence quotients, but these were not sufficiently low to be the sole explanation for the severe speech symptoms. In these instances the handicap of low intelligence had been coupled with other adverse factors in the training and background of the children, all of which combined to produce a more serious speech problem than any one of them could have caused by itself. As a matter of fact, in many of the seemingly unexplainable cases the individual factors may be so mild and unobtrusive that they escape detection in isolation; it is only when they begin to react upon each other that they become important.

Another reason why attempts to diagnose the speech troubles of some of these children may meet with failure is that the original causes may have disappeared or ceased to function but the speech symptoms remain, established and fortified by habit patterns which the individual is unable to change without help from the outside. A good example of such a circumstance is that of a child whose speech develops before his hearing, especially his speech sound discrimination, has sufficiently matured to enable him to speak correctly. By the time the teacher or speech clinician sees the child, the hearing may be perfectly normal, but the improper speech patterns may well have persisted.

As a matter of fact, in most cases a great deal may be done for the child who is delayed in his speech development, regardless of whether or not the cause has been discovered. It is always desirable, of course, to search carefully for the cause, so that it can be alleviated if it is still operative. Moreover, if the teacher knows the background out of which the difficulty has developed, the whole program of therapy can be organized and pointed up more effectively. On the other hand, in those instances where no satisfactory diagnosis can be made, the teacher should not hesitate to do what she can to help the child with his speech problem regardless. The application of sane mental health principles, the establishment of environmental conditions that will be conducive to the development of good speech and language, and a sound program of speech education and ear training in the schoolroom will harm no one and may do much to rehabilitate the linguistically retarded child, regardless of what the specific cause, or causes, may have been.

Moreover, much of what the teacher can do to assist the child with delayed or disordered oral communication can easily be made to fit in with regular classroom procedures and within the curriculum of the elementary school language arts program, especially at the level of the kindergarten and the first two or three grades. A number of specific suggestions will be found in the section which follows. Additional procedures and materials will also be found in subsequent chapters, especially Chapters v and xii.

Role of the Teacher and the School in Therapy

In those instances where some motor retardation is suspected as a causal factor in retarded speech, articulation drills and exercises to develop general bodily co-ordination and control would doubtless prove beneficial. Suggestions for articulation exercises that can be used to advantage for these children will be included in the following chapter on articulatory disorders. It may be more difficult for the classroom teacher to provide materials for the general motor development of the child. What such a child really needs is a program of calisthenics or corrective gymnastics of a type seldom available in the public school of today. As a substitute, the child can derive considerable profit from certain types of play activities and games demanding a relatively high degree of motor inhibition and control. For example, even such simple childhood pastimes as 'Peas Porridge Hot' and 'Simon Says Thumbs Up' have considerable value in developing eye-hand co-ordination and inducing motor inhibition and manual control. Many playground games, such as hop-scotch, jacks, ball bouncing, jump rope, baseball, and even follow-the-leader, also place a certain premium on steadiness, agility, and general motor co-ordination, as well as on more specific skills. These activities are adaptable to different age groups and most of them can be organized on either an individual or group-participation basis. Also, the motivation factor is automatically taken care of.

As a corollary to the program of motor development, the teacher who undertakes to help the child retarded in his speech would be well advised to encourage him to choose one hand or the other and to assist him in developing skill in that hand, so that he will become definitely right-handed or left-handed, as the case may be. Unless she has had special training in speech rehabilitation, however, it would be unwise for her to attempt to influence the child in his eventual choice of which hand is to be preferred for unimanual activities. If all outside influences are removed, the chances are good that the hand which the child naturally comes to prefer will be the correct choice for him. The point is that it should be one or the other; ambidexterity, whatever its merits may be for the average individual, is not to be encouraged in the child with delayed speech.

Unilaterality in manual activities can be developed by practicing every type of activity normally performed with one hand, from turning a doorknob or using a spoon in eating to pitching a ball. The most important unimanual activity from the point of view of the teacher, and the most critical from the point of view of the child's speech progress, is writing and related uses of a pencil or crayon. Here again, the child's own natural preference should be the determining factor. If he persists in using his left hand, no effort should be made to influence him otherwise; ordinarily it will be the same hand that he prefers for picking up things, for feeding himself, or for throwing a ball. The important point is not whether he is to become a left-handed or a right-handed writer, but that he should eventually be one or the other and should not shift indiscriminately back and forth in the process.

Ear training for the child with delayed speech is as important at school as it is at home, and many of the same devices can be used. The technique of reiterating in a natural way what the child has spoken imperfectly, to be recommended for parents, will also be found useful in the classroom. The teacher should speak clearly and carefully, but in a natural way, being careful to avoid a type of over-preciseness that will call attention to itself as being exaggerated and artificial. Story telling and story reading can again be used to good advantage, not only as ear-training material but also as motivation and speech stimulation devices. The child's interest should be aroused so that he will feel he is participating in the story himself; or perhaps the story can be dramatized simply, the various characters being assigned to members of the class, who respond with dialogue learned from listening to the story as previously read by the teacher.

No opportunity should be missed for drawing the child with delayed speech into a conversation or any other type of speech activity that is normally a part of the class routine or that can be made a part of the classroom procedure. If left to their own devices, many such children would prefer to sit silent in the back of the room, merely watching the other children perform, either because of a natural shyness from which many of them suffer or because they are painfully aware of their speech deficiencies, or perhaps for some other reason that may remain a complete mystery to everyone including the child himself. The teacher will need to exercise considerable ingenuity and tact with a great show of friendliness, animation, and interest to win the confidence of some of these youngsters and to give them motivation sufficient to make them respond verbally to the classroom situation. Others will present no difficulty with respect to this particular problem.

In those cases where the child needs to work specifically to correct individual sounds, certain poems, jingles, and specially selected stories can be found that stress the particular sound, or sounds, under consideration. A little poem about a bee 'buzzing,' for example, can be used to teach the sound of [z]. The familiar 'London Bridge Is Falling Down' contains a sufficient number of *l*'s to make it an effective vehicle for teaching the sound of [l]. A story about a rabbit would be effective in teaching the [r]. Some of the drill material listed under the various sounds discussed in the following chapter will be found useful in this connection. Books containing such specially prepared and selected material are also available to the teacher, some of which are included in the bibliography at the end of Chapter v and in the General References at the end of the book. Pictures, such as those found in the advertising sections of magazines, also furnish good drill material for the teaching of individual speech sounds. A picture of a birthday party with the inevitable cake occupying a prominent place will provide stimulus material not only for general spontaneous speech response, but also for ear training and drill on specific sounds, such as the [k] in *cake* and *candle*, the *th* [θ] in birthday, and many others. Chapter xii contains many specific suggestions for incorporating speech training into several of the regular subject-matter disciplines that make up the school curriculum.

At this point the teacher is reminded of the discussion in Chapter ii, which explains speech sounds as *sounds*, quite independent of spelling. In working with the child, she should always refer to them as sounds, never as alphabet letters. If it is the first sound in *Sam* that the teacher is attempting to correct, she should refer to it as [s] (like escaping steam) and not as 'ess.' In this way, the concept of words as combinations of phonetic units can be made clear to the child, and his attention can thus be called to the particular sounds to be singled out for special study. In the oral word *cake*, for example, the child's attention is focused on just two sounds, one of which is repeated—[kek]. The child is taught to hear the separate sounds and to be conscious of them as distinct entities. However, it is the *word* of which the sound is a part that in the end is important. Repetition or other drill on isolated sounds should be kept to a minimum and every effort should be made to emphasize the familiar words that contain the sound and their eventual correct pronunciation. Emphasis on the sound is merely a means to that end.

In accomplishing this phonetic awareness, the teacher will find it helpful to assign to each sound being studied some sort of identity, or name, that will be meaningful to the child. For example, the [s] is the 'snake sound,' *sh* [ʃ] is 'mother's shushing sound,' [z] is the 'bee sound,' *ch* [tʃ] is the 'train sound,' or 'sneeze sound,' and [r] is the 'puppy growling sound.' Not only is ear training materially facilitated by the use of this device, but the teacher will also find these names to be a convenient method of identification when referring to the sounds in the speech lesson.

Auditory stimulation, which constitutes the child's ear training and which is the most important single adjunct to his speech learning, must be supplemented wherever possible by other sensory reinforcements, such as the visual and kinesthetic. The child should not only hear what it sounds like to make an [l] or an [r], but often he must be shown, by watching someone else, where the tongue is placed for the [l], and he must learn what his own tongue feels like when he produces a proper [r]. To implement the visual approach, the child may be given a small mirror in which he can watch the movements and positions of his own tongue and lips as he forms sounds. He can then compare what he sees in the mirror with what he sees when he watches the teacher make the same sounds. For older children, pictures can be found or drawn that show the proper shaping of the lips and the tongue, as well as the recommended position of the jaw and the teeth, in the formation of the various sounds. While the auditory impression is the most potent sensory avenue of approach in speech teaching—the one that should be tried first and stressed most often—all three can be used to advantage to augment and strengthen each other, in whatever way fixes the speech-sound concept most firmly in the consciousness of the child.

Some Specific Activities for Group Work
1. The teacher should not forget that, for a number of possible reasons, the child with delayed speech may not process information received auditorially as rapidly as a normal speaker. Therefore, in all communication with language-disordered children she should slow down her normal rate of speaking, not so much as to make speech appear distorted and artificial or lacking in interest and vitality, but sufficiently to insure the children's easy comprehension.
2. Never mind the child's chronological age or his grade in school. Begin where the child *is* in his communicative development and go on from there.
3. Lessons and activities should be structured to provide the child with more successes than failures. Failures should be passed over but successes should be rewarded with smiles and praise.
4. As was recommended earlier, encourage the child to participate and get him to *speak up* to be heard by the teacher and the group.
5. Learning to listen discriminatingly is a basic step for the language handicapped child. Even though he may not present symptoms of word-deafness discussed earlier, he

may have developed the habit of passive, inattentive listening. Sharpen up his listening ability with the following activities, most of which can be turned into games:

    a. How does a pencil sound on paper, a crayon, chalk on a blackboard, et cetera?

    b. Have children all face in one direction and close eyes. Teacher at back of children jingles keys, opens desk drawer, sharpens pencil, et cetera. Children guess activity.

    c. Teacher reads prepared sentences; children listen for words that rhyme, or words that contain certain speech sounds, et cetera.

    d. Train the children in following directions: 'Mary, go to the board, draw a cross, open and close a desk drawer, then draw a circle, and come back here.' Directions can be made easier or more difficult. Others check on Mary.

6. To increase attention and visual memory, write something on the board. Immediately erase it and ask, 'What did I write?'

7. Put a variety of small common objects in a bag. Have the child reach in and describe what he is holding. The group guesses. Or he may withdraw his hand and describe through pantomime what he has touched.

8. Game of '20-questions'—this can relate to the activity described above, or the child can choose any person or object he wishes. Children take turns asking questions until the object is identified. This can be used to teach a child to ask good questions and give good answers.

9. 'Things that travel on wheels'—how many can the group suggest? There are many possible variations of this activity.

10. The child explains differences between objects that have some similarities, for example, baseball and basketball, automobile and truck, clock and watch, et cetera. Or the

teacher can go around the group getting one response from each child.

11. The many opportunities for teaching language in story-telling or story-reading should not be overlooked. Story-telling can also be participated in by the children. Try reading also, if ability permits.

12. It is surprising how easily and how enthusiastically children take to creative dramatics, 'acting out,' and use of hand puppets, which can be simple enough to be made out of small paper sacks with the bottoms folded down to form the upper half of the mouth and rest of the face, drawn on with crayon. It is surprising how a child too shy to participate himself can 'blossom forth' when he is speaking for a puppet. A small group playing store, for example, with one child playing the sales person and the others coming in to ask questions, make purchases, et cetera, can furnish many opportunities for language experience.[13]

Finally, the teacher must remember that when she is dealing with children, speech training can, and should, be fun. Much of it must be indirectly motivated in the form of games and other teaching devices. No progress in speech training can be made unless the teacher is able to secure a satisfactory response from the child. In order to accomplish this, a rather high level of interest and morale must be maintained. The child must be brought to the place where he is moved to respond, if not for the immediate purpose of improving his speech, at least in

13. Excellent additional suggestions for group activities to help language-retarded children can be found in Sima Spector's chapter entitled 'Implementing a Language-Development Program in the Elementary School' in Morris Val Jones's, *Language Development* and in the Teacher's Source Book for *The Junior Listen-Hear Program* by Jan Slepian and Ann Seidler. This latter is for children in the first grade and younger. Substantial help will also be found in the *Peabody Language Development Kits* by Lloyd Dunn and James Smith. All of these sources are listed in the References at the end of this chapter.

order to take his turn in the game, satisfy his curiosity, try his luck, or win his share of praise and attention. There are myriad ways of insuring satisfactory response in the speech lesson, most of which are not essentially different from those with which the successful teacher is already thoroughly familiar through previous experience in the ordinary classroom situation.

Remembering what a powerful influence the parents and home can exert on the child's development of speech and language, the teacher should peruse the paragraphs which follow for possible suggestions to use in parental counseling.

Role of the Parents and the Home in Therapy

In the case of the child in nursery school, kindergarten, and the lower grades, the classroom teacher will need to lean heavily on the co-operation of the parents. After she has learned something of the methods the parents have used in teaching speech to the child and has familiarized herself somewhat with his general environmental background, she will be in a position to make some suggestions looking toward the improvement of both of these potent factors.

1. *Motivation* Parents should be advised to keep a slight, but constant, pressure on the child to use the best speech of which he is capable in making known his wants. They should manifest considerable difficulty in understanding his careless and half-hearted approximations of words and phrases, if they have any reason to believe that he can do better. Grunts and gestures should never be accepted as substitutes for words, if the child is capable of speaking at all. Parents must realize that if an exclamation or pointing a finger will get the child what he wants, he will hardly be encouraged to exert the extra effort required to talk. Parents must also be very cautious not to anticipate their child's wants before he has made an effort to communicate them, nor to 'read his mind' solely from his general behavior when the situation calls for speech, or at least an attempt at it. Gesturing and unnessarily crude attempts at

vocal communication should be 'punished'; that is, the parents must pretend, if necessary, that they cannot understand the child and as a consequence he will not get what he wants. His best efforts to speak should be rewarded with praise and a prompt response, verbal or otherwise or both.

The teacher may discover in certain instances that anticipation of the child's wants is merely a part of a general pattern of over-protection on the part of the parents. They may not only wait upon him more than they should, but they may also worry and fret over him in other ways as well. In these instances a basic change in their general attitudes and methods of child training will probably be necessary before the speech problem can be solved satisfactorily. More often, however, it will be found that ignorance of the consequences and indifference, or simple expediency, are responsible for these practices. It is easier to wait on the child and get him what he wants, than it is to take the time and effort required to teach him to ask for it and wait for him while he does.

2. *Speech stimulation* Parents should themselves set a good speech model for the child. Speech that is on a slightly higher plane than the child is capable of reproducing easily will insure his constant progress. The words should not be too long, however, because the child's memory span has not as yet fully developed. The speech must be distinct and clear because the child's hearing may not be too keen and his speech-sound discrimination ability will not equal that of an adult. The tempo must be relatively slow, for his motor development does not as yet permit him to negotiate the quick shifts of position and the complicated adjustments of the articulators required by speech at the rapid tempo that characterizes much of adult talk.

If more than one language is spoken in the home, it would be advisable to delay introduction of the second language until the child has gained a solid grasp of the first one. The attempt to teach the child two languages at once may well result in confusion, with a consequent delay in his acquisition of skill in either one. In those instances where the use of two languages cannot be avoided, each parent should be consistent in the language which he uses when talking to the child. If he uses English sometimes and Spanish at other times, for example, confusion is more likely to result than it would if one parent consistently spoke to the child in Spanish, the other in English.

The child should be encouraged to play with children slightly older than himself, rather than younger, on the presumption that the older child will be more advanced in his language development and can thus furnish a better speech model. For the same reason it would be desirable to keep twins separated as much as possible for their play activities during the years important for the growth of speech and language. Twins who are together a great deal during their pre-school and early school years become very self-sufficient and interdependent, often developing a kind of jargon specifically for their use and understood only by them, and possibly the mother. Twins furnish relatively poor speech models for each other and are more often found to be retarded in their speech development than are single siblings.

Every opportunity for subjecting the child to speech and language experiences within the home should be exploited. A regular story hour should be established, preferably at bedtime when the child is relaxed and receptive (relatively, at least). Select a few simple stories and nursery rhymes and read them over and over to him until he comes to know them 'by heart.' This will not be difficult, for children seemingly never grow tired of hearing a favorite story or jingle repeated. As the child becomes familiar with the story, encourage him to participate in it with you, supplying key words and phrases at appropriate places in the narrative. For example, you are reading, 'On her way through the woods Little Red Riding Hoot met a ———'; you pause and look at the child expectantly and he supplies the word 'wolf.' Then you always repeat after him in a seemingly natural way, but very clearly and distinctly, 'That's right, it was a *wolf* that talked to her in the woods.' This device of repetition serves the important purpose of providing ear training for the child and avoids the odium that would become attached to constant correction of the child when he mispronounces. Later the child can be encouraged to tell most of the story himself, with the device of repetition again being used whenever the parent wishes to call attention to a sound missed or a word otherwise mispronounced. In this way the child will come to learn, without an issue being made of it, that the word is 'wolf' and not 'oof,' or whatever other approximation he may have attempted.

In addition to the story hour, other opportunities for speech learning should be provided at various times during the day's routine. For example, Molyneaux's study, previously referred to, revealed that mothers of the normal- and advanced-speech group reported more or less regular sessions of simple 'chatting' with their children about the day's activities and other items of interest at the moment. Moreover, they were in the habit of taking them on shopping trips down to the market, where there would be things to talk about and new words to be learned. Instead of having them left at home with baby-sitters, the mothers of this group indicated that their children were taken on trips to the zoo and on family excursions, where they could enjoy companionship with their parents and reap the benefits of talking with adults.

Parents should be advised to provide wholesome activities and constructive toys for their children, instead of leaving them to their own devices, simply to vegetate and grow self-centered. A carefully chosen selection of children's records should be provided, to which the children can listen at their pleasure, reproduced on simple machines they can operate themselves. A considerable selection of records that will furnish excellent ear training and superior speech models on a high level of interest and motivation is now available. Books that contain provocative and story-telling pictures will increase vocabulary and give children something to talk about. Painting and coloring books, drawing books, alphabet blocks, and small blackboards are constructive devices that encourage the use of speech and language.

Construction materials and toys of various kinds will stimulate the imagination and thought processes of the child and hence will further his language development. If he is to think constructively, he must have something to think with, and, for the average individual, word symbols become the tools of his thought processes. As the child builds the toy bridge, he is building it with words as well as with metal bars or wooden sticks. In general, parents must not forget that word meanings grow out of the child's experiences; the wider and more varied those experiences, the more stimuli there will be for communication and the greater the need to learn new words to match the new experiences. The child who sits at home alone or whose scope of activity is either severely limited or boringly monotonous will have neither the incentive nor the opportunity to progress as he should in his speech and language development.

3. *General procedures of effective speech teaching in the home*

   a. Encourage the child to vocalize. Within reasonable limitations, the child's practice of talking to himself while playing should be encouraged; he is merely thinking aloud, and as such he is improving his linguistic abilities. Even if his vocalization is confined largely to babbling, he should not be repressed on the theory that 'he is too old for that baby prattle.' He may simply be late in going through some of the earlier steps in normal speech deevlopment.

   b. Don't rush the child when he is talking. He should be made to feel that he has ample time to say what he wants to. A parent may be inviting serious trouble if the child becomes convinced that whatever he has to say must be got out in a hurry or he is likely to be interrupted, ignored, or cut off with some such admonition as 'Well, hurry up and say it!' or 'Can't you ever keep still and let someone else talk?' In defense of parents, on the other hand, it must be made clear that, quite naturally, the child cannot be allowed to monopolize every speech situation. It is essential, though, that he have his conversational rights and that he get an attentive and respectful hearing when his 'turn' comes and he has something to say that he considers important.

c. The matter of correcting the child when he makes mistakes must be carefully and judiciously handled. Too persistent and too frequent corrections can easily amount to nagging, which is likely to end in a negative attitude toward speech; or the child may simply grow so accustomed to the constant admonitions that eventually he does not even hear them. In general, and especially is this true of the younger child, parents will accomplish more if they keep their speech-teaching somewhat more subtle and indirect. For example, the child says, 'ee 'a baw' and mother responds, 'Yes, see the ball,' speaking very carefully and distinctly. The child is thus being corrected indirectly without being aware of the correction as such. This is a better procedure than shouting at the child, 'For Heaven's sake, don't say, "ee 'a baw" like a baby; say "see the ball." ' In the case of the older child whose habit patterns have become more deeply rooted, some more direct method may be needed to correct specific defects. Here it may be desirable for the parents to employ some of the techniques recommended for the teacher and explained earlier in this chapter.

d. Every effort should be made to prevent the child from becoming embarrassingly self-conscious about his speech problems. This is another reason why the practice of constantly reminding the child when he makes an error is not recommended. Great care should also be taken to make sure that the child is not teased because his speech is different. Undesirable speech habits can easily become fixated and entrenched by feelings of self-consciousness, guilt, or inferiority, or of being different from other people. When this happens, not only is there danger that undesirable attitudes and emotional problems will arise, but it also becomes more difficult to remove the speech impediment.

e. Parents can, and should, enjoy the various steps in the language learning process along with their children. Memorizing and reciting nursery rhymes can be a very pleasant experience for all, especially if some physical activity, such as clapping or finger play ('This is the church, this is the steeple,' et cetera), can be fitted in naturally with the words. Looking at pictures can also be fun, and animal pictures and stories have special appeal for children who often identify more easily with animals than with people. Animals 'talk'; what do they say? Be sure to pursue these activities when the child is in the mood or can easily be got in the mood; little good can come from thrusting them on him. As the child gets older, there are many family games requiring some mental exertion and use of language that would be more stimulating than watching television.

f. Don't forget that the child's oral communication comes basically from his socialization with adults and other children. If the child's environment restricts such contacts (there are few children to play with, the parents work, et cetera) and he is too young for regular school, serious thought should be given to sending him to nursery school. It can do wonders for the social development of children.

g. Take care that the child's 'baby-talk' isn't serving a useful purpose in your child's emotional and social life. If such speech wins attention for him, gets others to wait on him, or serves as an excuse for keeping him more dependent on his mother, he may unconsciously cling to it and refuse to improve. Perhaps it helps him to win attention away from his older brother, or places him in a better position to compete for attention with his baby sister. Perhaps he doesn't want to grow up and talk like a 'big boy.'

h. In line with the above, don't forget that speech and language are guides to a child's emotional and social maturity. If you treat your child like a baby, he may well continue to talk like one. Be careful not to resist the natural process of maturation. Encourage your child to develop a natural maturity and self-dependence commensurate with his age. Help him in the process of his 'growing up.' It should be natural for him to want to do things and to talk like a 'big boy,' not like a baby.

i. The happy, well-adjusted, emotionally stable child has many advantages in his favor which will show up in his speech and language development. Wise policies of discipline and child-rearing in general will pay big dividends in more ways than one. Develop in your child a sense of security, make him know that he is loved and wanted, be wise and consistent in your discipline, give him his share of legitimate attention, be realistic in your demands and in your expectations of him, give him opportunities to exercise his curiosity and to profit from new experiences, and see to it that he is well and physically fit. These are all important factors in assisting your child to develop better speech and language habits. More general suggestions will be found in Chapter ix.

References

Bangs, Tina, *Language and Learning Disorders of the Pre-Academic Child*, Appleton-Century-Crofts, New York, 1968.

Battin, R. Ray, and C. Olaf Haug, *Speech and Language Delay: A Home Training Program*, Charles C. Thomas, Springfield, Ill., 1964.

Berry, Mildred F., *Language Disorders of Children*, Appleton-Century-Crofts, New York, 1969.

Birch, Herbert G., ed., *Brain Damage in Children: The Biological and Social Aspects*, Williams and Wilkins, Baltimore, 1964.

Blake, James Neal, *Speech, Language, and Learning Disorders*, Charles C. Thomas, Springfield, Ill., 1971.

Burns, Paul C., and Leo M. Schell, *Elementary School Language Arts: Selected Readings*, Rand McNally, Chicago, 1969, Part II.

Dunn, Lloyd M., and James O. Smith, *Peabody Language Development Kits*, American Guidance Service, Minneapolis, 1965.

Eisenson, Jon, J. Jeffery Auer, John V. Irwin, *The Psychology of Communication*, Appleton-Century-Crofts, New York, 1963, Parts i and iv.

Frankenburg, W. K., and J. B. Dodds, *Denver Developmental Screening Test*, University of Colorado Medical Center, Denver, 1967. For children under six.

Greene, Margaret C. L., *Learning To Talk: A Parent's Guide for the First Five Years*, Harper and Row, New York, 1960.

Johnson, Doris, and Helmer Myklebust, *Learning Disabilities, Educational Principles and Practices*, Grune and Stratton, New York, 1967.

Johnson, Wendell, et al., *Speech Handicapped School Children*, Harper and Row, New York, 3rd ed., 1967, Chap. 6.

Jones, Morris Val, ed., *Language Development: The Key to Learning*, Charles C. Thomas, Springfield, Ill., 1972.

Kugelmass, I. Newton, *The Autistic Child*, Charles C. Thomas, Springfield, Ill., 1970.

Lee, Laura, *The Northwestern Syntax Screening Test*, Northwestern University Press, Evanston, Ill., 1969.

Lewis, M. M., *How Children Learn To Talk*, Basic Books, New York, 1959.

Lillywhite, Herold, and Doris Bradley, *Communication Problems in Mental Retardation*, Harper and Row, New York, 1969.

Maietta, Donald F., and Don Glen Sandy, *Baby Learns To Talk*, Stanwix House, Pittsburgh, 1969.

McElroy, Colleen W., *Speech and Language Development of the Preschool Child*, Charles C. Thomas, Springfield, Ill., 1972.

Mecham, M. J., J. L. Jex, J. D. Jones, *Utah Test of Language Development*, Communication Research Associates, Salt Lake City, Utah, 1967. For children of school age.

Menyuk, Paula, *The Development of Speech*, Bobbs-Merrill, New York, 1972.

National Institute of Neurological Diseases and Stroke, *Learning To Talk*, U. S. Government Printing Office, Washington, D. C., 1970.

Pennington, R. C., and James E. Pennington, *For the Parents of a Child Whose Speech Is Delayed*, Prentice-Hall, Englewood Cliffs, N. J., 1965.

Riley, Glyndon D., *Riley Articulation and Language Test*, Western Psychological Services, Beverly Hills, Calif., 1966. For kindergarten and first grade.

Slepian, Jan, and Ann Seidler, *The Junior Listen-Hear Program*, Follett, Chicago, 1968.

Templin, Mildred C., *Certain Language Skills in Children: Their Development and Interrelationships*, University of Minnesota Press, Minneapolis, 1957.

Travis, Lee E., ed., *Handbook of Speech Pathology and Audiology,* Appleton-Century-Crofts, New York, 1971, Chaps. 43, 44, 45, 46, 47.

Van Riper, Charles, *Speech Correction,* Prentice-Hall, Englewood Cliffs, N. J., 4th ed., 1963, Chaps. 4, 5, 6.

——, *Teaching Your Child To Talk,* Harper and Row, New York, 1950.

West, Robert, *Childhood Aphasia,* Proceedings of the Institute on Childhood Aphasia, California Society for Crippled Children and Adults, San Francisco, 1962.

Wood, Nancy, *Delayed Speech and Language Development,* Prentice-Hall, Englewood Cliffs, N. J., 1964.

Wyatt, Gertrude, *Language Learning and Communication Disorders in Children,* Free Press, New York, 1969.

V

Articulation Disorders

Articulation disorders of various kinds, including those associated with delayed speech, account for approximately 75 per cent of the total speech defects found among the public-school population. Articulatory problems present a wide range of symptoms and degrees of severity, varying all the way from a mild slovenliness of speech to a speech pattern so defective that it becomes unintelligible. The majority of problems with which the teacher needs to concern herself most, however, will be found somewhere between these two extremes, characterized typically by defective sound production, such as a lisp, a substitution of [w] for [r], or an improperly formed [l].

In Chapter II articulatory disorders were classified into seven main types: (1) disorders involving specific sounds, which may be omitted, substituted one for another, or improperly produced; (2) oral inactivity, or generally unclear speech; (3) slow and labored articulation; (4) rapid, slurring speech that 'hits the high spots' only; (5) immature articulation; (6) foreign dialect; (7) regional dialect. Also included were articulatory tests for analyzing the speech of the child to determine his particular problems. The present chapter will deal largely with the first four of the categories mentioned above, although some of the material can also be applied to improving the speech of the child who exhibits dialectal pronunciation, a problem to be presented in more detail in the following chapter. Immature articulation was discussed in the previous chapter on delayed speech and language.

Causes of Articulation Disorders

As with other types of speech disorders, it is important to discover the cause of the articulatory deficiency in each instance in order to eliminate it or mitigate it, if such is possible or feasible. Even in those cases where apparently nothing can be done to modify the cause, it is important for the teacher to be aware of the probable origins of the difficulty, because such knowledge may greatly influence the approach that should be used in individual instances. There are seemingly myriad reasons why the child's articulation may vary from the norm for his age, some of which are often obscure and difficult to locate. Only the more common and readily discoverable will be described here.

Structural Deviations

The most common assumption of the layman, in which category most parents must be placed, is that any abnormality of speech exhibited by the child is caused by some deficiency in his speech mechanism—there must be something 'wrong' with his mouth or throat. Such is actually more often the exception than the rule. Actually only a relatively small percentage of the articulatory disorders found among school children are structural in origin. It is well, however, to be on guard, for structural deviations do occur in school children, and the teacher should be able to recognize at least the more obvious cases when she sees them.

1. *The lips* If the lips are not functioning properly, the defect will most likely show up in those sounds dependent upon lip action for their proper formation, principally [p], [b], [w], and [m]. If the lower lip is also involved, [f] and [v] may be disturbed too. The most serious, and most obvious, lip malformation is known as cleft lip. In these cases there will be a cleft or gap beginning at the lower border of the upper lip and extending upward toward the nostril opening on one side or both. The cleft will be a little to the right or left of the central ridge of the lip and may be slight or complete. The surgical repair of cleft lip is usually completed while the child is quite young. There is little that the classroom teacher can do for the child with an unrepaired cleft lip that is at all serious, a situation unlikely to be seen these days.

The teacher should also look for scar tissue on the lips which may be impairing their mobility. Such a symptom would call for a program of lip exercises to improve their flexibility and precision of movement. Such exercises will also benefit the child whose lips appear excessively full and flabby, resulting in 'lip-lazy' speech. Sometimes the upper lip appears to be abnormally short or is kept in a retracted, chronic-smile position exposing the front teeth. In some of these cases the upper lip appears to be unusually short; in others, protruding front teeth or a habitual facial expression has apparently been a contributing factor. In any case, where functional inadequacy of the upper lip is involved, exercises to bring it down where it will make effective contact with the lower lip are indicated. Drills containing such sounds as [p], [b], and [m] are especially useful here. Particular attention should be called to the function of the lips in the production of these sounds.

If the lips are kept too tightly together during the production of speech, resulting in oral inactivity of the mumbling variety, some psychogenic factor may be involved. Sometimes individuals resort to this practice in order to hide ugly or irregular teeth of which they have become self-conscious. The teacher should also be on the lookout for signs of asymmetry in lip position or movement, which may be indicative of muscular imbalance or neurological malfunctioning. Have the child smile or alternate between the lip positions for [u] (rounded) and [i] (spread); the movements should be reasonably the same for the two sides. If they are not or if the child habitually talks out of one side of his mouth, the possibility of paralysis or of some other physiological condition should be investigated.

2. *The bite* The term 'bite' refers to the occlusion of the teeth, or the way in which they come together when the jaws are closed. For speech purposes we are concerned principally with the occlusion of the front teeth. There are several sounds, chief among them being [s] and [z], that call for a rather precise adjustment of the upper and lower incisors, not only with respect to each other but in relation to the tip of the tongue as well. If there is any malformation of the jaw structure or of the dental arch that makes these adjustments difficult or impossible, an articulatory disorder may result. Such malformations of the bite are referred to as malocclusions. There are three main types, all of which render the proper formation of certain sounds, notably the [s] and [z], difficult if not impossible in some cases.

   a. An overbite occurs when the upper front teeth protrude beyond the lower teeth to a greater degree than normal (fig. 1). This is often associated with a receding lower jaw. Some form of lisp is likely to occur in these cases, but fortunately it is not difficult to correct, provided the overbite is not too pronounced.

   b. The underbite is the opposite of the condition described above—the lower jaw protrudes to such an extent that the lower incisors mask all or part of the upper incisors when the jaws are closed (fig. 2). This is also called the undershot jaw, or the 'bull-dog' bite. This condition, fortunately more rare than the overbite, is more difficult to compensate for through speech training and is likely to affect a larger number of speech sounds.

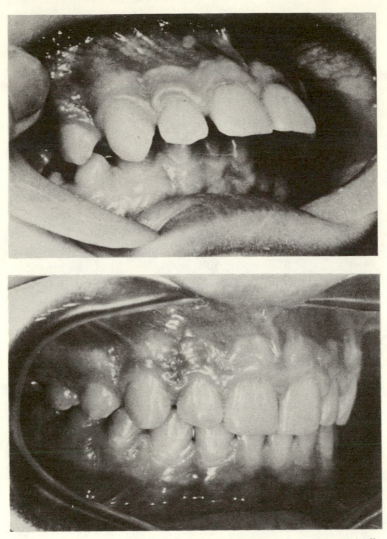

FIGURE 1. A case of overbite. The severe malocclusion existing originally (above). The same mouth seventeen months later after orthodontia had been completed (below).

c. The open bite can be recognized by the space that appears between the upper and lower front teeth when the back teeth are brought together (fig. 3). The alignment of the teeth is such that it is impossible for the individual to get the edges of his incisors together. This condition is not as commonly found as the overbite, but it is more difficult to deal with. The [s] and [z] are most likely to be defective as a result of this condition, although most of the front-of-the-tongue sounds may also be affected if the condition is sufficiently severe.

In all cases of malocclusion the possibility of correction through orthodontia should be considered. Virtually all types of malocclusion and dental irregularities, no matter how severe, can be either completely corrected or greatly improved through the process of orthodontia, if the work is begun at the right time. The possibilities for correction are dramatically illustrated in figures 1 and 4. Where such treatment is in prospect, it would be unwise to attempt any serious speech training for those defects arising from the malocclusion until the orthodontia has been completed, for several reasons. In the first place, speech re-education is at best a slow and difficult process where serious structural deviations or deficiencies are present. Then, too, whatever speech habits are acquired as a result of such training may need to be modified and relearned after the articulatory structure has been altered. All in all, it is generally better to delay speech training until after the orthodontia has been completed. Whether any will be needed then will depend on a number of factors, among them the severity of the original malformation, the age of the child, and his intelligence and general adaptability.

3. *The teeth* Irregular, missing, or poorly spaced teeth, particularly the incisors, can result in defective production of the sounds that are dependent in part at least on the teeth for their acoustic properties. This group includes [f], [v], [θ], [ð], [ʃ], [ʒ], [s], and [z]. Prognosis is relatively good in the case of most

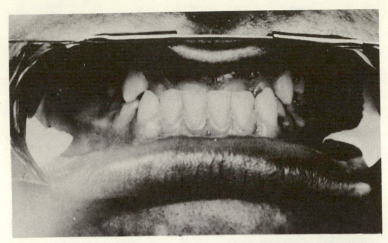

FIGURE 2. An example of underbite

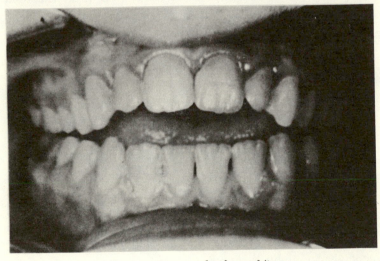

FIGURE 3. An example of open bite

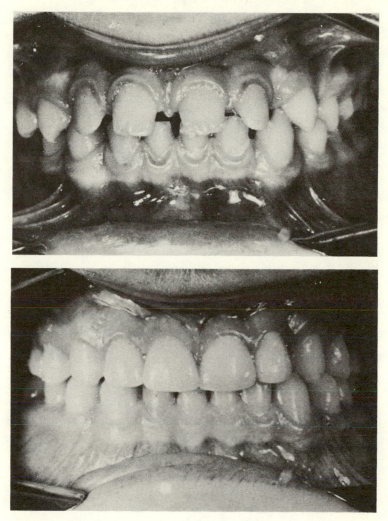

FIGURE 4. An example of serious dental irregularity involving the incisors especially (above). The same mouth after orthodontia had been completed sixteen months later (below).

speech defects involving dental irregularities of various kinds. Through experimentation, an adjustment will usually be found that will produce an acceptable sound, even though the adjustment departs somewhat from that normally used by the average speaker.

Again, the possible advantages of orthodontia or dental prosthesis should be carefully considered (fig. 4). Crooked teeth can be straightened, gaps between them can be closed up, and missing teeth can be replaced. Where such procedures are feasible, they are much to be preferred to speech training that is designed merely to compensate for deficiencies of dental structure.

4. *The tongue* In the thinking of the average individual, the tongue is so vital to the speech process that almost any speech defect will be thought of in terms of some malformation or malfunctioning of the tongue, usually referred to as tongue-tie. Actually true tongue-tie (an abnormally shortened frenum of the tongue), as well as other malformations of tongue structure, is comparatively rare. Therefore, although the individual with a speech problem may be convinced that his tongue is too large or too small or too long or too short, seldom will any such condition be found upon actual examination.

Have the child protrude his tongue and attempt to touch his nose and then his chin with the tongue-tip. If he can elevate the tip toward his nose without the middle of the tongue appearing depressed and tied down or if he can extend the tip downward beyond the red border of his lower lip, he is not tongue-tied. If he can protrude his tongue and move it from side to side or run it out and in as a cat does in lapping milk, there is no serious deficiency of neuromuscular control. Have the child open his mouth with his tongue lying relaxed in a natural position. The right and left halves should be approximately even in height and similar in appearance. If one side is lower than the other or gives the impression of being shriveled up, some atrophy or functional imbalance may be present.

On the whole, the teacher may be comforted by the assurance that the tongue itself is rarely at fault, so far as any structural deficiencies are concerned. In those instances where some malformation is suspected, the child should be referred to a physician for diagnosis. The tongue is a very adaptable organ, however, and in those few instances where some irremediable structural deviation may be present, a little training can often accomplish a great deal to improve the articulation, given good hearing, adequate motivation, and other favorable factors.

5. *The hard palate* The most serious malformation of the hard palate, or roof of the mouth, is a cleft, or opening, along the central line of the palate up into the nasal cavities. This condition, which will be discussed in more detail in Chapter vii, is usually congenital and is known as cleft palate. Individuals suffering from this condition have no way of shutting off the mouth from the nasal passages when producing those sounds that should be made in the mouth, with the result that the voiceless consonants will pass through the nose as puffs of air or as variously produced friction sounds, while the vowels and voiced consonants will be improperly nasalized. Only the nasals [m], [n], and [ŋ] retain their natural quality. In serious cases, articulation will be so distorted that speech is virtually unintelligible.

The palatal cleft may be closed by surgery or by means of a plastic artificial palate known as an obturator, or by a combination of the two. Until and unless one of these steps is taken, speech training is pretty hopeless. After the repair has been completed, a protracted period of speech training is usually needed to modify the old habit patterns and establish new ones that utilize the new mechanism. Such a program will, in most instances, require more time and training than the classroom teacher has at her command; hence it must be left as the primary responsibility of the speech clinician.

A more common and less serious condition can be seen when

the palate appears to be unusually high and narrow. This is often accompanied by a typically narrow upper dental arch as well and possibly protruding upper incisors. Such a condition may interfere with the proper formation of sounds that depend upon the tongue-tip making contact or establishing other relationships with the upper gum ridge or front part of the palate. These include the [t], [d], [n], [l], [ʃ], [s], and [z]. If a malocclusion is also present, the palatal contour may well be improved by the orthodontia that should be undertaken.

6. *The soft palate* (*Velum*) Have the child open his mouth with his tongue lying relaxed. The velum should hang at the back of the mouth in a relaxed position, fairly even on both sides, with the uvula suspended at the center. Observe any asymmetry of structure and look for evidence of cleft or scar tissue. Have the child say a good oral 'ah'; the velum should rise up and back in a fairly even, symmetrical fashion, and the posterior walls of the pharynx should pull in somewhat until the velum and pharyngeal wall approximate to form a complete, or almost complete, closure. If the velum does not rise sufficiently to close with the pharyngeal wall, or if, after rising, there is still an appreciable gap between them, either a paralysis or a structural inadequacy of the velum is indicated. Likewise, if one side seems to be higher than the other or moves up farther when the velum is raised, some type of functional or structural inequality may be present.

Have a physician take a look at the child if there is any cause for suspicion either in the action of the child's velum or in his speech. Common symptoms of a malformed or malfunctioning soft palate are very similar to those previously listed for cleft palate, although they may not be quite so severe. Vowels will be nasalized to some degree, and many of the consonants will show a leakage through the nose, some of them going through the nasal passages as puffs of air, or 'nasal snorts.' Such nasal leakage can often be tested by placing a small feather or crumpled piece of tissue on a card held directly under the child's nostrils as he pronounces such words as *tent-pole, paper, chicken,* or *teeter-totter.* If there is substantial escape of air, the feather or paper will be blown off on such sounds as [p], [t], [tʃ], and [k].

Physiological Deficiencies

Any condition that contributes to a malfunctioning of organs involved in speech is likely to produce a speech disturbance as a result. It has been found, for example, that approximately 75 per cent of children suffering from the previously discussed cerebral palsy also exhibit associated speech defects because they do not have normal control over the muscles of the lips, jaw, tongue, and throat. It is not probable that the classroom teacher will be able to do much for the child whose speech problem is caused by paralysis; such training must be left for the speech therapist.

In the preceding chapter it was pointed out that retarded motor development may be a causal factor contributing to delayed speech. Children differ considerably at all age levels with respect to motor ability, and it is no surprise to discover that speech, which is basically a motor process, appears to be rather closely related to that ability. Experimental studies have produced some evidence to indicate that those children with so-called functional defects of articulation tend to score significantly lower on tests of motor ability than children who speak normally. One such study was conducted by Jenkins and Lohr in which a group of first-grade children with articulatory defects involving three or more consonants were matched with a control group of normal speakers.[1] Using the Oseretsky Tests of Motor Proficiency, they discovered a significant difference (beyond the .01 level of confidence) between their two groups when the Oseretsky scores were compared. Moreover, there was a consistent difference between their two groups on each of the six categories making up the Oseretsky tests.

1. Edna Jenkins and Frances E. Lohr, 'Severe Articulation Disorders and Motor Abilities,' *Journal of Speech and Hearing Disorders,* August 1964, pp. 286–92.

It is highly probable that children with such disabilities would profit from a program in general physical training involving agility, control, balance, and co-ordination, because motor skill can be developed, up to a certain point at least. More specifically, the child who is clumsy with his speech mechanism would profit from properly selected and administered articulation exercises designed to improve the speed, precision, and timing with which he is able to manipulate his articulatory mechanism. A certain amount of this increased skill can be made to carry over into his speech patterns. A number of suitable articulation drills are included later in this chapter.

If the child's motor inferiority is at all marked, a physical examination should be arranged for him. It is possible that some remediable factor is contributing to the poor muscle tonus or the inferior co-ordination, such as an endocrine dysfunction, malnutrition, or a neuropathology.

Tongue-Thrust—Abnormal Swallowing

Although presently surrounded by a degree of uncertainty and controversy, the subject of so-called tongue-thrust should probably be included among possible causes of articulatory disorders. Although this abnormal pattern of swallowing has been known to orthodontists for many years, only recently has there been general recognition of the extent of the problem and widespread interest in its possible relationship to articulation and especially its suspected role in causing malocclusions.

Simply stated, tongue-thrust has been described as the forward and/or lateral thrusting of the tongue between the teeth during swallowing. Additionally, swallowing appears to be more effortful than normal, with contraction of the facial muscles, especially those surrounding the mouth, with lips slightly protruded, but compressed and seemingly pressing in on the incisors during the act. If the observer is quick to push the lips open with the thumb and forefinger of each hand at the height of the child's swallow, the tip of the tongue can actually be seen between the teeth. The swallow itself may be inefficient, with crumbs or liquid left at the corners of the mouth, necessitating extraneous tongue activity to clear the lips and surrounding tissues. Apart from swallowing, many children habitually carry the tongue too far forward in the mouth with the tongue-tip protruding between the teeth or pressing outward against the incisors.

Orthodontists are convinced that tongue-thrusting is a positive contributor to malocclusions, especially the open bite type, with the overbite also involved in many cases. There is also some evidence to indicate that children who exhibit tongue-thrusting habits are more likely than normal swallowers to display distortions of those sounds involving the tip or front of the tongue, especially the sibilants, such as [s], [z], [ʃ], [tʃ], and [dʒ].[2] These sounds, and possibly others as well, are produced with the front of the tongue too far forward and too low in the mouth. Of course, if an actual malocclusion does result from the tongue-thrust habit, that also may contribute to defective speech sound production.

There are a number of theories as to what may cause tongue-thrust, one of which is that it may represent an abnormal persistence of what has been found to be the normal infantile swallowing pattern.[3] Others blame it on use of the wrong kind of nipple in bottle feeding, on an imbalance and lack of proper synergic coordination of the muscles normally involved in swallowing, and it has also been suggested that forward thrusting of the tongue may arise from avoidance of pain or discomfort in the back of the throat, perhaps involving the tonsils, pharynx, et cetera.

If the teacher should observe any of the symptoms mentioned above or have any other reason to suspect that a child is a tongue-thruster, she should consult with the speech clinician

2. Samuel G. Fletcher, Robert L. Casteel, and Doris P. Bradley, 'Tongue-Thrust Swallow, Speech Articulation, and Age,' *Journal of Speech and Hearing Disorders,* August 1961, pp. 201–08.
3. James A. Lewis and Richard F. Counihan, 'Tongue-Thrust in Infancy,' *Journal of Speech and Hearing Disorders,* August 1965, pp. 280–82.

if one is available. If not, she should involve the school nurse, school dentist consultant if there is one, or suggest that the parents have the child examined by an orthodontist or children's dentist. In many cases the habit is correctable.

Sensory Deficiencies

The importance of hearing, including speech-sound discrimination, to the speech-learning processes was discussed in Chapter III. There it was stressed that the probability of a child's producing any given sound properly in his normal speech pattern is contingent upon his ability to hear that sound, which implies more than merely being aware that some sort of sound is being produced. Hearing, so far as speech production is concerned, involves the ability to distinguish one sound from another—the ability to perceive the fine distinctions that make a particular speech sound different from all others. That this ability is positively related to articulation ability is supported by a number of research studies, typical among which is one by Sherman and Geith who found differences in discrimination scores significant beyond the .001 level in favor of kindergarten children who ranked high in articulation ability when compared with children ranking low.[4] In summary, they state, 'According to present results, a reasonable assumption is that low speech sound discrimination ability is in general causally related to poor articulation.' There is some evidence from other studies that this close relationship may not apply to children older than about eight or nine years of age.

In every case of defective articulation, especially those where the cause is not immediately apparent, the teacher should insist on some assurance that the child's hearing is functioning properly. This precaution becomes particularly important if the defective, missing, or substituted sounds happen to be those of high frequency and low intensity, such as [s], [f], [θ], and

4. Dorothy Sherman and Annette Geith, 'Speech Sound Discrimination and Articulation Skill,' *Journal of Speech and Hearing Research*, June 1967, pp. 277–80.

[ʃ]; other sounds may be involved as well, depending on the type and severity of the hearing loss.

Although for purposes of diagnosis there is no substitute for an audiometer test of hearing, it is possible for the teacher to gain some notion of the child's auditory abilities, especially his discrimination of speech sounds, by employing a rather simple type of speech test, examples of which are included in the Appendix. If the child's discrimination appears to be poor, an intensive concentration on ear training is indicated in addition to whatever speech training is needed, or rather as an accompaniment of it. Moreover, as was pointed out earlier, in such cases special emphasis may need to be placed on other sensory approaches, the visual and the kinesthetic specifically.

While there is no question that the auditory sense modality is the most essential, so far as the learning and production of speech are concerned, there may be other sensory feedback mechanisms also important in the formation of speech sounds. For example, for those sounds that are relatively invisible, such as [l], [r], [k], [g], and [j], it is probable that the tactile sense, as well as the kinesthetic sense, may well play an important role. This may be illustrated by the difficulty one has in speaking when certain sensory nerves of the mouth are immobilized by the injection of novacain during dental surgery. It doesn't *feel right* when we try to talk.

An ingenious experiment was conducted by a group from Purdue University in which various small objects were introduced into the mouths of blindfolded subjects who were then required to tell with respect to two successive objects whether they were alike or different.[5] An experimental group of 60 eight-year-old children with varying degrees of articulatory impairments were compared with a similar control group of normal speakers. When scores on the oral tactile discrimination tests were compared, it was found that the experimental children

5. Robert Ringel et al., 'Some Relations Between Orosensory Discrimination and Articulatory Aspects of Speech Production,' *Journal of Speech and Hearing Disorders*, February 1970, pp. 3–11.

made more errors than the children with normal speech and, furthermore, there was a clear and significant tendency for errors to increase as a function of the severity of the articulation defect. These results would indicate that certain children who are inferior in speech production may not be as aware of what their tongues are doing, for example, as normal speakers are. When the word doesn't sound right, they are not as clever at making the necessary articulatory adjustments.

The sensory ability under study in this investigation is doubtless, in part at least, a native ability. To what extent, if any, it might be improved through training has not been scientifically established. It is quite possible that work on such articulatory exercises as are included later in this chapter might well serve to call the child's attention to what was going on in his mouth and increase his ability to make appropriate adjustments in his articulatory mechanism to correct certain defects in the production of speech sounds. It might be worth a try.

Mental Deficiency

The close relationship between speech and intelligence has been stressed in previous chapters. There it was pointed out that, although a speech defect is not necessarily a symptom of mental retardation *per se*, the likelihood of defective speech is definitely increased as the intelligence drops below normal. There are a number of reasons why this should be so, only a few of the more important of which can be mentioned here. In the first place, as mental capacity declines, motor ability also suffers—the mentally deficient are likely to be below normal in general motor co-ordination and development. This factor, as we have seen, might very likely be reflected in articulatory losses.

Even more important are the generally low standards and the poor motivation of the less intelligent individual. There is not the incentive for him to improve because he is not sensitive about his speech, and it is difficult for him to see the value of good speech. Moreover, the general perceptive powers of the individual with a low I.Q. are likely to be duller than are those of his more gifted contemporary. It is more difficult for him to see and hear that his speech is different from that of others, a factor which makes speech training a tedious and uncertain process in these cases.

The speech symptoms likely to be exhibited by the child who is below normal in intelligence will follow in general the speech pattern that is characteristic of the normal child of the same mental age. That is, a child of eight with a mental age of six will tend to talk like a normal child who is six years old. In an older person the speech patterns would be those normally identified with carelessness and laziness: difficult sounds will be omitted or easier ones substituted for them, many sounds will be distorted, words and phrases will be telescoped and run together, and the whole speech will lack precision and clearness. The vocabulary will be simple and restricted, and grammatical errors will be common. The degree to which these symptoms will appear in the speech of a given individual is, of course, dependent on a number of factors in addition to intelligence. An unusually favorable environment, for example, may offset a considerable loss in intelligence, with the result that the speech may show no obvious deficiencies at all. The situation is particularly critical, however, when mental retardation happens to be accompanied by other unfavorable factors; such situations are the ones most likely to result in serious speech problems.

All of these factors considered together perhaps provide the clue to successful therapy for such an individual. The attack must be a multipronged one. As many avenues of approach as possible must be utilized, and all available factors must be turned into positive forces that will help him. For example, in these cases it is important that the speech of those with whom the person comes in contact should constitute a good model for him and that other factors in the environment should be favorable. Methods must be found to motivate the individual to appreciate the value of adequate speech and to strive to attain an established goal through consistent effort and attention.

Adverse Environmental Factors

A large proportion of the poor speech found among school children is merely a reflection of an unfavorable speech environment. Many of their bad speech habits are simply the result of imitating the bad speech of their elders, who are often unaware of their own communicative shortcomings and the effect such poor models may have upon the speech of their children. Recently a mother brought her lisping daughter to a speech clinic, with the explanation, 'I uthed to lithp mythelf,' but she thought she no longer lisped and could not understand how her small daughter had acquired such a bad *s!* If the child has been exposed to hurried, slurred, dialectal, or otherwise inadequate speech at home, it can hardly be expected that his own speech will be free of similar faults.

Many of the environmental factors discussed in the two previous chapters in relation to oral language development and retardation also apply importantly to articulation and its deviations. After all, articulation is an integral part of language and behaves like many of its other facets.

Adverse Personality Factors

It is obvious that attitudes and habits of carelessness, lassitude, and indifference are hardly conducive to the development of superior speech, or even to the prevention of serious defects. The source of many of the speech faults found in the school can be listed simply as laziness, indifference, and ignorance of proper standards. Youngsters are very much inclined, and perhaps understandably so, to take the path of least effort, which very often involves sound omissions, substitutions, slurring, and other similar articulatory short cuts.

There may also be a relation between style of speech and certain personality traits, or personality types, if they can be called that. The slow-moving, sluggish, phlegmatic individual is very likely to display some of those personality characteristics in his speech, resulting in a slow tempo and 'mushy,' poorly formed sounds and words, referred to as oral inactivity. Such people are inclined to be lip-lazy and tongue-lazy, and the final result in extreme cases is a kind of mumbling drawl. The opposite temperament also produces its special brand of speech pattern. The nervous, high-strung, hyperactive person is likely to talk fast, and, because he is not able to execute the proper articulatory adjustments so rapidly, many sounds are dropped out or are distorted. Such a person tends to 'hit the high spots' only and his speech rhythm may be jerky and broken. Then there is the shy, bashful person who is literally afraid to open his mouth. In such cases the voice is likely to be light and weak, and this lack of intensity, coupled with the oral inactivity, often renders the speech very difficult to understand.

While it may be difficult or impossible to alter personality traits in these cases, speech training must be aimed at compensating for the adverse personality factors. The phlegmatic individual can be taught to speak more precisely, the high-strung person can be trained to speak more slowly and carefully, and the timid child can be encouraged to speak up with more emphasis and force. The task is not easy, but persistent efforts can produce results in the end.

More specific emotional factors may be involved where a lisp or signs of baby-talk seem to be symptoms of regressive tendencies or may be used as attention-getting devices. In these instances some psychotherapy may be needed as an accompaniment of the speech training. A young girl in junior high school was getting help from the speech clinician to overcome a lisp. The speech problem was a very simple one, but after a period of time, very little, if any, progress had been made. Further investigation finally disclosed that the girl, although giving lip-service to the desirability of improving her speech, was actually resisting efforts to rid her of the lisp because she was convinced that the boys thought it was cute.

A more complete discussion of behavior and personality problems most likely to be found in childhood and their possible relation to speech and language disorders, as well as to environmental factors, will be found in Chapter IX.

Testing Articulation

It is always a good plan to form as complete a picture as possible of the speech problem. This may be simple; through close association with the child over a period of time, the teacher may have had ample opportunity to observe his natural speech and may have discovered which sounds are defective and under what circumstances the defects appear. In those instances where the teacher has not had the opportunity to observe the child's speech or where a more thorough analysis of the articulation is needed, a regular articulation test is recommended. A number of such tests, suitable for use with children of various age levels, were included in Chapter II.

These are simple screening tests suitable for the classroom teacher and others whose time and technical knowledge are limited. Where the articulation problem is more involved or serious, a more complete diagnostic testing is recommended to be done by a trained speech clinician.

General Procedures in Training

Making the Child Aware of His Problem

In most cases of articulatory disorder among older children and adults it is desirable and necessary to make the individual aware of his speech deficiency and to secure his co-operation in removing it. A different practice must be followed with younger children, since their awareness of their problem might well result in undesirable self-consciousness and anxiety. Until the child is in the third grade or so, the wisest procedure is to approach the situation somewhat more indirectly, showing the child what he needs to do and training his ear to recognize the proper pattern without direct reference to any specific deficiency on his part. As soon as the child is old enough to understand, however, and is otherwise capable of assuming a reasonably objective attitude toward his speech problems, they should be discussed with him, and a clear understanding arrived at concerning what needs to be done.

It is often difficult for another person to realize how and why an individual can be blissfully unaware of defects and bad habits in his own speech when they can appear so obvious and distracting to others. The explanation involves two types of factors—psychological and physiological. As we have seen, the speech process evolves as an unconscious process in the child and it is likely to remain so throughout life unless attention is called to it in one way or another. The speech habits exhibited by an individual are likely to be of relatively long standing, and any major changes which may have occurred since the establishment of speech probably came about gradually without the individual's being aware of them.

Then, too, the structure of the ear is such that it prevents an individual from hearing his own voice and speech in the same way that another person hears them. We hear our own voice partly by way of direct conduction of sound through the bones of the neck and head from the origin of the sound in the larynx or articulatory mechanism to the end-organ of hearing in the inner ear, while another person hears it only through sound waves in the air impinging on the sound-detecting and sound-conducting mechanism of the outer and middle ear. The result is that our own voice actually does sound different to us from the way it sounds to another person. The nature and extent of this difference are partially demonstrated when we listen to our speech played back to us after it has been recorded. Such a disclosure is always a shock to a person who is experiencing it for the first time because what he hears on the recorded sample sounds so different to him from what he thought he sounded like. The inevitable response from such an individual is, 'Do I sound like that?' And it is usually a perfectly honest reaction.

Such considerations not only explain why a person may be unconscious of his own speech faults, but they also point up the necessity of bringing such problems to the attention and full realization of the individual. Unless this is done, he is working largely in the dark because he does not know what is wanted of him. Speech improvement is difficult and improbable under such conditions. This procedure does not apply to the young child, of course, for here, as explained above, the approach must be quite different.

The Use of Recording Equipment

There are only two practical ways of making clear to the individual what it is in his speech that is different from the normal and what should consequently be changed. One way is for the teacher to imitate the child's defects. This method has certain advantages, especially for the teacher, for in so doing she may discover how and why it is that the child speaks the way he does. When she begins to talk as the child does, she may discover, for example, the particular adjustments of the articulators that produce the observed deviations and can thereby gain insight into the nature of the child's problem and as a result can assist him more effectively.

On the other hand, there are certain limitations and disadvantages to this procedure as a means of helping the child identify his errors. In the first place, it is difficult, if not impossible, for one individual to imitate exactly either the mechanics or the acoustic properties of a speech sound as produced by another person. The mechanism involved is too complex for that. Then, too, there is always the tendency for the child to feel that the teacher is exaggerating merely for the effect—he really cannot sound as bad as the teacher is making it appear. The teacher is warned that unless imitation is carefully and judiciously employed some harm may result. Care must be taken to avoid developing self-consciousness in the child or suggesting that either the child or his speech is being subjected to ridicule.

Undoubtedly the most satisfactory and effective method of objectifying an individual's speech is to record it on sound-recording equipment and let him hear for himself what the machine reproduces. One such experience may be sufficient not only to convince the child that something is seriously wrong with his speech but to motivate him to do something about it as well. A boy of eighteen with very defective articulation was brought to the speech clinic. He omitted many sounds and numerous others were substituted or were grossly distorted. He was asked to read a simple story and a recording was made of it, which was then played back to him without comment. The seriousness of his speech problem was graphically impressed upon this young man as he realized with amazement that he himself could not understand what he had said. For the first time, in all probability, he had heard his speech as it really was and was shocked to discover that it was unintelligible even to himself. The experience was highly motivating!

Another way in which recordings can be used to good advantage is to take interim samples of the child's speech from time to time throughout the course of his training. These give the teacher some measure of her progress with the child and they provide a basis for appraising the effectiveness of the methods being used. For the child, such periodic check-ups constitute a source of great encouragement and satisfaction when they indicate improvement, and they contribute to his motivation as he strives to make the next one show an even greater change.

On the other hand, the point must be made that there is no magical benefit to be derived from the mere recording and playing back of a pupil's voice. Even after he hears his speech objectively, he will need help and guidance in appraising it and in organizing a program of training to improve it. Merely calling attention to speech defects serves only to make the individual self-conscious and distressed about them, unless he is also shown what he can do about them and is given some assurance that improvement is possible.

Ear Training

The importance of ear training in the process of re-educating a child's speech can scarcely be exaggerated. If the child is to become aware of his bad speech habits and is to change these into good speech habits, it is essential that he learn to hear and identify the undesirable speech pattern and recognize it as being different from what he is attempting to acquire. This process involves ear training. Again, a recording device can be used to good advantage. If a permanent recording is made of the child's speech and if he is allowed to listen to it a number of times, he will be aided in his efforts to isolate and identify the defective sounds or the faulty speech pattern. Once the child is able to hear objectively the mistakes he makes, it will not be difficult for him to become aware of the difference between what he is saying and what he should be saying.

As a necessary part of the process of ear training, the child must be made to realize that words are made up of speech-sound units, and he must be trained to listen for these sounds and to be able to isolate them. In this connection the teacher is reminded of the discussion of the sound scheme of English presented in Chapter II. There it was stressed that the teacher must learn to think in terms of speech sounds rather than of alphabet symbols, that the oral word *cat*, for example, is made up of the three sounds [k], [æ], [t], and not the alphabet letters *cee, ae, tee*. Therefore, whenever the teacher wishes to call the child's attention to a speech sound, she should produce the actual sound and not refer to it by its alphabet symbol. Moreover, to avoid confusion, the teacher should produce only the sound itself, with no accompanying vowel or other sound to distort it and complicate the picture. If it is the initial sound of *top* that is under consideration, for example, the teacher would produce only [t], a mild explosion of unvocalized breath, being careful to avoid making it sound like 'tuh,' [tə] or [tʌ]. On the other hand, the voiced consonants such as [d] or [g] will be produced with an unstressed neutral vowel following and will become [də] and [gə].

With older children the phonetic symbols can often be used to good advantage as a means of identifying the individual speech sounds, especially since by this means some visual representation of the sound can be used in addition to the oral. Incidentally, phonetic symbols produce additional motivation by catering to the child's natural fascination for any form of 'secret' writing. It is impossible for the child, or the teacher either, to develop even a 'nodding acquaintance' with the phonetic alphabet without becoming aware of the individual sound components that go to make up the words and phrases of spoken language.

When working with younger children, other techniques of ear training and sound identification must be developed. As was pointed out in Chapter IV, one of the most useful is to give each speech sound being studied a name by which it can be referred to and identified. Thus [s] becomes the 'snake sound,' [z] is the 'sound the bee makes,' [tʃ] is the 'sneeze sound,' [ʃ] is 'mother's shushing sound,' and [θ] can be the 'windmill sound' or any other that the teacher and the children wish to agree on. With this basis of common understanding established, the teacher can say, 'Does the word *see* begin with the "snake sound" or the "windmill sound"? All right, then, let's hear the "snake sound" when you say *see*.'

Various listening projects can be worked out that will provide both fun and valuable ear training for the child. Jingles, poems, and stories can be read to the child, especially those that repeat the sound being studied. Read a poem about a bee that goes 'buzzz-z-z-z-z' at frequent intervals, or the goose that says 'hiss-s-s-s-s-s-s' every time anyone comes around. Stress the sound somewhat when you come to it and later encourage the child to help you out when you come to that part; or he can play the part of the bee and the goose himself, supplying the 'z-z-z-z-z-z-z-z' and 's-s-s-s-s-s-s-s-s' at the appropriate places. Somewhat older children can either read the jingles themselves or memorize short ones.

There are many jingles and stories that have been especially written to exploit this technique of ear training and sound identification. Some of them are in the form of action poems constructed to permit a sort of pantomimic accompaniment of appropriate activity as the child or the teacher recites the lines. This provides an effective means of reinforcing the auditory impression received by the child, and it can also motivate what might otherwise be merely another speech exercise. Many of these specially prepared jingles also lend themselves to simple choral reading or to a primitive form of dramatization if individual parts can be assigned. Recommended collections of such material are listed in the bibliography at the end of this chapter and in the General References at the end of the book.

Another favorite technique of teachers is to read a poem or story containing repetitions of the sound being studied. Part of the time the sound is correctly produced, but part of the time the teacher imitates the child's error when she comes to the sound. The child is to try to catch the teacher in every error by raising his hand or indicating in other ways that he knows the difference between the correct and incorrect forms when he hears them. This speech game is also adaptable to groups of children by having one child read and the others listen for errors. Or the teacher-pupil relationship can be reversed, the child reading to see whether the teacher can tell when he is speaking correctly and when he is deliberately making the error. The chief value of this latter exercise is that it develops the child's ability to alternate between the old habit and the new pattern consciously and at will. When he can do that, he is on the way to eventual mastery of the problem.

A great deal can also be done with objects or pictures, the teacher hiding a number of them about the room and instructing the child to see how many he can find whose names begin with the sound being studied, the [s], for example. Then as he brings them to the teacher he must pronounce correctly the name of each one, stressing the [s] as he does so. Van Riper[6] has listed and explained a large number of games and other devices that are useful in promoting ear training and in helping the child recognize and identify his errors in relation to the proper speech pattern. Additional suggestions for incorporating ear training and sound discrimination in many of the regular activities of the classroom are included in Chapter xII.

Group Work with Children

Either from choice or from necessity, a large proportion of the work for children with speech problems will be conducted in groups. While it is quite possible, and profitable, to give 'speech improvement' training to an average classroom of unselected children all at one time, groups of actual speech defectives should be kept as small as possible so that a maximum amount of individual attention can be given to each child.

There are certain advantages inherent in group or classroom work, and the teacher should exploit them as fully as each individual situation permits. Ear training can be facilitated by setting up lesson projects in such a way that the children will check on each other. Learning to listen analytically to speech and to recognize deviations from the norm when they occur is one of the first and most important steps in the development of ear training. Motivation can be greatly increased in group work because the teacher can utilize a much wider variety of games and other teaching devices where there is sufficient interest inherent in the activity itself to carry it along and the speech training with it. Furthermore, the natural interest children have in competition can be a powerful motivating force and can contribute greatly to the general progress of the training if properly directed and controlled.

A typical example of the kind of activity that is adapted to

6. Charles Van Riper, *Speech Correction: Principles and Methods*, 4th ed., Prentice-Hall, Englewood Cliffs, N. J., 1963, pp. 249–65.

groups of intermediate age children and that illustrates some of these values is the speech game known as 'A Trip to the Country.' Now, on a trip to the country it is necessary to take along an assortment of accouterments for the pleasure and comfort of the journey. It may be agreed that names of all of the objects to be taken must begin with some specified sound, must contain the sound in some other position, or must meet any other specification the teacher wishes to make. If it is a class of lispers, it may be agreed that names of all objects must begin with [s]. The child selected to start the game begins by saying, 'I went to the country and I took with me a suitcase (his choice of a suitable word beginning with s).' The child next to him continues, 'I went to the country and I took with me a suitcase and a sandwich (his choice).' The next child continues, 'I went to the country and I took with me a suitcase, a sandwich, and my sister.' Thus, each child adds one object of his own choice, but he must also repeat all of the other objects named previously.[7] The game has motivation value, contributes to ear training, and gives training and practice in the sound being studied. It can also be used to overcome oral inactivity, to counteract shyness, and for a number of other purposes.

'A Trip to the Country' is merely one example of many similar types of activity that are adaptable to group work in speech training. A variety of such games will be found in the references later and at the end of this chapter and many will be included in Chapter XII. The teacher will think of others herself. Often such simple equipment as toy telephones, for example, can be used to advantage in setting up situations that approximate real-life activities, such as ordering groceries from the store or inviting friends to a party. In addition to the factor of motivation in such activities, they provide an ideal medium

---

7. This procedure may become a bit cumbersome with a larger group or an entire classroom. Here the teacher may prefer to have each child in turn merely add his item without trying to remember all of the others that have accumulated. Or repeating three such items, for example, would provide additional practice on the sound under study.

for effecting the vital 'carry-over' of new speech habits from the classroom situation to real life outside of school, always a difficult step to accomplish in the course of any special training.

Methods of Teaching New Sounds—
The Acoustic Approach

As was stated earlier, there is no substitute for ear training in attempting to teach a new sound or alter the improper production of an old one. Often this is all that is needed to make the entire problem clear to the child. When he becomes aware of what is wanted, he may be able, without further instruction, to produce the sound perfectly. And often he may do so without being conscious of the particular mechanics involved. Once he has heard the teacher produce [s] clearly in isolation, for example, he may be able to imitate her merely by listening and without knowing the exact position of the tongue and teeth, even though he may not habitually use [s] at all in his speech. This is called the acoustic approach to speech training.

In every case of articulatory disorder, except those where serious hearing loss is involved, the teacher should try the acoustic approach first, and if the child can produce satisfactory results without an explanation of the mechanics, so much the better. The teacher can then proceed directly to the next step in the training—the incorporation of the new sound into syllable, word, and phrase combinations. Such an approach is simple to use and easy to motivate, since the tendency to imitate comes naturally and readily to most children and can easily be made to present something of a challenge to them.

Therefore, it is wise at the beginning of training to have the children hissing like geese, buzzing like bees, and 'shushing' like mother to see who can do it the best. Although general ear training is of considerable value to the child with any type of articulatory defect, special emphasis should be placed on the new sounds, or the correct form of the old sounds, that are to be learned. The next step in the process will be discussed in a later section.

Methods of Teaching New Sounds—
The Phonetic Placement Approach

In those cases where mere imitation of the sound proves inadequate as a means of producing the desired response, the teacher will need to utilize some more direct means of securing the proper formation of the sound, or sounds, in question. Attention must then be called to the mechanics of the sound as determined by the position and movements of the articulatory organs, especially those of the tongue, lips, and teeth. Here the teacher must resort to visual, tactile, and kinesthetic approaches, in addition to the auditory. The child must see where his tongue should go, for example, and he must feel its position and movement.

A small mirror which the child can hold in his hand will enable him to adjust his own tongue, lips, and teeth to correspond with what he can see when his teacher makes the sound. Or the teacher and the child may work in front of a large mirror side by side so that both can watch each other more readily. What the child is able to observe visually will naturally be supplemented by a verbal explanation of the mechanics involved, the extent and importance of the explanation being determined by the child's ability to comprehend it and profit from it. Pictures of the lip and tongue positions may be used to supplement the explanation, or simple diagrams may be drawn on the blackboard. Such pictures and phonetic diagrams are available in a number of sources, some of which are given in the bibliography at the end of this chapter.

As a reinforcement of the auditory and visual stimuli, the teacher should also utilize tactile and kinesthetic sensations, especially in those cases where the child's response to what he sees and hears has been slow. In some cases the teacher can assist the child in securing the proper articulatory adjustment by actually placing his lips, tongue, or jaw in the right position by the use of her fingers or with the aid of such simple equipment as wooden tongue depressors or applicator sticks. Once the proper position has been achieved, the child should be encouraged to identify the *feeling* of that adjustment so that he can reproduce it again voluntarily. Young and Hawk[8] explain in some detail and illustrate with pictures a method whereby the teacher can assist the child mechanically in achieving the desired adjustment for virtually all of the speech sounds.

In following the phonetic placement approach to speech training, however, the teacher should keep its chief limitation in mind—that, except within rather vague and flexible limits, there is no strictly 'standard' articulatory adjustment for any of the speech sounds. When really accurate methods of measurement are applied, we find that no two people make the 'same' sound in exactly the same way. For most of our speech sounds the adjustment is a complex one, the variations in the position or movements of one articulatory organ being compensated for by complementary variations in the others. The acoustic result of this composite adjustment is the important thing, not the specific placement or movement of each individual organ. For example, despite the traditionally vital role the tongue is supposed to play in the production of many of the consonants and all of the vowel sounds, Goldstein[9] reports the case of a man who, after complete surgical removal of his tongue, could produce speech well enough to carry on his trade as a plumber and to be readily understood over the telephone. His rehabilitated speech was self-taught and was acquired within a few weeks after the operation.

In the light of such evidence, it is perhaps unwise to be too dogmatic about the exact position of this or that organ in the production of a given sound. Rather, it is the total adjustment and the composite movements that are important in determining the final product. This is not to imply that the mechanics of speech can be totally ignored, but the complex nature of the mechanism must be constantly kept in mind.

8. Young and Hawk, *Moto-Kinesthetic Speech Training*, op. cit.
9. Max Goldstein, 'Speech Without a Tongue,' *Journal of Speech Disorders*, March 1940, pp. 65–72.

Special Techniques and Devices

Procedures to Insure Motivation

A young child cannot be expected to apply himself diligently to his speech work merely for the sake of self-improvement. Various supplementary interest-arousing devices must be employed. Even in the case of the older child, speech training can be, and should be, fun. Fortunately speech training lends itself readily to presentation in the form of games and other stimulating devices. Some profitable speech games have already been referred to and many others will be found in Chapter xii and in the references later in the present chapter. The possibilities are unlimited, and the teacher herself can invent many attractive devices as she goes along or can adapt them from her other teaching.

An exercise in relaxation becomes a game, for example, if the children can imitate rag dolls or clothes fluttering on the line. Tongue drills take on new life if the child can pretend that he is a cat lapping milk or if a little friendly competition is introduced into a contest to see who can touch the tip of his tongue to his nose or the point of his chin. Songs, jingles, choral readings, and simple dramatizations, all have great possibilities as speech-training media. Songs and jingles not only contain sounds and words as training materials, but they are also useful for teaching rhythm. Many of them combine action with language and can be used to promote co-ordination and motor control as well as to reinforce the speech training with a related and appropriate motor response. If the child can combine the spinning of a pointer with practice on the sound of [s] as he learns to use it in the word *spin*, tangible and lasting results will be more readily forthcoming because the exercise will take on real meaning for him.

It should be pointed out here, however, that the use of games and contests as motivational devices can be overdone, with a consequent loss to the actual speech-learning involved. Two possible dangers must be kept in mind: (1) The child may become so engrossed in the game or contest itself, that speech improvement is largely lost sight of; the main objective becomes obscured. (2) The game or play activity may be so complicated that time spent in explaining and supervising it far overshadows any real speech correction. For example, Mowrer reports a study[10] in which it was discovered that speech clinicians outtalked the children in their classes on an average of 10 to 1! Furthermore, much of the clinicians' talk had little or nothing to do with changing the children's speech behavior.

In another article Mowrer[11] recommends less emphasis on games to insure motivation and more attention to positive reinforcement of the wanted behavior and negative reinforcement of the unwanted behavior. Praise or some other type of reward should follow a successful performance or a sincere attempt, while lack of success may be disapproved by a frown, or perhaps the child actually loses tokens or other tangible rewards he has earned by previous successes. Mowrer concludes by observing:

In view of the research findings we have at this time, it would appear that speech clinicians would increase their effectiveness in modifying speech behavior if they: (1) present positive reinforcers contingent upon correct responses, (2) indicate with a mild aversive consequence when incorrect responses are emitted, (3) teach the child to monitor his own responses, and (4) provide effective cues designed to evoke the correct response.[12]

It is true that Mowrer was writing with professional speech clinicians in mind, but much of what is said also applies to the classroom teacher who is attempting to improve the oral communication of her pupils.

---

10. Donald E. Mowrer, 'An Analysis of Motivational Techniques Used in Speech Therapy,' *ASHA*, October 1970, pp. 491–93.
11. Donald E. Mowrer, 'The Management of Consequent Events in Speech Therapy,' *Educational Technology*, April 1971, pp. 58–61.
12. Ibid. p. 61.

In any case, it is true that motivation, an important ingredient in all learning, becomes particularly vital in speech training because of the peculiarly personal nature of the communicative process. The child will profit little from his speech lessons if they are forced upon him or if he finds doing them unpleasant or boring. Speech training can so easily be motivated, and must be, not only for the pupils but for the teacher herself as well. The moment she becomes too dignified, self-conscious, 'prissy,' or bored, much of the value to the pupils will be lost. Enthusiasm, vitality, imagination, creativeness, and a sense of humor command a high premium in all speech work, especially where children are involved.

The Use of Toys and Other Teaching Materials

One little girl of six had allowed a progressive negativistic 'streak' to develop to the point where she refused to respond at all after the first few minutes of her lesson. Finally the teacher hit upon the device of giving the speech lesson to the child's doll, which she insisted upon bringing with her each time. Of course, the doll could not respond, so the little girl had to do the doll's talking for her and thus got the benefit of the training in the end. This trick was good for several weeks, during which time the negativism gradually subsided and the little girl was quite willing to respond as herself once more. In this and similar ways many of the toys and 'impedimenta' with which children like to surround themselves can be used to advantage by the alert teacher who can see in almost any object a stimulus for producing a new sound, an excuse for starting a conversation that will elicit a desired speech response, or the point of departure for a new game that the group can play.

Among the most useful materials are those adaptable to creative activities, such as modeling clay, crayons, blocks, paints, and toy furniture. Here the child verbalizes as he creates, the new speech pattern taking on practical significance because it is associated with a meaningful activity. As the child works the clay into a thin roll, he imitates the sound that the snake makes and has a chance to practice the [s] as he talks about his new creation.

One student teacher completely 'sold' himself and his program of speech training to several classes of first- and second-grade children with the aid of Pluto, a small jointed wooden dog put together with cord and springs in such a way that he could be made to perform in a most astonishing fashion. When a child responded correctly, Pluto would nod his head in enthusiastic approval, but when a child forgot or a mistake was made, Pluto would shake his head in a most disapproving way. In his enthusiasm over an unusually good lesson, he might be persuaded to sit down or stand on his head. Those children worked considerably harder for Pluto than they would have for the teacher himself.

Of course, the experienced teacher does not need to be told that although such devices can be used to great advantage if properly handled, they can also become very distracting and cumbersome if they are allowed to get out of hand, as was pointed out earlier. After all, they should be nothing more than mere devices to gain a certain objective, and they must always be kept subservient to that end. When the game or the apparatus becomes so engrossing in itself that the speech training is merely incidental, then it has defeated its purpose and becomes an impediment rather than an aid to teaching.

Paired Words and Syllables

With the older children the technique of pairing syllables and words to capitalize on the similarities or differences between certain speech sounds has many advantages. For example, if a child lisps because he allows his tongue to fall too low in the front of his mouth, the proper position of the tongue in the production of [s] may be made clear by comparing it with the tongue position for [t], provided, of course, the individual's [t] is properly made. Word pairs, such as *tea-sea, top-sop, tip-sip,* and *tat-sat,* are useful, therefore, in getting the tongue-tip up and away from the front teeth if some of the feeling associated with the beginning of [t] in the first word of each pair can be made to carry over to [s] at the start of the second word. Likewise, there is a sufficient similarity between [d] and [l] to insure considerable likelihood of getting the tongue-tip on the upper gum ridge where it belongs for [l] if the feeling of [d] can be made to carry over. Therefore, such pairs as *dee-lee, doe-low, dim-limb,* and *die-lie* can be used to advantage in teaching the proper tongue position for [l].

This phonetic device can also be used to demonstrate dissimilar characteristics of sounds. If an individual has an interdental lisp, for example, and substitutes a sound resembling [θ] for [s], an effective technique is to pair such words as *saw-thaw, sin-thin, sum-thumb,* and *pass-path,* having him repeat each pair slowly several times and then reverse the order. Since the words of each pair are obviously different, it will soon become apparent to the lisper that something is wrong with his speech when they sound and feel alike as he pronounces them. In this exercise he strives to make the two words as different as possible by carefully differentiating between the [s] and the [θ] both mechanically and acoustically.

Sequence of Steps in Training

More satisfactory results will be obtained if a certain sequence is adhered to in the training, or retraining, of an individual with an articulatory disorder. While there is naturally some overlapping among the steps explained briefly in the following paragraphs, in general they form a progressive pattern in which the abilities acquired during one phase of the training carry over to the next succeeding step.

After the individual has been made aware that he has a speech problem, if that proves to be a desirable step, and some ear training has been started, his next task is to learn to produce the new sound, or sounds, in isolation and in nonsense syllables. It is usually necessary to begin with the sound itself, rather than with a word in which it occurs, because the average individual has never learned to break a word down into its phonetic components. To him a word is a complete and separate unit, and he is not aware of the specific sounds of which it is composed until they are called to his attention and he learns to recognize and reproduce them individually. For example, if the child habitually substitutes [w] for [r], as some children do, he has learned that the traditional harbinger of spring with the familiar red breast is a 'wobbin.' That is what it is, and it does not do any good to admonish him, 'Don't say "wobbin," say "robin," ' because he does not distinguish between what you have said and what he says; it all refers to the same thing—the familiar bird whose name is 'wobbin'—because that is the way he has learned it.

It is better to begin with something he has not learned incorrectly, such as the syllable *rah*, as contrasted with the syllable *wah*. Here it can be explained that *rah* begins with a new sound, the sound that the puppy makes when he growls— [r-r-r-r-r]. The position of the tongue can be studied and ear training can be employed to enable him to recognize the sound when he hears it and to distinguish it from all other sounds, especially [w]. After he has become thoroughly familiar with the sound itself in such combinations as [rɑ], [ræ], [ri], [ro], and [ru], then it is time to begin looking for some words that also contain the puppy sound. If the training has been successful up to this point, he will recognize that *robin* is one of these words, and that it is really a 'robin' after all, and not a 'wobbin.' At this point he is ready to begin the next step in his training.

In learning to use the new sound in familiar words and phrases, a great deal of unlearning must naturally precede and accompany the new learning. Old habit patterns must be changed and new ones developed in their place. This is a laborious process, and in the accomplishment of this step there will be many lapses when the child will unconsciously fall back into the old pattern. He will see the bird, and it will automatically be a 'wobbin.' During a considerable period in his training, he must stop and think whether this is one of the words that contain the growling sound and must remember how that sound is made and must consciously produce it. In a sense, he is actually learning a new vocabulary, not just a new sound, for the word is *robin*, not 'wobbin'; the color is *red*, not 'wed'; and his friend's name is *Fred*, not 'Fwed.' These are really different words for the same thing.

This stage in the child's training must be carefully and solidly built up because it is a crucial one. The new sound must be thoroughly reinforced and securely established in the child's consciousness through as many avenues of sensory and motor approach as possible. He must learn which words contain this sound through listening to poems, stories, and other material in which it is frequently repeated in familiar words. If he is a younger child, he must have objects and pictures to identify and talk about that illustrate the use of the new sound in names for things. If he is an older child, lists of words and phrases in which the sound occurs can be used for him to read and practice on. The motor pattern involved in the production of the sound can be strengthened if the individual is given exercises in which he pronounces and at the same time writes words and phrases containing the sound.

Continued practice in the use of the new habit pattern can be given by having the pupil read specially prepared sentences and specially chosen selections of prose and poetry that illustrate the use of the new sound in all of its various combinations with other sounds. The next step involves the use of the sound in original speaking situations which are carefully prepared and carefully controlled. The gap between reading and speaking can be bridged somewhat if the child is encouraged to talk about what he reads; or the teacher can ask him questions about what he has read as a speech exercise, such questions to be answered in the same careful manner in which the reading was done. For the child too young to read, memorized material or carefully chosen pictures and objects must be substituted.

During this phase of the training the teacher should accept no substitute for the very best that the pupil is capable of doing.

It is very easy, after the enthusiasm of the first success has passed, to settle down into a sort of compromise between the old, incorrect pattern and the best that the pupil is able to do. The result is something definitely better than the old habit, but not as good as it should be. Such a compromise is unsatisfactory because, since the difference is so slight between the new and the old, there is too much danger that the child will slip back into his old habit without realizing it.

The next, and final, step in the training involves the habitual and natural use of the new sound in ordinary real-life speech situations—in the classroom, on the playground, and at home. This, in some respects, is the most troublesome phase of all to complete successfully, partly because it is harder to observe the child's speech in those natural speech situations. It may not be difficult to bring the child to the place where he speaks perfectly when he is with the teacher because he is aware of his speech and is careful and conscious of his words. But the moment he is in another situation where restraint and supervision are removed, he may forget and revert to his old pattern. This is particularly likely to occur if the speech training has seemed to the child to be something artificial, restricted, or divorced from the everyday uses of speech. If he can see no sense in it and finds it just another kind of lesson required of him at school, then naturally he will not be likely to absorb the training and take it with him when he leaves the room where he had to be on his good verbal behavior because he was having a speech lesson. All of this points to the value of making speech training as practical and functional as possible, of integrating it with all of the other activities in which the child engages during the day and in which speech plays a part. Here the classroom teacher enjoys a decided advantage over the special speech clinician, who may see the child for only a short period two or three times a week. Every use of speech during the day can be a speech lesson and can present an opportunity for the child to establish the new habit pattern if the teacher is alert to the child's problem. The co-operation of the parents may also need to be enlisted if the child is to practice his good speech habits at home.

Standards of Pronunciation and Articulation

So far as pronunciation is concerned, the teacher would be well advised to encourage the child to use the type of pronunciation that is considered standard in the locality where the child lives, even though such pronunciation may differ from that which the the teacher herself uses. For example, if the teacher 'drops her r's' in such words as *barn* and *never* but the majority of speakers, including the child, pronounce these words as [bɑrn] and [nɛvɚ], she should make no effort to change his basic pronunciation pattern, since General American is a perfectly good regional standard.

The problem of articulation is a bit more complicated, however, and perhaps a word of caution may not be out of place here. Emphasis on 'correct' articulation and clear speech can be overdone. After all, the final objective is normal conversational speech, not the over-precise, artificial articulation that may have come into certain stages in the process of training the child to recognize and produce a specific sound. A certain amount of exaggeration for emphasis may be necessary at first, but the teacher should make sure that the distortion of a natural speech pattern is not carried too far. The child can hardly be expected to develop over-precise articulation that differs markedly from what he hears around him.

For example, it is only natural that words are 'run together' somewhat in phrases and sentences. No one pronounces the final sound of a word with the same clarity and force he uses for the initial sound, and often sounds and perhaps whole syllables are omitted from words in connected speech. To illustrate, the *for* becomes a weak 'fer' in the phrase *come for me* [kʌm fɚ mi]; the *t* in *lists* is often dropped out in ordinary speech and the word becomes merely [lɪs]; the phrase *miss you* becomes a single word [mɪʃu]; and the word *probably* loses a whole syllable when it becomes [prɑblɪ], as it often does in natural conversation.

These are not necessarily examples of careless or 'sloppy' speech, but rather easy, informal usage developed through the influence of certain phonetic processes referred to as assimilation, unstressing, et cetera. As is obvious, we do not ordinarily speak in terms of individual speech sounds or even individual words. Sounds and words flow together in an unbroken stream within the phrase or even longer unit of oral communication. In this process certain things happen to some of the individual sounds, and new 'transition' sounds develop as the speaker progresses from syllable to syllable and from word to word. Research studies show, incidentally, that speech intelligibility depends as much, or more, on these transition phenomena as on the actual speech sounds themselves. Therefore, the teacher must not make the mistake of insisting upon 'drill' articulation when the time comes to transfer the training into natural conversational speech.

Habituating the Child to the New Speech Pattern
A certain amount of self-consciousness can be expected, especially in the case of an older child or an adult, while the new speech habits are in the process of acquisition. Any departure from an accustomed style of speaking is likely to appear strange and unnatural to the speaker at first. The teacher must recognize this tendency and must be prepared to assist the pupil in discounting it. Some degree of deliberate exaggeration during the drill period of the training program may be justifiable and helpful, as was mentioned above. If the individual learns to overdo the movement or overstress the sound in practice, perhaps enough will be left, after the loss of transfer, to constitute a normal pattern when the sound has been incorporated into natural speech. Moreover, the exaggeration may serve to habituate the child to the new pattern, so that it is not likely to appear as strange as it otherwise would when carried over, in somewhat reduced form, into ordinary communication. As

stressed in the previous section, however, such exaggeration must be carefully limited and controlled.

This habituation can be further facilitated during the training period by organizing a series of lessons that incorporate or simulate real-life speech situations. With older children, group discussions can be organized in which the immediate interest in the discussion and the desire to contribute to it overshadow, for the moment, the realization that it is merely a speech-training exercise. The child begins to behave as he would outside of the classroom. With younger children, various play situations can be set up, such as playing store, a visit to the doctor, or mother's afternoon tea. With smaller groups or with individual children the teacher can have simple conversations during which the child forgets the formal training situation in telling about his new pet, the parade he saw, or a recent family picnic. Or a 'show and tell' session in class may accomplish the same thing.

Training Materials and Techniques

There is a strong feeling among many educators that specialized improvement in oral communication should not be reserved solely for those already gifted in this ability or for those exhibiting a handicap. Rather they feel, and with good reason, that the average child, especially in the kindergarten and first five or six grades, could profit greatly by some training and supervised experience in what has come to be known as speech improvement. This would not only help the child to perform better in his current school work, but would also help to insure his future progress and success in his other language activities and in his school work generally and would contribute to his personal and emotional maturation and growth. As was stated earlier in this book, adequate skill in oral communication, while of first importance to the young child in school, too often fails to receive the attention it deserves in the elementary curriculum.

As the teacher studies the suggestions offered in the present chapter, as well as those in Chapter IV, she can see that many of the exercises, assignments, and other activities are readily adaptable as classroom exercises for the whole class. Additional suggestions are offered in Chapter XII for the natural integration of speech improvement with routine activities involving other subjects in the curriculum. In this way the teacher avoids the necessity of singling out for special attention those pupils exhibiting communication disorders. This is not to suggest that some pupils may not need special help with their problems, either individually or in small groups, but such concentrated effort can be greatly lessened through more emphasis on oral communication activities in the general classroom. And don't forget, it is the quiet child who sits back and seldom volunteers who may need help the most. Don't let the class be taken over by the 'eager beavers.'

It is obvious that the following specific drills and exercises under the individual sounds most likely to be defective have been designed basically for the pupil who can read. For non-readers, changes in the handling of the material must be made. Specific adaptations will occur to the teacher, who is doubtless already aware that pictures are often a very good substitute for reading. For advice regarding this problem, as well as assistance in setting up classroom projects for general speech improvement, the teacher should, of course, consult with the speech and hearing specialist, if one is available in the school system.

Excellent material designed for speech and language training can be found in the references at the end of the present chapter, and Chapters IV and XII, and in the General References following Chapter XII. Some of these sources also feature games and other motivational devices, of which the following are typical: *Speech Correction Through Listening* by Bryngelson and Mikalson; *Language Development* by Jones, Chapter 13; *Talking Time* by Scott and Thompson; *Speech Correction* by Van Riper; *Listening for Speech Sounds* by Zedler; *Language Arts in the Elementary School* by Los Angeles City Schools.

Similar helpful instructional guides are published by the school systems of many other larger cities, as well as by departments of education or public instruction of the various states.

General Drills and Exercises

Relaxation Exercises

For many reasons, some of which have been discussed elsewhere in this book, the child with a speech disorder is likely to be more tense and fidgety than the average child. Sometimes such tenseness operates as a basic cause of the speech disorder, or it may result from it, or, in other instances, the connection between the two may be more remote and indirect. In any case and whatever the relationship, an initial emphasis upon relaxation during the speech lesson is often a very wise procedure. For one thing, it serves to quiet the child and make him more receptive to the training that is to follow. Motor control and skill are also enhanced. A variety of standard relaxation exercises for the arms, legs, torso, neck, and jaw will in all probability be familiar to most teachers.

With younger children, as well as with those of intermediate age, some form of psychological approach to relaxation will be found helpful. This involves getting the child into a frame of mind, or a state of feeling, that will induce relaxation. With younger children it will also usually be advantageous to motivate the exercises by making a game of them. The following exercises are suggested as representative of those the teacher can use.

1. If the children are sitting around a table or on chairs that have writing arms, have them lay their heads on their arms with eyes closed or buried in the arm. Otherwise, have them assume a comfortable position with hands in the lap and eyes closed. Say to them in a quiet, even voice, 'This is our quiet time. I want you to imagine that it is a warm summer day and you are lying out under a tree in the shade. You can hear the bees softly humming in the blossoms, and near by a little brook is

bubbling and gurgling. You are tired and you almost go to sleep.' This description can go on as long as the teacher sees fit to prolong this exercise. The children should be 'brought to' quietly and easily, not with a start that will jar them out of whatever benefit they may have gained from the relaxation experience.

2. The exercise above can be varied in many ways. The children can imagine that they are lying on a cloud sailing softly across the sky, or that they are relaxed in their favorite chair or sofa at home. Or, each child may be allowed to imagine the most quiet place he can think of. Some teachers use music to good advantage in helping to establish the proper mood of relaxation. All talking during this period should be even, quiet, and soothing.

3. A more direct approach to the problem is provided by a modification of the well-known game of charades. Each child is told to assume some tense and perhaps awkward position, into which he freezes, like the Tin Woodsman in *The Wizard of Oz*. One child is chosen to play the Good Fairy, who goes among the children touching each in turn with her 'magic wand.' As each is touched, the spell is broken and he immediately becomes limp and relaxed. This game can be modified to involve just one arm, both arms, or the whole torso. It has the advantage of contrasting the feeling of relaxation with that of tenseness.

4. The children can be told to imitate clothes on the line fluttering in the wind. This exercise is adaptable mainly to relaxation of the arms.

5. The game of rag doll is always good to secure relaxation of the arms, legs, and neck. The child is to imitate a rag doll, which has no bones, is soft, and cannot hold up its head or arms. If you lift up an arm, it falls right down again.

6. The child is asked to play elephant. He links his two hands together and bends forward at the hips, allowing his head to hang limp and his two arms to dangle like the trunk of the elephant. As he walks slowly across the room with a

lumbering gait, his 'trunk' will sway from side to side, if his arms are fully relaxed.

7. To relax the throat and neck, instruct the child to drop his head forward, chin toward the chest, the muscles of the neck thoroughly relaxed. Then he should gradually lift the head to its original position. Repeat a number of times.

8. The child should drop the head forward as before, then rotate the head from the shoulders. Notice that when the jaw is fully relaxed, the mouth falls open as the head reaches the backward position.

9. To relax the jaw, have the child practice vocalizing words and syllables ending in [ɑ] allowing the jaw to fall open and remain relaxed following the final sound. Repeat, *yah, fah, pah, po-pah, bo-bah,* etc.

10. Instruct the child to repeat *fah* rather rapidly with a gross movement of the jaw, keeping the tongue relaxed and motionless, and moving the jaw up and down in a loose, lazy fashion: *fah-fah-fah-fah-fah,* etc.

11. With his jaw motionless but open and relaxed, have the child repeat the following in a smooth, easy rhythm with a gross movement of the tongue:

a. Yah-yah-yah-yah-yah, etc.
b. Yuh-yuh-yuh-yuh-yuh, etc.
c. Yaw-yaw-yaw-yaw-yaw, etc.
d. Yo-yo-yo-yo-yo-yo, etc.

12. The child should take a deep breath and sigh. Be sure he fully relaxes on the sigh, 'giving up' to it. Then he should take another deep breath and sigh audibly.

Articulation Drills for Oral Inactivity

The chief enemies of clear articulation are a tight jaw, lazy tongue, and immobile lips. In the majority of instances nothing is wrong with the mechanism structurally; it is simply a matter of bad speech habits. Articulation drills can serve a number of useful purposes, among them the important function of making the child conscious of the movements of the articulatory organs and their various roles in the production of speech sounds. A large part of this re-education is kinesthetic; the child becomes aware, often for the first time, of what it feels like to open his mouth adequately in phonation, to use his lips vigorously in the formation of various sounds, and to perform certain important movements with his tongue. In exaggerating the articulation drills, he tends to lose the self-consciousness and feelings of strangeness that might otherwise result from using the articulatory mechanism in unaccustomed ways when making new speech patterns. Furthermore, there is probably some actual increase in motor skill as a result of such training. Just how much increase can be expected and what portion of that may be carried over into actual speech production in the form of improved articulation are questions to which exact answers have not as yet been found. In the meantime, the teacher is safe in assuming that in cases of oral inactivity a reasonable amount of time spent in general articulation exercises is quite justifiable.

In general, such exercises should be spread out over a period of time, devoting a certain portion of the lesson each day to this activity, rather than concentrating such training within a given period. An entire lesson spent merely on articulation drills would be boring and unprofitable, but devoting the first four or five minutes of a lesson period to a 'warming up' session of such exercises can produce worthwhile results.

There are many possibilities for introducing the spirit of competition into the following exercises by making games of them, especially where groups are involved. The group can be divided into 'sides,' with individuals performing in turn from alternate sides. The premium can be placed upon speed, accuracy, length of time that an exercise can be sustained without a mistake, or any other feature to which the teacher wishes to call attention.

Exercises for the Tongue

1. Try lapping like a cat; run the tongue in and out as rapidly as possible.
2. Extend the tongue as far as possible and try first to touch your chin, then the tip of your nose.
3. Extend the tongue and move it rapidly from side to side.
4. Explore the roof of the mouth with the tip of the tongue as far back as possible, beginning on the upper gum ridge. With younger children, some form of motivation may need to be used in this and other exercises in this section. For example, Mrs. Lingua sweeps the cobwebs off the ceiling in this exercise.
5. Repeat rapidly, but clearly, lee-lee-lee-lee-lee, etc. Substitute other vowels such as [ɑ], [o], and [u] in place of the [i] and repeat as before.
6. Repeat tee-lee, tee-lee, tee-lee, etc. Repeat also using lee-ree.
7. Develop various rhythm patterns, using the syllable *la*. A few are suggested below. The italicized syllables are to be stressed and prolonged slightly; the others are given a quick, light touch. No sounds should be lost; all must be clearly audible. *La* is sounded as [lɑ].

   a. *la*, la *la*, la *la*, la *la*; etc.
   b. *la*, la la *la la*; *la*, la la *la la*; etc.
   c. *la*, la la la *la la*; *la*, la la la la *la la*; etc.

8. Repeat Exercise 7, using *la, da, ka,* and *ga*.
9. Repeat clearly the following sequences, at first slowly and then more rapidly, stressing each syllable equally:

   a. la-lay-lee-la, la-lay-lee-la, etc.
   b. ta-tay-tee-ta, ta-tay-tee-ta, etc.
   c. ka-kay-kee-ka, ka-kay-kee-ka, etc.

10. With an easy motion of the tongue repeat the following syllables, allowing no 'break' in the tone between them. Vary the speed with different trials.

    a. ya-ya-ya-ya-ya-ya, etc.

    b. yaw-yaw-yaw-yaw-yaw, etc.

    c. yo-yo-yo-yo-yo-yo, etc.

    d. yu-yu-yu-yu-yu-yu, etc.

11. Practice the 'locomotive yell,' stressing the action of the tongue and using the jaw and lips as little as possible. Begin slowly, gradually increasing the tempo: rah, rah, rah, rah, rah, rah, rah, etc.

Exercises for the Lips

1. Repeat rapidly, but clearly, me-me-me-me-me-me-me, etc.
2. Repeat Exercise 1, substituting: wee, my, mo, and may.
3. Repeat the following sequences several times rapidly and clearly:

    a. ee-oo, ee-oo, ee-oo, ee-oo, etc.

    b. me-may-my-mo-moo, me-may-my-mo-moo, etc.

    c. we-way-wie-woe-woo, we-way-wie-woe-woo, etc.

4. Repeat and exaggerate: ee-ah-oo. Lips should be drawn back tightly for *ee*, mouth open for *ah*, lips rounded for *oo*.
5. Exaggerate the lip movements in pronouncing the following exercises and sentences:

    a. wee-woe-wee-woo. Repeat several times.

    b. pree-pray-prie-proe-proo. Repeat several times.

    c. Peter Piper picked a peck of pickled peppers.

    d. We went away for a while.

    e. We will wait for Will.

    f. The wire was wound round the wheel.

Exercises for the Jaw

1. Drop the jaw lazily and allow the mouth to fall open.
2. Move the relaxed jaw from side to side with the hand.
3. Move the jaw around in a circle.
4. Pronounce *ouch*; open the mouth wide. Repeat a number of times.

5. Repeat *ah-ger* [ɑ-gɚ] a number of times, opening the mouth wide on *ah*.
6. Repeat exercise 5, substituting *ah-wa*, *ah-ee*, and *ah-oo*.
7. Repeat the word *gobble* rapidly several times, opening the mouth wide on the first syllable, [gɑ].
8. Pronounce the following sentences carefully, exaggerating the mouth opening for all of the stressed vowels:

    a. Humpty-Dumpty sat on a wall.
    b. The wagon wobbled wildly.
    c. Around the rough and rugged rock the ragged rascal ran.
    d. Go out and get me some water from the well.
    e. Come back when you want some more money.

Defects of [s] and [z]

Of all speech defects involving faulty articulation, improper formation of [s] and [z] is by far the most common, at least for the age range found within the elementary schools. Three causes for this frequency of occurrence are immediately suggested: (1) Because [s] contains some of the highest frequencies found in any of the English speech sounds, keen hearing is essential for the proper articulation of this sibilant. If the child is unable to hear this sound clearly, he can hardly be expected to produce it correctly. (2) The sound is of relatively weak intensity. (3) From the point of view of the articulatory adjustment involved, these two sounds are very complex ones. All of the organs of articulation must be adjusted with such co-ordination and precision that even a relatively slight deviation may be sufficient to change the quality of the resulting sound. These deviations may spring from structural deficiencies in the mouth, or they may arise merely from improper habit patterns. Much of what is true with respect to [s] applies with equal force to its voiced analogue [z], except that the former sound occurs much more frequently in speech than the latter one, and irregularities of formation are likely to show up more prominently in [s] than in [z]. The two sounds are formed similarly, except that [s] is an unvoiced sound while [z] is voiced.

Briefly stated, the hiss-like sound we call *s* is produced with the tip of the tongue retracted slightly from the position for [t], and with the sides of the tongue in tight contact with the upper teeth and gums approximately as far toward the front of the mouth as the canine teeth. A fine stream of air is then blown through the narrow groove formed between the tongue tip and the front of the hard palate, really the upper gum ridge.[13] This air stream is directed against the sharp cutting edges of the upper and lower front teeth (incisors), which should be held fairly close together but not tightly closed. The resulting sound should be relatively high in pitch and its quality should be that of a clear hiss, but not a whistle.

From a physical point of view, the minimum essentials are that a thin stream of air should be directed against a sharp cutting edge. An easily recognizable [s] can be produced merely by pursing the lips tightly and blowing air against the edge of a filing card or sheet of paper. Whenever these essentials are present, we have the potentials of a good *s*; the thin stream of air is formed between the tongue tip or middle front and the gum ridge, and the sharp cutting edges are provided by the incisors. When some factor operates to interfere with this mechanism, a speech defect is likely to result. Many such factors can, and do, operate to produce defects of [s] and [z], but only the more common categories will be described briefly.

Structural Deficiencies

Malocclusions and dental irregularities are among the more common structural causes of [s] and [z] defects. When these conditions are present, it becomes difficult or impossible to align the front teeth properly so that they can intercept the

13. In the speech of certain individuals the tongue position for [s] varies from that described here. These speakers keep the tip of the tongue back of the lower teeth and arch the middle front of the tongue upward toward the gum ridge to make the narrow groove described above. The sounds produced in these two positions are acoustically similar.

breath stream to form the sharp cutting edge required. The breath stream may pass out between the teeth through an opening so wide that it does not strike the sharp edges at all. This situation is particularly likely to result from the types of malocclusion referred to earlier as open bite and overbite. In the case of underbite, the lower incisors, which are the ones primarily involved in forming the cutting edge, are masked by the upper teeth so that it becomes difficult or impossible to direct the breath stream against them. As a form of compensation in most cases of malocclusion, the individual will have developed the habit of keeping the front of his tongue low in his mouth with the tip near the edges of the upper incisors, with the result that a sound very closely resembling [θ] is likely to result—a form of lisp known as the interdental, or frontal, lisp.

Missing, poorly spaced, or irregular teeth may operate in a similar fashion to make proper alignment of the cutting edges difficult. A frequent, though customarily temporary, cause of *s* defects among younger children, for example, may result from the loss of their deciduous teeth, especially the incisors. In most cases the appearance of the permanent teeth will remedy the situation, and no special training will ordinarily be needed. Sometimes defects of [s] in older children can be traced to a period when they had orthodontia appliances in their mouths that made proper positioning of the tongue uncomfortable or difficult. The habits acquired during this time may persist after the bands have been removed and the orthodontia has been completed. Usually such cases yield readily to training because the orthodontia will have provided a basically normal structure to work with.

At this point attention is called to the discussion, given earlier in this chapter, of anomalies of the tongue, some of which may operate as causal factors to produce defects of [s] and [z]. If there is a unilateral paralysis or atrophy of the tongue, the tongue will probably not be strong enough on the affected side to prevent leakage of air out of the side of the mouth, and a lateral emission of the *s* is likely to result. The result is referred to as a lateral lisp. True tongue-tie, as was pointed out earlier, is relatively rare, but in those few cases where it does occur, it is likely to impair the proper positioning of the front of the tongue, resulting in an interdental lisp.

Physiological Dysfunctions

Naturally any form of paralysis or other physiological condition that interferes with adequate control of the organs of articulation, especially the tongue, is very likely to manifest itself in some form of [s] and [z] deficiency, because of the precise and complicated nature of the adjustments necessary to produce these sounds. Some diagnostic aids in recognizing such conditions were suggested earlier in this chapter.

Hearing Deficiencies

The importance of hearing to the proper development of articulation has been referred to several times previously in this book. Since frequently a hearing impairment manifests itself first in a loss of sensitivity for the higher frequencies, [s] is usually one of the first sounds to suffer when a hearing loss develops. Therefore, in the absence of any obvious cause of the [s] defect, the teacher would be wise to have the child's hearing tested.

If this proves to be impossible or unfeasible, a superficial check at least should be made. This can be done very simply if the teacher will produce the *sound* of [s]—a hiss—first on one pitch level and then produce it again on a different pitch, either higher or lower than the first. With a little practice, this should not be difficult, since the higher pitch can be made simply by tensing the tongue and pressing it more tightly upward and forward against the upper gum ridge. During several trials, the child should be asked to indicate each time which [s] sounds higher to him and if he responds successfully each time, it is reasonably safe to conclude that his hearing is not the cause of his sibilant defect.

Functional Defects

There will be many instances of defects of [s], and other sounds as well, when no probable cause can be found even though a careful search is made. It must be assumed that many of these cases are attributable to such factors as environmental influences, imitation, certain personality manifestations, or general bad habits of speech that have developed for reasons that are often obscure. With respect to a possible psychogenic basis, it must be remembered that lisping is one symptom of immature speech. Therefore, it may appear as a form of infantile perseveration or it may be a symptom of regression or effeminacy. It may also be cultivated as a bid for attention or it may be displayed by coy young girls because they think it is cute and attractive to the opposite sex. It is obvious that counseling as well as speech rehabilitation is indicated in some of these cases.

Types of [s] *Defects*

1. The Interdental, or Central, Lisp. In this form of lisp the tongue is held too low in the mouth so that the tip approximates the edges of the front teeth. Often a portion of the tip can be seen protruding between the teeth when the *s* is produced. The result is a sound resembling [θ], making the word *sum* sound like *thumb*. The correction here involves getting the tongue away from the front teeth and up back of the gum ridge where it belongs.

2. The Semi-Lisp or Dull [s]. A number of factors may contribute to produce a dull, low-pitched, 'mushy' *s* which is not an interdental lisp, but which lacks the clear sibilant quality of a good [s]. Such a sound is likely to result if there are uneven or widely spaced incisors, or if the jaw is dropped too far, or if too much air is allowed to issue through the opening formed between the tongue and the upper gum ridge. The first two conditions may be structural, but the latter one is more likely to be caused by lax and inexact positioning of the front of the tongue. As in the case of the interdental lisp, retraining in-

volves getting the tongue tip closer to the gum ridge so that the stream of air which issues between them will be more concentrated. In correcting *s* defects remember that, other factors being constant, the tighter the contacts and the smaller the openings through which the breath stream is forced, the higher in pitch the resulting sound. The looser contacts and larger openings produce sounds that are lower in pitch, often to the point of defectiveness. The two openings principally involved are the one formed between the edges of the incisors and the other between the tip or front of the tongue and the upper gum ridge.

3. The Lateral Lisp. This not uncommon defect results from failure of the tongue to maintain tight contact with the upper teeth and gums at one or both sides. As a result, air is allowed to escape at the side, usually over the canine or first biscuspid tooth. Since these teeth are not sharp enough to provide a suitable cutting edge for the stream of air emitted, the resulting sound will be dull and 'fuzzy' and, in extreme cases, suggestive of a voiceless [l]. Sometimes the breath stream can be heard striking the inside of the cheek on its way out. The general effect is likely to be very noticeable and unpleasant.

4. The [ʃ] Substitute. A sound resembling [ʃ] will result if the tip of the tongue is dropped and the middle front of the tongue is allowed to rise too high toward the palate during the production of [s]. Conditions that interfere with the muscular control of the tongue, such as paralysis, are among the causes of this type of defect.

5. The Too-Prominent or Whistled [s]. Occasionally the [s] is defective simply because there is too much of it; the individual prolongs the sound unduly and builds up too much breath pressure in its formation. In these cases some de-emphasizing of the sound is indicated. A whistled effect may result if the tongue is allowed to groove too deeply in the middle as it is brought up into the *s* position.

The Correction of [s] *Defects*

The following steps and suggestions constitute a general program of training to be pursued in the treatment of [s] defects.

1. The acoustic approach should be attempted first; ear training is very important in establishing the sound pattern that is wanted. Often all that is needed to elicit the proper response from an individual is to produce the sound for him and ask him to imitate it. If the child can be made to hiss like a snake, the problem may be solved and it may not be necessary to consider the mechanics which produce the sound. The individual may not even be aware of how he makes the sound; if the quality is acceptable, that is all that is necessary. Usually the correction is not this simple, however.

2. Care should be taken not to build up too much breath pressure in the production of this sound. No great amount of breath is required for a good [s], provided the articulatory adjustments are right.

3. The sound should not be unduly prolonged or stressed. The effect is better if [s] is passed over quickly and easily, and the sound that immediately follows is stressed.

4. The sides of the tongue should at all times maintain tight contact with the upper teeth and gum ridge as far front as the cuspids (canine teeth).

5. The tip of the tongue should never be allowed to fall so low in the mouth that it approaches the interdental position, nor should the tip be allowed to blanket the sharp, cutting edges of the upper or lower incisors.

6. The incisors should be adjusted so that their sharp edges intercept the breath stream as it is directed downward and over the tip of the tongue. The edges should be fairly close together, with the upper teeth slightly in advance of the lower, leaving a thin space between them. Many defects of [s] are traceable to improper adjustment of the teeth and they can often be corrected merely by directing the individual to bring the edges of his teeth closer together. This alignment of the teeth becomes especially important in cases of overbite, since

the most essential step in the therapy involves teaching the individual to bring the lower jaw far enough forward to get the upper and lower teeth into the proper relationship. Fortunately, this is not difficult to do, provided the malocclusion is not too serious, since the lower jaw is capable of considerable forward movement. Such a procedure is usually very difficult, if not altogether impossible, in cases of underbite and open bite. About the best that the teacher can do in these cases is to utilize the acoustic approach to assist the individual in effecting a better total adjustment of the tongue position, often through experimental trial-and-error procedure. The lips must at all times be spread sufficiently to keep the edges of the incisors free.

In the correction of *s* defects it will often be found expedient to approach the problem of a good tongue position for [s] by studying the beginning position for [t] and noticing the similarity between the two. This technique can be used to aid the individual in keeping his tongue away from the cutting edges of the front teeth. Lists of paired syllables and words can be used to demonstrate that in many respects the tongue is in the same position for [s] as it is for [t], the chief difference being that for [s] the tip is retracted and the center grooved sufficiently to allow a thin stream of air to pass through. As the pupil practices this exercise, he should attempt to carry the feel of the initial *t* position over into the production of [s]. Such pairs as the following can be used:

[ti–si]	tea–see	taw–saw	till–sill
[te–se]	told–sold	tub–sub	tat–sat
[ta–sa]	top–sop	tell–sell	toil–soil
[tɔ–sɔ]	too–Sue	tip–sip	tent–sent
[to–so]	teal–seal	tight–sight	toe–so
[tu–su]	tame–same	turf–serf	tank–sank

Some modification of this procedure may be necessary when dealing with a lateral lisp. The chief concern here is to prevent a break in the contact of the sides of the tongue with the upper teeth and gum ridge during the formation of [s]. The pupil should be instructed to begin with the implosive (closed) phase of [t], holding the tongue tight all the way around, including the tip in front, while moderate breath pressure is built up in the mouth as if the individual were going to say [t]. Instead of exploding the [t], however, the pupil should hold the pressure while he very slowly releases the tip of the tongue until a thin stream of air is coming through, all the while keeping the sides tight against the teeth. The result should be a sound approximating [s]. The pupil must be cautioned to release the tip slowly enough so that he can determine where the first break in the *t* contact is going to come. In this 'slow-motion' process he may be able to prevent the release from coming at one side of the tongue, and he may be able to break the contact first at the tip, where it should occur. If the slow-motion has been successful, the result should approximate [tsssi], [tssse], [tsssɑ], et cetera, with a very light [t] and a slow, prolonged [s]. The transition can be gradually speeded up until the syllable resembles [tsi], [tse], [tsɑ], et cetera, the first two sounds being very similar to the pronunciation of the German *z*. The beginning *t* effect can be dropped as soon as the pupil has mastered the central release of the tongue, and the [s] can then be started from the normal tongue position without the initial closure.

In the case of interdental lispers especially, the technique of paired words beginning with [θ] and [s] respectively will prove helpful in demonstrating the essential difference between these two sounds. Such pairs as the following should make it clear to the lisper as he pronounces them that two essentially different sounds are involved in the initial position.

thin–sin	thump–sump	thank–sank	path–pass
theme–seem	thumb–sum	think–sink	growth–gross
thaw–saw	thigh–sigh	neath–niece	bath–bass

The following material can be used for practice. The words and selections should be read slowly and carefully with special attention being paid to each [s] and [z].

INITIAL		MEDIAL	FINAL
seal	swan	acid	this
sip	sleep	lesson	vase
save	spin	missing	rice
send	skate	peaceful	dates
soap	smile	aside	grapes
soda	snow	rest	once
say	stop	catsup	box
sun	split	master	rugs
sand	scrape	whisper	juice
soon	street	receive	bass
soy	splash	baseball	pass
south	slant	beside	noise
spick and span		sink or swim	small and slender
sour and sweet		step by step	soft and smooth

1. Six times six are thirty-six.

2. Can you spell *sister?*

3. I was in school yesterday.

4. Seven birds sang in the sun.

5. Some sailors came to see the starfish.

6. Sister Susie is sewing shirts for sick soldiers.

7. Nancy said, 'How much does a bus ticket cost?'

8. Susan went skating with Buster and slipped on the ice.

9. Simple Simon met a pie-man
     Going to the fair;
   Said Simple Simon to the pie-man,
     'Let me taste your ware.'

   Said the pie-man to Simple Simon,
     'Show me first your penny';
   Said Simple Simon to the pie-man,
     'Indeed, I have not any.'

10. Swan, swim over the sea;
    Swim, swan, swim.
    Swan, swim back again;
    Well swam, swan.

11. As I was going to St. Ives,
    I met a man with seven wives.
    Each wife had seven sacks,
    Each sack had seven cats,
    Every cat had seven kits:
    Kits, cats, sacks, and wives,
    Now tell me how many were going to St. Ives.

12. As Tommy Snooks and Bessie Brooks
    Were walking out one Sunday,
    Says Tommy Snooks to Bessie Brooks,
    'Tomorrow will be Monday.'

13. An apple pie, when it looks nice,
    Would make one long to have a slice,
    And if the taste should prove so, too,
    I fear one slice would hardly do.
    So to prevent my asking twice,
    Pray, mamma, cut a good large slice.

14. Boats sail on the rivers,
    Ships sail on the seas;
    But clouds that sail across the sky
    Are prettier far than these.

15. Swift and sure the swallow,
    Slow and sure the snail;
    Slow and sure may miss his way,
    Swift and sure may fail.

16. There's no dew left on the daisies and clover,
    There's no rain left in heaven;
    I've said my 'seven times' over and over—
    Seven times one are seven.

17. This is the song of the bee,
    Buzz, buzz, buzz.
    A jolly good fellow is he.
    Buzz, buzz, buzz.
    In days that are sunny
    He's making his honey
    Buzz, buzz, buzz.
    In days that are cloudy
    He's making his wax.
    Buzz, buzz, buzz.

Defects of [r]

The consonant [r], as found in the word *rat,* belongs to a group of four speech sounds called glides, the other three being [j] (as in *yet* [jɛt]), [w], and [l]. Because these sounds have a certain acoustic similarity, there is a considerable tendency to confuse them and exchange one for another, especially in the speech of the child or of others whose articulation is inclined to be faulty. The most common substitutions are [w] for [r], [w] for [l], [j] for [l], and [l] for [r]. The prevalence of the [w] substitution is undoubtedly accounted for by the relative simplicity of the sound and the fact that the mechanics of its production are easily visible. The other three, especially the [l] and the [r], are much more complex and their production is largely invisible, being inside the mouth.

The consonant [r] is begun from an articulatory position that can be described as follows: The sides of the tongue are in contact with the inner borders of the teeth as far forward as the first or second bicuspid. The tip is elevated toward, but does not touch, the hard palate slightly back of the upper gum ridge.[14] The position of the tongue must be judged largely through the kinesthetic sense, since the tip does not make actual contact with the palate. This fact explains for the most part why it is difficult to determine definitely just where the tongue actually is in the production of this sound; and it also partially explains why there is considerable variation from individual to individual in the way [r] is produced, and why it is

---

14. It should be made clear that the [r] being discussed here is the prevocalic *r* (followed by a vowel) as in the words *red* and *around.* When the [r] follows a vowel or is in the final position, as in *farm* or *ever,* it is produced somewhat differently and varies considerably in the manner of its production, not only among individuals, but from one section of the country to another. The post-vocalic [r] is generally weaker than the prevocalic variety, disappearing altogether in the speech of those individuals who 'drop' their *r*'s. Everyone should pronounce a good, clear [r], however, when it is followed by a vowel.

frequently found to be defective. From the starting position explained above, the tongue moves, or glides, to the position required for the sound that follows. It should be noticed that [r] is primarily a tongue sound; it should be produced with a minimum of dependence on lip movement. To the extent that lip movement is allowed to intrude, the sound will take on a [w] quality.

Causes of [r] Defects

It has been observed that many individuals suffering from a hearing loss exhibit certain defects of [r]. The defective sound is usually thick in quality and is made rather far back in the mouth. Apparently in these cases the hearing is not adequate to the task of keeping the quality of the [r] 'true' and of preventing the tongue from wandering from its rather vaguely located position.

Lack of motor control is an important cause of [r] defects, since a rather complex adjustment of the tongue is required. Any condition, such as paralysis, for example, that deprives the individual of adequate control over his tongue will in all probability be reflected in various modifications of the [r] sound.

A foreign language background may very easily result in nonstandard variations in the production of [r], since all languages have one or more varieties of this sound and most of them are different from the varieties found in English. As one point of difference, the *r*'s of most foreign languages are trilled in some manner, while the *r* of American English is never trilled in ordinary usage.

It is surprising how often a defect of [r] cannot be traced to any definite cause but rather appears to be the product of speech habits acquired in some unknown way, perhaps during the early speech development of the individual. The [r] is one of the later sounds to appear in the normal speech of the child, being dependent on the maturation of certain motor skills, for one thing. An *r* defect, therefore, is one of the chief symptoms of infantile perseveration in speech.

Types of [r] *Defects*

1. The [w] Substitute. A true [w], or a sound very closely resembling it, may be substituted for [r], especially in the speech of children. Since [w] is a visible sound and is very simply made, it appears much earlier in the speech development of the child than does the more complex, largely invisible [r]. For this reason it is often substituted for [r], an infantilism that may persist into later childhood or even into adult life unless it is corrected.

2. The Back [r]. If the [r] is made with the tip and front of the tongue low in the mouth and the back humped up, the resulting sound will have a quality somewhat suggestive of [w]. Upon first hearing the back [r] used, the teacher may mistake it for a [w] substitution, but closer examination will reveal that the sound is being produced primarily with the tongue rather than with the lips, and the quality is not that of a true [w].

3. The [l] Substitute. This defect is likely to be found among Orientals, who frequently confuse and interchange [l] and [r] in pronunciation.

4. The Omission of [r]. One of the common defects among children whose speech is delayed or is otherwise defective is the omission of initial [r] and of [r] in certain other combinations as well. Thus, *red* becomes simply [ɛd], and *brother* sounds like [bʌvə].

5. The Various Forms of Trilled *r*'s. Since [r] is not normally trilled in American speech, a trilled [r] is almost certain to reflect a foreign language influence. There are many varieties of such trilled sounds in foreign languages, some produced by vibrating the tip of the tongue and others made in the back of the mouth with the aid of the uvula.

The Correction of [r] *Defects*

Where excessive lip movement is present during the production of [r], which should be primarily a tongue sound, the child must be taught to use his tongue more and his lips less. Such exercises as the 'locomotive yell' explained previously are helpful in accomplishing this if they are performed with the lips largely immobilized and the tongue used to the fullest extent. The tendency to use the lips can be checked by having the child watch himself in a mirror as he performs, or by instructing him to keep his fingers lightly on his lips so that he can feel their movement. The pairing of words beginning with [w] and [r] will tend to make the distinction between the sounds more obvious. There should be considerably less lip action when the second member of each pair is pronounced. Such combinations as the following can be used:

wing–ring	won–run	woo–rue
weep–reap	wipe–ripe	way–ray
wed–red	wake–rake	wag–rag

The tongue position for [r] may be established by comparing it with the position for [d]. When the two syllables [dɑ] and [rɑ] are compared, for example, it will be found that in the production of [r] the tip of the tongue is drawn back and elevated slightly from the gum ridge where it rests for [d]. With a point of departure thus established, the position from which the glide [r] is begun will be easier to determine. Paired words such as the following can be used to exploit this comparison still further:

doe–roe	Dan–ran	dope–rope
dip–rip	dub–rub	doom–room
deem–ream	day–ray	dice–rice

It will be observed that the consonant [r] begins from the tongue position characteristic of a rather extremely retroflexed vowel [ɝ], which is sometimes referred to as a 'burred r.' This static position of [r] is not difficult to teach in most cases, especially if adequate ear training is also used. In the case of children the sound can be referred to as the 'motor or growl sound,' and they can be encouraged to imitate the sound of the motor or puppy by prolonging the *r-r-r-r-r* until the acoustic characteristics and the feel of the tongue are firmly established in their minds. This position should be assumed and held for a moment before the tongue is allowed to slide into the true [r] glide. At first, short words should be pronounced to sound like *r-r-run, r-r-rat, r-r-rip*, et cetera, with considerable stress being placed on the first part of the sound. Gradually, as facility in the use of the [r] develops, the beginning vowelized *r-r-r-r-r* can be shortened and finally eliminated altogether.

Visual imitation can also be used in the teaching of [r]. If the teacher assumes the tongue position for the beginning vowel position [ɝ] and opens her mouth a bit, it is quite possible for the pupil to see approximately where and how the tongue is placed. With a small mirror, or if teacher and pupil both work in front of a mirror, the pupil should be able to manipulate his own tongue into the same position. A few gentle prods with an applicator stick or the split half of a wooden tongue depressor may be needed to assist the child in attaining the correct adjustment. Various exercises for the tongue, such as those described previously in this chapter, will render it more mobile and responsive. Defects of [r] are inclined to be persistent faults, and considerable effort may be required to modify or eliminate the old habit patterns and establish the proper ones in their place. In addition to the exercises already suggested, lists of words, phrases, and sentences, to be followed by selections stressing the [r], should be provided for frequent practice. Begin with the initial [r] followed by a vowel in short words, such as *run* and *rope*, and then proceed to the medial [r] also followed by a vowel, as in *around* and *arrive*. The so-called *r*-blends, in which another consonant, or two other consonants, precede the [r] are more difficult and should be attempted only after some progress has been made with the initial sound. The following material will be found useful:

INITIAL [r]		MEDIAL [r]	
rock	Richard	arrive	tomorrow
reel	ripple	arrow	story
ran	rowboat	marry	parachute
roll	rabbit	parade	terrible
room	roof	very	borrow
rug	robin	carrot	hearing

[r] BLENDS

rap–trap–strap	rim–prim–brim–trim
ride–tried–stride	ray–pray–bray–tray
roll–troll–stroll	rye–pry–fry–try
ripe–tripe–stripe	rip–trip–drip–strip
rest–pressed–crest	rank–frank–prank–crank
rag–brag–crag	rue–crew–true–through

1. The rabbit ran around the rock.

2. Robert tried to catch the frog in the pond.

3. Have you ever seen a red-nosed reindeer?

4. Ruth wore a brown dress to school.

5. He ran down to the river in the rain.

6. Wee Willie Winkie runs through the town,
   Upstairs and downstairs in his nightgown;
   Rapping at the window, crying through the lock,
   'Are the children in their beds?
   For now it's eight o'clock.'

7. Little Robin Redbreast sat upon a tree,
       Up went Pussycat and down went he;
   Down came Pussycat and away Robin ran;
       Says little Robin Redbreast, 'Catch me if you can.'

8. Pit, pat, well-a-day!
       Little Robin flew away.
   Where can little Robin be?
       Up in yonder cherry tree.

9. Rock-a-bye, baby, on the tree top!
       When the wind blows, the cradle will rock,
   When the bough breaks, the cradle will fall;
       Down will come baby, cradle and all.

10. The rain is raining all around,
        It falls on field and tree;
    It rains on the umbrellas here
    And on the ships at sea.
    	R. L. Stevenson

11. When a merry maiden marries,
    Sorrow goes and pleasure tarries;
    Every sound becomes a song.
    All is right and nothing wrong!
                    W. S. *Gilbert*

Defects of [l]

The consonant [l] is the only sound in English that is emitted laterally—around the sides of the tongue. The tip of the tongue remains in contact with the upper gum ridge in front in approximately the same position as for [d]. However, contact between the tongue and the teeth is initially broken at the sides so that the sound can issue laterally. As a matter of fact, this sound is an extremely variable one, there being virtually as many varieties as there are sounds that may precede or follow it. The shape and position of the body of the tongue as well as the shape of the lips will determine what particular resonance or quality the [l] will have. Final *l* is more obscured than the initial sound.

Causes of [l] Defects

Since this sound is also among the last to develop, it is often found to be defective in the speech of the young child. Being relatively invisible and involving a rather specialized action of the tongue, the [l] requires adequate auditory discrimination and motor control for its correct production. Therefore, any deficiency in these abilities may manifest itself in a defective [l]. Also, regression and babyish tendencies may be reflected in [l] defects, since such defects are among the most common characteristics of so-called baby-talk.

Types of [l] Defects

1. Perhaps the most common defect is a substitution of [w], as in the case of [r]. The child with this substitution says 'wam' for *lamb,* or 'fawing' for *falling.*

2. Common in adults, as well as in children, is the substitution of a vowel resembling [ɔ] or [ə], especially when [l] is final or when it precedes a consonant. Some people pronounce *milk* as [mɪək] and *well* as [wɛɔ]. This variation is also referred to as a 'dark' *l*.

3. The glide consonant [j] may be substituted for [l], in which case the word *lady* sounds like [jedɪ].

4. The tendency for individuals with an Oriental background to confuse [l] and [r] and substitute one for the other has already been mentioned under the discussion of [r].

The Correction of [l] *Defects*
The best approach will often be to capitalize on the similarity between [d] and [l] with respect to the initial position of the tip of the tongue. This similarity can be demonstrated by means of paired words, the first member of each pair beginning with [d] and the second member beginning with [l]. The pupil should be taught to observe the position of the tongue tip as he starts the first word beginning with [d], and he should attempt to carry over this feeling as he begins the [l] in the second word. The second word should be started just as if the first were being repeated. Then, after the tip of the tongue has been properly placed, the sides are released first; next the tip is dropped as the tongue passes from [l] into position for the following sound. A great deal of ear training should accompany this exercise. The following pairs can be used:

deep–leap	dome–loam	dip–lip
dead–lead	dove–love	dark–lark
dine–line	dawn–lawn	dame–lame
dad–lad	doom–loom	dear–leer

As another exercise, the tongue is held in the beginning [d] position with particular attention being paid to the tip, which rests against the upper gum ridge. With the tip still tight against the ridge, the sides of the tongue are released in a mild explosion, resulting in the combination [dl̩], as in the final syllable of *saddle*. As long as the tip is maintained against the gum ridge, the tongue is in position for the start of the glide [l], as found in such words as *leap* and *lad*. The combination [tl] as found in *little* can also be used to achieve this same starting position for [l].

If a small mirror is used, the child can learn a great deal about the position and movements of the tongue in the production of this sound by observing the position of the teacher's tongue as she makes the sound and then attempting to imitate her with the aid of the mirror. Under close scrutiny, [l] is not an invisible sound.

As soon as the child is able to produce a satisfactory [l], simple exercises involving the sound should be assigned. Begin with single syllables consisting of [l] plus a vowel, such as *lah*, *lay*, *lee*, et cetera. Later, various combinations of these syllables can be built up for practice. Several such drills were included in an earlier section of this chapter devoted to general articulation exercises.

After progress has been made on the initial [l], the medial and final sounds can be undertaken; these will usually be more difficult to pronounce correctly. Production of the medial [l] can be facilitated if at first words are chosen in which it is both preceded and followed by a vowel, as in *alone* and *alive*. If a slight pause is made just before the [l] is pronounced, so that the child can get properly 'set' for it, it will take on some of the characteristics of the initial [l], and hence will be easier to say properly. In such cases the pronunciation will resemble [ə-lon] and [ə-laɪv], with the [l] receiving considerable stress. More difficult combinations include the [l] before a consonant, especially a back consonant as in *milk*, the final [l] as in *ball*, and the so-called syllabic [l] as in the final sound of *little*. In the production of these sounds, however, the teacher should keep in mind that, even in normal speech, they are ordinarily more subdued—more dull or 'dark'—than when the sound is initial or otherwise precedes a vowel.

The following drill material can be used to advantage in carrying out the steps explained in the preceding paragraphs:

INITIAL		MEDIAL			FINAL	
lady	late	alone	cliff	help	heel	little
leave	left	eleven	blame	milk	hill	camel
let	lunch	yellow	play	colt	sale	saddle
lie	lard	silly	sleep	heels	pal	uncle
lamp	loud	dolly	flock	field	ball	giggle
law	leap	only	glass	health	pole	whistle
loop	lip	alive	split	wolf	cool	puzzle
load	lead	belong	slope	lily	file	table

1. Louise likes to sleep late in the morning.
2. Charley's mother told him to drink all of his milk.
3. Billy's brother walked slowly down the long lane.
4. The little kitten quickly lapped up all of the milk.
5. The children laughed when the lamb followed Mary to school.
6. The pilot landed the plane safely.
7. Alice was limping after she hurt her leg.
8. A meadow lark flew up into that tall tree.
9. The lady laughed at the little children playing ball.
10. Nellie fell into the lake and yelled for help.

11. Willie was a Piper's son,
     He learned to play when he was young;
     But the only tune that he could play,
         Was 'Over the hills and far away.'

12. As I was going along, long, long,
     A'singing a comical song, song, song;
     The lane where I went was long, long, long,
     And the song that I sang was long, long, long,
     And so I went singing along.

13. Little Bo-peep has lost her sheep,
         And can't tell where to find them;
     Leave them alone and they'll come home,
         Wagging their tails behind them.

14. Little Mary had a lamb,
         Its fleece was snowy white,
     That followed her around all day,
         And slept by her at night.

He followed her to school one day,
  Which was against the rule;
It made the children laugh and play
  To see a lamb at school.
'What makes the lamb love Mary so?'
  The eager children cry.
'Oh, Mary loves the lamb, you know,'
  The teacher did reply.

15. Baa, baa, black sheep, have you any wool?
      Yes sir, yes sir, three bags full;
    One for my master, one for my dame,
      And one for the little boy that lives in the lane.

16. Little Boy Blue, come blow your horn!
      The sheep's in the meadow, the cow's in the corn.
    Where's the boy who looks after the sheep?
      He's under the haystack, fast asleep.

Defects of [ʃ], [ʒ], [tʃ], and [dʒ]

The sounds in this group are all inter-related, and a defect of
any one of them is likely to be reflected in the others as well.
There is no single symbol in conventional spelling to represent
any of these sounds; each one is spelled in a number of different ways, the spelling usually having but little relation to the
actual sound. For example, [ʃ] is most commonly spelled with
sh, but it is a distinctly different sound from either [s] or [h].
The [ʒ], the voiced equivalent of [ʃ], may be spelled with *z* as
in *azure*; the most common spelling of [tʃ], which combines
both [t] and [ʃ], is with *ch* as in *chip*; and the usual spelling of
[dʒ], the voiced equivalent of [tʃ], is with *j* as in *joke*, although
g is also common as in *gem*. Since [ʃ] is the key sound of this
group, more or less, and since it is the one most likely to exhibit defects in production, this discussion will be concerned
with this sound for the most part. When the problems involved
in its production are solved, it will be a simple matter to deal
with the others.

The [ʃ] is formed, as is [ʒ] also, with the point of the tongue somewhat retracted and lowered from its position for [s] and with the middle of the tongue considerably more raised toward the hard palate. Also in contrast to the [s], there is a noticeable lip rounding in the production of [ʃ].

Causes of [ʃ] and [ʒ] Defects

More often than not, no adequate cause can be found for deviations in the production of these sounds. Often such defects must be listed as functional, which means that improper speech habits, perhaps arising from imitation of poor speech models, must be offered as the explanation. Since [ʃ] is a relatively high frequency sound, it has been found to be defective in certain cases of hearing loss, especially those involving the higher frequencies.

Types of [ʃ] and [ʒ] Defects

1. An infrequent defect is the substitution of [s] for [ʃ], making *ship* sound like *sip*.
2. A more common defect of [ʃ] occurs when the middle front of the tongue is allowed to rise too high toward the hard palate, in which case it becomes much higher in pitch and takes on a quality suggesting the sound of the German *ch* as in *ich*. This defect may be accompanied by inadequate lip rounding in the formation of [ʃ].

The Correction of [ʃ] and [ʒ] Defects

In almost every instance of a defect of [ʃ], the quality of the sound can be improved if the pupil is instructed to round his lips properly as the sound is formed. This lip rounding can usually be attained if the child is reminded that this is mother's 'shushing sound' and if he is asked to imitate mother in saying 'sh-h-h-h-h-h.' Lip rounding is also facilitated if the [ʃ] is combined with some of the rounded back vowels, such as [u] and [o]. Such combinations as *shoe* and *show* can be used to advantage here, the natural lip rounding of the vowel contributing to the rounding of [ʃ].

Combining [ʃ] with the middle and back vowels, in the formation of which the tongue is low in front, is also a good technique to use when dealing with the defect of [ʃ] in which the pitch is too high because the middle front of the tongue is too close to the hard palate. Such syllables and words as *shah, shaw, shoe,* and *hush* make good practice material for individuals with such a defect.

Although late in appearing in the speech development of many children, [tʃ] and [dʒ] usually present few problems, once they have been acquired. Perhaps the most common defects are found in foreign dialects, which will be discussed in the following chapter.

To correct the [s] substitution for [ʃ], the technique of paired words can again be used, the first member of each pair beginning with [s] and the second member beginning with [ʃ]. The essential differences between the two sounds should be carefully explained, including the factor of lip rounding, and the child should be cautioned not to allow the second word to sound like the first. Pairs such as the following can be used:

seat–sheet	sown–shown	Sue–shoe	sip–ship
sake–shake	suit–shoot	so–show	Sal–shall
sun–shun	save–shave	saw–Shaw	sign–shine

The following drill material will be found helpful in correcting defects of the sounds discussed in this section:

INITIAL		MEDIAL		FINAL	
shade	shout	wishing	notion	hush	selfish
short	shop	ocean	insure	wash	wish
shark	shut	bushel	bashful	bush	crash
shook	should	issue	dishes	rush	leash
shore	shawl	seashore	fisher	fresh	mash

1. She sells seashells at the seashore.
2. John rushed out just in time to catch the dog that was running down the beach.
3. She climbed aboard as the fishing boat left the shore.
4. Shall we buy some dishes in this shop?

5. The sailor shouted for help as the rising water reached his chin.
6. The boy was pushing a little cart in which he kept his shoe-shine boxes.
7. The sheep were rushing about in every direction.
8. Are you sure that you caught a big fish on your vacation?
9. Shirley helped her mother wash the dishes.
10. The ocean was so rough that waves washed over the ship's deck.

11. Shoe the wild horse, and shoe the gray mare;
    If the horse won't be shod, then let him go bare.

12. Here's sulky Sue. What shall we do?
    Turn her face to the wall till she comes to.

13. Jack, be nimble, Jack, be quick;
    Jack, jump over the candle stick!

14. Tommy kept a chandler's shop,
    Richard went to buy a mop;
    Tommy gave him such a knock
    That sent him out of the chandler's shop.

15. I had a little hen, the prettiest ever seen
    She washed me the dishes, and kept the house clean.
    She went to the mill to fetch me some flour,
    She rushed it back home in less than an hour;
    She baked me my bread, she brewed me my ale,
    She sat by the fire and told many a fine tale.

Miscellaneous Substitutions

Defects of [θ] *and* [ð]

In conventional spelling these two sounds are both represented by the digraph *th*, although they are in no way related to either [t] or [h]. Moreover, the spelling does not distinguish voiceless [θ] from its voiced analogue [ð]; it must be learned from observation when the sound is voiced, as in *this* [ðɪs], and when it is unvoiced, as in *thin* [θɪn]. The troublesome problems that many foreigners are likely to have with these two sounds will be discussed in the following chapter.

A common infantile substitution is [f] for [θ], as 'fum' for *thumb,* and [v] for [ð], as 'muvver' for *mother.* Sometimes these perseverations will continue after the child has started to school, in which case there is danger that other children will ridicule him with bad effects upon the child if the defect is not removed forthwith. Ear training, as well as the visual approach, should be used. As part of the former, the [f] can be called the 'angry kitty sound' and the [θ] can be given the name of the 'goose sound.' The child should have ample opportunity to imitate both the 'angry kitty' and the 'goose' until he can distinguish the sounds and can produce them at will. Along with auditory stimulation, the child's attention should be called to the difference in the formation of the two sounds. With the aid of a mirror, he should be taught to imitate the tongue position of the teacher as she sounds [θ].

With the young child for whom reading is limited, simple pictures can easily be found to illustrate the sound, such as *thread, thimble, thumb, toothbrush,* et cetera. The child should be reminded that these words contain the 'goose sound' and he should be given practice in using that sound in them. He should also be able to catch up the teacher when she pronounces some of them with the incorrect 'angry kitty sound' to see whether he can tell the difference.

A similar technique can be used to correct the [v] substitution for [ð], except that different names will have to be found. In this case, the [v] can be the 'very angry kitty sound,' to distinguish it from [f]. With the somewhat older child, the technique of paired words can again be used to demonstrate that different words take different sounds. Such pairs as the following should make him more conscious of [f] and [v] in relation to [θ] and [ð]:

fin–thin	fum–thumb	fought–thought	van–than
free–three	Fred–thread	first–thirst	vine–thine

1. I thought I saw Thelma buying some thread at the store.
2. Ruth usually thinks things out thoroughly.
3. The player got three free throws at the basket.

4. Thirteen is just three more than ten.

5. Next Thursday Theodore will have his seventh birthday.

6. My brother hurt his thumb when he picked up the thistle.

7. Thirty thousand thoughtful boys
Thought they'd make a thundering noise;
So, with thirty thousand thumbs,
They thumped on thirty thousand drums.

8. Bertha sews with thin thread,
    Martha sews with thick,
For Bertha sews a thin silk scarf,
    But Martha sews a smock.
So Bertha sews with thin thread,
    Though Martha uses thick.

9. For healthy warmth in all the weathers
Some birds build nests with snug warm feathers;
Feathers thick and feathers thin,
With thick without, and thin within.

Drill Material for General Improvement of Articulation

The Bug and the Beetle

Little Black Beetle said one day,
'Little bug, you're in my way!
Little bug, don't bother me,
I'm a big bug, don't you see?'
Little bug said, 'I can do
Quite as many things as you.'

The Grasshopper and the Crickets

A grasshopper once had a game of tag
    With some crickets that lived near by,
When he stumbled his toe, and over he went
    Too quickly to see with your eye.
Then the crickets leaned up against a fence,
    And chirped till their sides were sore,
But the grasshopper said, 'You are laughing at me,
    And I won't play any more.'
So off he went though he wanted to stay,
    For he was not hurt by the fall,

And the gay little crickets went on with the game,
    And never missed him at all.

The Crooked Man

There was a crooked man, and he went a crooked mile;
    He found a crooked sixpence against a crooked stile;
He bought a crooked cat, which caught a crooked mouse,
    And they all lived together in a little crooked house.

Fishing

When I go fishing,
I'm always wishing
Some fishes I will get;
But while I'm fishing,
The fish are wishing
I won't; just harder yet.

And all those wishes
Of the fishes,
Every one comes true;
But all my wishes
To get fishes
Never, never do.

Mr. Jumping Jack

Mr. Jumping Jack is a very funny man,
He jumps and jumps as fast as he can.
His arms fly out, his feet fly too;
Mr. Jumping Jack, how do you do?

Santa Claus

A jolly old fellow,
Whose hair is snow white,
And whose little bright eyes are blue,
Will be making his visits
On Christmas night;
Perhaps he will call on you!

Just Like Me (A dialogue)

I went up one pair of stairs.
    Just like me. (to be read by a second person)

I went up two pairs of stairs.
   Just like me.
I went into a room.
   Just like me.
I looked out the window.
   Just like me.
And there I saw a monkey.
   Just like me.

Humpty-Dumpty

Humpty-Dumpty sat on a wall,
Humpty-Dumpty had a great fall;
All the king's horses and all the king's men,
Couldn't put Humpty-Dumpty together again.

Morning

Awake, arise, pull out your eyes,
   And hear what time of day;
And when you've done,
Pull out your tongue,
   And see what you can say.

Seeing Things

Amidst the mists and coldest frosts,
   With barest wrists and stoutest boasts,
He thrusts his fists against the posts,
   And still insists he sees the ghosts.

The Fly and the Flea

A fly and a flea in a flue
Were imprisoned, so what could they do?
   Said the fly, 'Let us flee!'
   'Let us fly!' said the flea;
So they flew through a flaw in the flue.

Poor Robin

The North Wind doth blow,
And we shall have snow,
And what will poor Robin do then?
He will hop to a barn,

And to keep himself warm,
Will hide his head under his wing,
   Poor thing!

A *Fellow Named Hyde*

A silly young fellow named Hyde
In a funeral procession was spied;
  When asked, 'Who is dead?'
  He giggled and said,
'I don't know; I just came for the ride.'

Noise

Harry is singing and Willie is clapping;
 Baby is waking, his little arms flapping;
Mother is saying, 'Stop singing! Stop clapping!
 You're waking the baby who ought to be napping.'

The Fat Man of Bombay

There was a fat man of Bombay
Who was smoking one sunshiny day;
  When a bird called a snipe
  Flew away with his pipe,
Which vexed the fat man of Bombay.

The Chubby Little Sister

A chubby little sister
Was rubbing at her tub;
A chubby little brother
Came up to help her rub.
The chubby little brother
Fell in with a cry;
The chubby little sister
Then hung him up to dry.

A *Funny Thing*

The funniest thing in the world I know,
Is watching the monkeys in the show.
Jumping and running, and racing around
Up to the top of the pole, then down.
First they're here and then they're there,

And just almost any and everywhere!
Screeching and scratching wherever they go,
They're the funniest things in the world I know.

The Man with Bandy Legs

As I was going to sell my eggs,
I met a man with bandy legs—
Bandy legs and crooked toes,
I tripped up his heels, and he fell on his nose.

The Little Bird

Once I saw a little bird come hop, hop, hop;
So I cried, 'Little bird, won't you stop, stop, stop?'
And was going to the window to say, 'How do you do?'
But he shook his little tail, and far away he flew!

References

Anderson, Virgil A., *Training the Speaking Voice*, Oxford University Press, New York, 2nd ed., 1961, Part II.

Bryngelson, Bryng, and Elaine Mikalson, *Speech Correction Through Listening*, Scott, Foresman, Chicago, 1959.

Byrne, Margaret C., *The Child Speaks: A Speech Improvement Program for Kindergarten and First Grade*, Harper and Row, New York, 1965.

Carrell, James A., *Disorders of Articulation*, Prentice-Hall, Englewood Cliffs, N. J., 1968.

Fairbanks, Grant, *Voice and Articulation Drillbook*, Harper and Row, New York, 1960, Chaps. 1–9. For older children.

Garbutt, Cameron W., *The Road to the Land of 'R,'* The Interstate, Danville, Ill., 1970.

Goebel, Jane O., *Speechcraft: A Speech Therapy Workbook for Any Sound*, The Interstate, Danville, Ill., 1967.

Irwin, John V., *Disorders of Articulation*, Bobbs-Merrill, Indianapolis, 1972.

Johnson, Wendell, et al., *Speech Handicapped School Children*, Harper and Row, New York, 3rd ed., 1967, Chap. 3.

Larr, Alfred L., *Tongue Thrust and Speech Correction*, Fearon Publishers, San Francisco, 1962.

Matthews, Jack, et al., *The Best Speech Series*, Stanwix House, Pittsburgh, 1959.

Mellencamp, Virginia, *Play and Say It*, Prentice-Hall, Englewood Cliffs, N. J., 1962.

Miller, Diane May, and Alfred L. Miller, *Carryover Articulation Manual*, Charles C. Thomas, Springfield, Ill., 1971.

Parker, Jayne Hall, *Sounds Like Fun*, The Interstate, Danville, Ill., 1962.

————, *My Speech Workbook*, Prentice-Hall, Englewood Cliffs, N. J., 1964.

Slepian, Jan, and Ann Seidler, *The Listen-Hear Books*, Follet, Chicago, 1964.

Travis, Lee E., ed., *Handbook of Speech Pathology and Audiology*, Appleton-Century-Crofts, New York, 1971, Chaps. 28, 33, 34.

Van Riper, Charles, *Speech Correction*, Prentice-Hall, Englewood Cliffs, N. J., 4th ed., 1963, Chaps. 9, 10, and Appendix B.

West, Robert W., and Merle Ansberry, *The Rehabilitation of Speech*, Harper and Row, New York, 4th ed., 1968, Chaps. 4, 13.

Young, Edna Hill, and Sara Stinchfield Hawk, *Moto-Kinesthetic Speech Training*, Stanford University Press, Stanford, California, 1955.

Zedler, Empress Young, *Listening for Speech Sounds*, Doubleday, Garden City, N. Y., 1955.

(See also General References near end of book.)

VI

Dialects

In contrast to the articulatory problems discussed in the previous chapter, there is another form of atypical speech with marked articulatory deviations that also typically involves different linguistic patterns and is more closely related to the racial-cultural environment from which the child comes than any other type of speech deviation. The speech may be a cause for concern not just because certain specific sounds differ from Standard English but because the entire pattern of speech and language is sufficiently different to interfere with communication or cause unwanted attention to be directed toward the speaker. Foreign dialects can come under this classification, as can certain other patterns of speech, some of which are sufficiently well defined to be classified as deviant forms of American dialects.[1] It must be pointed out, however, that in many instances the American dialect has its roots in some foreign language influence, as in

1. It should be noted that the word *dialect* refers, in its broadest sense, merely to a homogeneous style or pattern of speech or language as used by a considerable number of people. It follows, therefore, that dialects are inherently neither good nor bad but can be classified as either, depending on how widely used they are, who uses them, and who is doing the evaluating.

the case of the speech and language representative of certain sections of New York City or the Pacific Southwest.

In previous chapters it has been explained how and why a child naturally comes to use the speech he hears in his environment. During early childhood before the child enters school, by which time his basic speech habits are normally pretty well established, the greatest single influence is the speech he hears in the home spoken by the parents and others with whom he comes in daily contact. The next most important factor is the example set for him by his playmates and other acquaintances in the immediate neighborhood. If one of these factors is unfavorable, there is, unfortunately, a strong possibility that the other will be also, since there is a tendency for foreign dialects and various other deviant forms of communication to be centered in certain districts and areas over the country. The problem of dialectal speech and language is likely to be more concentrated, therefore, in certain schools and school districts or systems than in others, in contrast to most forms of speech disorders that are found more or less universally.

True, it can be argued that the pattern of speech and language the child brings to school may reflect more than simply his immediate language background; it is a part of his cultural heritage, functions as his medium of thought and learning, and provides him efficient communication with his associates. While these contentions may be true in some cases, it is also true that as the child gets older, his world ought to expand beyond the confines of his childhood environment and he may find his habitual comprehension and means of expressing himself inadequate to his more complex needs. Moreover, there is little doubt that a seriously deviant form of oral communication will prove to be a handicap to the average individual born in this country as he pursues his work in higher education, begins to look for a job, or attempts to enter almost any of the major professions. Therefore, it is to the child's advantage to learn the standard language of the larger community in which he expects to live, even if it means learning it, and perhaps using it, especially at first, as a second language, with his natural language used for informal communication at home and among his friends.

It is also true that in many instances the child may not represent any special ethnic group or culture, but may come from merely a culturally limited or even a culturally deprived and economically impoverished family or neighborhood. In this case the child's speech is likely to be a degraded form of English that must be called simply substandard.

In any case, whether the child is simply to be taught English as a second language or whether his communication generally needs upgrading, the teacher in the early grades will be the first individual in a position to help him acquire the communicative skills he will need as he progresses through school and through life. The problem will be little different basically from what confronts the teacher of the child who habitually uses such language as 'I ain't got none' or 'His old man done the work.' In either case habits of long standing will need to be eradicated or severely modified and more acceptable patterns of communication developed, a process that is seldom easy and which is made more difficult by environmental influences that continue to be adverse.

Where speech is concerned, the re-education begins with intensive ear training, since the child is often not aware that his speech is different from anyone else's, although the teacher will also encounter the opposite situation, especially where foreign dialect is involved—the child may be painfully aware that his speech, and perhaps many other things about himself as well, is distinctly different from that of his playmates without knowing exactly how or why. The result may be a backward and unhappy child with distinct feelings of inferiority and insecurity with which the teacher will have to deal.

Foreign Dialect

It is difficult for any of us to shake off the linguistically naïve conviction that English is inherently easy to learn to speak and that foreign languages are more difficult. Mark Twain was aware of this natural tendency, and he is credited with observing in one of his essays that the Germans must be a very intelligent people because there even the small children spoke German more fluently than he could. Anyone who has studied languages objectively, however, has soon discovered that any language is difficult to master only after a native language has been spoken. This is particularly true of pronunciation, chiefly because each language has its own individual system of vowels, diphthongs, and consonants, and the sound scheme of one language may be distinctly different from that of another. While most languages of the world, for example, contain at least close approximations of such vowels as *ee* [i], *ah* [ɑ], and *oo* [u] and such consonants as [s], [m], and [t], very few of those languages use the vowels short *i* [ɪ], short *a* [æ], and short *u* [ʌ] or the consonants *th* [θ], *th* [ð], and *wh* [hw], all of which are commonly found in English. Conversely, other languages contain sounds, such as the French nasal vowels and the German umlauts, that are not present in English. Moreover, intonation and stress patterns are different in different languages, as well as word order and general sentence structure.

The problem faced by an individual attempting to learn to speak a language other than the one he has acquired 'naturally,' therefore, involves a rather thorough auditory retraining, for he must first come to hear the new sounds and intonation patterns before he can hope to reproduce them. The natural tendency is for the individual to hear the sounds of the new language in terms of the sound scheme of the old. He hears the word *look*, for example, but since he has no auditory image for the vowel o͝o [ʊ], he actually thinks that he hears the vowel *oo* [u], which in his own language is the sound most like the new one. Consequently he pronounces the word as [luk], using the vowel in *who*, usually without realizing that what he is saying is different from the way others pronounce it. The principle operating here is that the ability to produce a given sound normally depends on the ability to hear, distinguish, and identify that sound. Ear training, therefore, becomes the key, not only to the teaching of a new language for use in oral situations, but to the correction of foreign accents and other undesirable forms of American pronunciation.

It can be seen from the foregoing that each type of foreign dialect will present its own individual problems, and the teacher, if she were ideally prepared for her task, would need to be familiar with the structure of each foreign language with which she attempted to work. Unfortunately, this ideal is rarely attained, nor is such preparation really necessary from a practical point of view. The teacher who attempts to assist individuals with a foreign language background will discover that there are a large number of sound distortions and sound substitutions that are fairly common among English-speaking individuals with a foreign background, regardless of the particular foreign language involved. Some of the more common of these problems involved in the retraining of individuals whose speech betrays a foreign background will be discussed briefly in the paragraphs that follow.

Vowels and Diphthongs

1. The vowel *ee* [i], or a sound resembling it, is likely to be substituted for the so-called short *i* [ɪ] in such words as *big, sit, sing,* and *little,* making them sound like 'beeg,' 'seet,' 'seeng,' and 'leetle.' In comparing these two sounds, the teacher will discover that [ɪ] is usually a shorter sound than [i], and that the pronunciation of words containing [ɪ] can be improved merely by cutting the vowel sound a bit shorter. She will also find that for [ɪ] the tongue is held slightly lower in the front of the mouth than for [i], and that it is somewhat more relaxed.

The use of paired words that differ only in these two sounds will help an individual distinguish the difference between them. Such lists as the following can be made up:

heat–hit	leak–lick	feast–fist	team–Tim
seat–sit	sheep–ship	leap–lip	meat–mitt

Pairs like these can be used in a number of different ways: the student can read them, making the proper distinction between the members of each pair; pictures corresponding to the words can be found for non-readers; the child can be asked to point to the proper word or picture as the teacher pronounces the words, alternating between the correct and incorrect form. A humorous approach can also be utilized if the teacher obviously mispronounces the [ɪ]-word in a sentence where the meaning would also be affected, such as 'The sailor was standing on his sheep [ship].' Stories or sentences can be read by the teacher, the child being asked to hold up his hand each time the teacher mispronounces a word containing [ɪ]. The child can then demonstrate how the teacher should have pronounced it. Sentences containing words utilizing both [ɪ] and [i] sounds will be found useful:

   a. He hit the little tree with a big stick.
   b. Jim listened to the wind singing in the trees.
   c. The little kitten seemed to be sick, for he didn't want to drink his milk.
   d. Dick liked to sit in his own seat.
   e. Tim's teacher took him to see the big city.

   2. The substitution of *ah* [ɑ], the vowel in *father*, is probably the most common foreign dialect problem in the pronunciation of words containing the short *a* or [æ], such as *hat, land, man*, and *back*. The distinction between the two sounds will be somewhat heightened if the teacher remembers that [æ] is a shorter sound than [ɑ] and that it is made more toward the front of the mouth with the jaw raised slightly from the lower position.

   3. The vowel [ɑ] is also likely to be substituted for short *u* [ʌ] in such words as *come, up*, and *mother*, in which case they will sound like [kɑm], [ɑp], and [mɑðɚ], or perhaps more likely [mɑðə]. The teacher should observe that [ʌ] is a shorter sound than [ɑ], and that it is made with the middle of the tongue raised slightly higher in the mouth.

   4. The vowel *oo* [ʊ] as found in such words as *look, could, pull*, and *push* is almost certainly to be improperly pronounced by an individual with a foreign accent. These words become

[luk], [kud], [pul], and [puʃ] in most foreign dialects, the familiar vowel *oo* [u] being substituted for the unfamiliar o͝o [ʊ], which is found in very few languages other than English. The chief points of difference between these two sounds are that [ʊ] is a shorter sound than [u], and that for the production of [ʊ] the lips are somewhat less rounded and the back of the tongue is lowered and relaxed slightly from the high, tense position for [u].

Some of the same techniques suggested for [ɪ] can also be used for the correction of [ʊ], although it is somewhat more difficult to find pairs of words containing [u] and [ʊ] that are within the comprehension of younger children. The following are illustrative:

pool–pull	fool–full	food–foot	boot–book
cool–cook	hoot–hood	noon–nook	tool–took

It will be observed that the spelling often does not distinguish words containing these two sounds, for in many cases *oo* is used for both [u] and [ʊ]. This sort of confusion in spelling is one of the factors that make English a very difficult language to learn to speak. Sentences such as the following can be used in training the child to recognize the difference between the two sounds:

a. The woman put the wool into the basket.
b. She took the book from the shelf and put it on the table.
c. Are you sure that the woman stood on just one foot?
d. He could go if he would.
e. The cook took a good look at the poor boy.

5. As generally pronounced throughout the country, long *o* [o] as in *go* and long *a* [e] as in *say* are in reality diphthongs. Phonetically the *o* is properly written as [ou] and the *a* as [eɪ], which means that during the production of *o* the sound glides, as it were, from [o] to [ʊ], and in the production of *a* the glide is from [e] to [ɪ]. If the words *go* and *say* are pronounced slowly, this gliding action can easily be heard and the final sounds become much more obvious. In most foreign languages these two

sounds are straight vowels pronounced as [o] and [e] with no gliding action at the end. The effect is to make the [o] resemble [ɔ], the vowel in *law*, and the [e] resemble [ɛ], the vowel sound of *let*. Thus, for the foreigner, who tends to hear new sounds in terms of the sounds of his own language, the word *coat* will sound somewhat like 'caught' and *gate* will resemble 'get.'

The correction of these sounds involves training in the diphthongal quality involved. In both ear training and training in actual usage of the new sounds, the diphthongal elements should be clearly stressed and exaggerated if necessary until the pupil becomes fully aware of the second element of the glide and has learned to reproduce it. Once this has been accomplished, these two sounds should offer no further difficulty.

6. The long *u* [ju] of such words as *union* and *cute* is likely to present some difficulty for the foreigner, since this sound, a diphthong, does not appear in many languages. Inasmuch as the alphabet letter *u* represents the sound of [u], as in *who*, in the majority of foreign languages, the most common and natural substitution will be the vowel [u] for the diphthong [ju]. The following pairs of words and sentences may be found useful in teaching the distinction between these two sounds:

coo–cue	coot–cute	moo–mew	food–feud
ooze–use	fool–fuel	who–hue	pooh–pew

   a. Hugh likes to study music in school.
   b. The new pupil in our room has a huge dog.
   c. The cute little girl had a beautiful doll.
   d. Few people ever leave the United States.
   e. Human beings can use tools easily.

7. The vowel *er* [ɚ], or [ɜ] as it is pronounced in certain sections of the country, presents a special difficulty for the foreigner, partly because it is spelled in so many different ways in English. It is the vowel sound of such words as *girl, work, her, heard, fur*, et cetera. The alphabet letters that would ordinarily be pronounced as vowels are not pronounced separately in these and similar words, but rather the letter is combined with *r* to produce

a single vowel, which is pronounced as [ɝ] or [ɜ]. There is a tendency for the foreigner to apply a spelling-pronunciation to these words, with the result that he will attempt to pronounce the vowel sound that seems to be represented by the spelling plus the following *r* as a consonant. The effect is a pronunciation of [work] for *work*, [hɛr] for *her*, something resembling [hɪrd] for *heard*, et cetera. Considerable ear training and drill may be necessary to eliminate this particular problem.

Consonants

A number of consonant distortions and substitutions are also characteristic of foreign dialects in general, but in some respects consonants are easier to handle than vowels because the mechanics of consonant production are relatively demonstrable and in some cases actually visible. This does not mean that ear training is less important than in the case of vowel mispronunciation, but it does mean that other sensory avenues of approach, such as the visual, the tactile, and the kinesthetic, can be used to supplement the auditory. For example, in the production of [t], not only can the child see fairly clearly where the tip of the tongue should be, but he can feel it touch the gum ridge above the upper teeth (tactile), and he can also sense its general shape and position in the mouth (kinesthetic). Only the more common difficulties will be discussed in the following sections.

1. The two sounds represented by the spelling *th*, [θ] as in *thin* and [ð] as in *this,* are found in very few languages other than English and hence are characteristically faulty in most foreign dialects. The most common fault is the substitution of [t] for [θ], 'tin' for *thin,* and [d] for [ð], 'dis' for *this,* although occasionally [s] or [z] will be heard. A mirror can be used to help the individual see how to place the tip of his tongue lightly against the lower edge of his upper front teeth and blow air through the narrow opening between tongue and teeth. The visual approach can be used to good advantage too, since the tip of the tongue can readily be seen between the front teeth in

the production of the *th* sounds, although the teacher should bear in mind that the tip is not actually protruded between the teeth. Rather, it is the friction produced by the air being expelled between the tongue tip and the lower borders of the upper incisors that constitutes the sound. One of the big problems will be to get the foreigner to hold the sound and make a continuant out of it, rather than a plosive, in the case of *t* and *d* substitutions.

Again, the technique of paired words can be used to good advantage. Begin with the following:

tin–thin	tank–thank	taught–thought	bat–bath
tick–thick	tie–thigh	true–through	toot–tooth
tree–three	team–theme	tread–thread	Pat–path

a. Ten thousand people marched through the town.
b. Tom thought that he could find the path through the woods.
c. Their mother sewed a feather on Bertha's new hat.
d. The farmer gathered all of the thorns and thistles together.
e. Martha had trouble getting the heavy thread through the thick tick.
f. All day they were so thirsty they thought they were going to die.
g. The three brothers wanted to travel through the country.
h. Take this birthday present over to Arthur's house.

2. The consonant [r] is one of the most variable sounds, not only from language to language, but also within a single language. There are many varieties of [r] in English, but most foreign languages contain still other variants not found in our language. One of the most common characteristics of the [r] in the speech of the individual with a foreign language background is that it is trilled in one way or another. Since the sound is not ordinarily trilled in English, the foreigner must be taught to make it as a smooth glide with no vibration of the tongue, uvula, or of any other part of the speech mechanism. It is recommended that the teacher refer to the discussion of [r] in the

preceding chapter and utilize the techniques and exercises suggested there for teaching the proper production of this sound. Many of the methods explained in Chapter XII will also be found useful.

3. Although some form of the consonant [l] appears in most languages, [l], like [r], varies considerably in the way it is formed and hence in acoustic quality. In most foreign languages it is pronounced somewhat farther forward in the mouth than it is in English and hence possesses what is referred to as a 'clear' or 'light' quality. While perhaps not classifiable as an actual fault of pronunciation, this 'light' [l] often becomes distinctly noticeable in the speech of the foreigner, especially when it occurs in positions where Americans characteristically use a relatively 'dark' [l], such as finally or when *l* precedes a back vowel or consonant. Again, the teacher is referred to the discussion of this sound in the preceding chapter for a more complete description as well as for recommended procedures for teaching its correct production.

4. The consonant [ŋ], spelled with *ng* as in *sing* or with *n* as in *bank*, often causes the foreigner some difficulty. A common fault involves the addition of [g] or [k] after the [ŋ] in words where such sounds do not belong, as when *singing* is pronounced as [sɪŋgɪŋ], with or without a suggestion of [g] or [k] at the end, although [g] is more likely to be present than [k]. If the teacher will compare the pronunciation of *singer* with *finger*, she will discover that the [g] is included in certain words and not in others, but that the spelling makes no distinction. Although there are rather detailed rules that can be applied to this problem of when to use [ŋ] and when to use [ŋg],[2] perhaps the teacher would be well advised to adopt the simpler procedure of attempting to teach the correct pronunciation of each word as it appears without regard to rules and generalizations, at least as far as this problem is concerned.

2. Charles K. Thomas, *An Introduction to the Phonetics of American English*, 2nd ed., Ronald Press, New York, 1958, pp. 81–82.

Ear training must be used when working with this problem so that awareness of the added plosive will be developed. Practice on the following pairs should hasten that awareness and should teach the individual when to use [ŋk] or [ŋg] and when [ŋ] alone is the proper sound.

bank–bang	sink–sing	linger–singer
kink–king	rank–rang	longer–longing
clank–clang	rink–ring	finger–wringer
hunk–hung	sunk–sung	hunger–among

a. The king learned that there was great hunger among the peasants.
b. Is it wrong to sing that song?
c. The bell rang out with a loud clang.
d. The young man was going along the wrong road.
e. Bring me something to eat.
f. The young bird had broken his wing.

g. I'll sing you a song,
   Though not very long,
Yet I think it's as pretty as any;
   Put your hand in your purse,
   You'll never do worse,
And give the poor singer a penny.

h. Robin is singing a song of cheer,
   Telling us that the spring is here,
   High in the top of an old oak tree,
   His tiny throat is bursting with glee.
   Hark! he is singing, cheerie, cheerie.
   Happy springtime is here, cheerie!

5. The consonants [w] and [hw], as found in *wear* and *where*, are likely to be confused with [v] by the foreigner, and there will be substitutions both ways. Fortunately these sounds are readily visible, and the distinction between [w], made with the two lips in a rounded position as for the vowel [u], and [v], produced by friction of the air passing between the lower lip and the upper teeth against the lower borders of which the lip is

lightly held, should not be difficult to teach. Such pairs as the following should be found useful:

| vine–wine | vent–went | vest–west | V–we |
| vale–whale | vie–why | vim–whim | veal–wheel |

6. The symbols [dʒ] are used to represent a consonant combination in English, although the sound is often spelled with only one alphabet symbol—*j* in the case of such words as *jump* or *g* as in *gem* or *age*. Not only is this sound missing from many foreign languages, but there is another complicating factor—the letter *j* in most foreign languages is used to represent the sound [j], which we usually spell with the letter *y* as in *yet*. Therefore it is to be expected that [dʒ] will be improperly pronounced by most foreigners and that the most common substitution for it will be [j]—in which case *jump* will become 'yump' [jʌmp] and *joke* will sound like 'yoke' [jok]. Paired words can again be used to teach the distinction between these two sounds:

| Yale–jail | yam–jam | use–juice | yet–jet |
| yoke–joke | year–jeer | yes–Jess | yell–jell |

In addition to the substitution of [j], other foreign dialect variations in the pronunciation of [dʒ] include the substitution of *zh* [ʒ], especially among those who have spoken French, and the tendency to unvoice [dʒ] particularly when it occurs in the final position, a practice that results in changing [dʒ] into *ch* [tʃ]—in which case *age* becomes 'aitch' [etʃ] and *ridge* sounds like 'rich' [rɪtʃ].

7. The voiceless consonant combination [tʃ], spelled typically with *ch* as in *chin*, will cause some difficulty for foreigners, although not as much as its voiced correlative [dʒ], discussed in the preceding section. Various substitutions may occur for [tʃ], a common one being *sh* [ʃ], making *chin* sound like 'shin' and *chip* become 'ship.' One of the chief distinctions between the two sounds—which should be taught foreigners—is that the new sound [tʃ] begins from a stopped or closed position with the tongue tip against the upper gum ridge and is therefore more like a plosive or exploded sound, while [ʃ] is a continuant.

Pairs containing these two sounds are readily available for use in teaching the difference between them:

ship–chip	shoe–chew	shin–chin	wish–witch
share–chair	sheet–cheat	sheep–cheap	cash–catch

8. There is a tendency among foreigners to omit the consonant *h*, a practice that becomes noticeable only when the [h] occurs in a prominent or stressed syllable. In such a sentence as *He wanted to go home* the omission of [h] from *home* would be considered a fault; but in *Did you see him go?* there is very little, if any, sound of [h] in *him* even when a person is careful to be 'correct,' provided of course he speaks in a natural, conversational manner. If the teacher studies the sound we designate as *h*, she will discover that it is produced in the throat with a sort of whisper quality while the mouth is already shaped for the sound that is to follow. Foreigners must be taught to expel this whispered air before beginning the voiced sound in words in which the *h* occurs and is pronounced, such as *Harold, home,* and *help,* when these words receive any degree of stress or emphasis.

Some drill on pairs such as the following should convince the foreigner that words he may have been in the habit of pronuncing alike are in reality quite different words and consequently should be pronounced differently.

all–hall	eel–heel	old–hold	add–had
and–hand	E–he	ear–hear	Ed–head

Some Further Characteristics of Foreign Dialect

In addition to the pattern of sound distortions and sound substitutions that characterizes a foreign dialect, some of the more important examples of which have been presented in the preceding sections, there are other factors of spoken language that also tend to make the speech of the foreigner sound 'foreign.' These are often more obscure and, in some respects, more difficult to deal with than speech-sound changes, but where time and facilities are available, some effort at least should be directed toward these more general problems, which are presented in very brief form in the following sections.

1. *The aspiration of voiceless plosives* It is characteristic of spoken English that the voiceless exploded consonants, [p], [t], and [k], are produced by a perceptible explosion of air accompanying their release. This can easily be detected if the hand is held close to the mouth while such words as *pie, two,* and *can* are pronounced. While the expulsion of breath is not quite as forceful after [k] as after [p] and [t], it is nevertheless obvious as a part of the pronunciation of these three sounds. The foreigner will be inclined to omit this explosion of breath, or aspiration as it is called, causing these plosives to resemble their voiced correlatives [b], [d], and [g]. Thus, in foreign dialect *pan* tends to sound like 'ban,' *time* will resemble 'dime,' and *cap* sounds to us like 'gap.'

Such devices as having the pupil hold either his hand close to his mouth or a feather or lighted candle that will be noticeably blown by the aspiration can be used to good advantage in teaching the proper production of the voiceless plosives.

2. *The melody pattern of spoken English* It is obvious to anyone who has listened to foreign languages being spoken that they sound different, irrespective of whatever actual speech sounds may be involved. Each language has its own melody pattern—it sings its own song, so to speak—and there is a strong inclination for the foreigner to transfer to the new language the familiar melody pattern of his native tongue. As a matter of fact, this melody form may be the last vestige af the foreign language to disappear among individuals or nationalities with a foreign language background.

Speech melody tends to remain an obscure aspect of spoken language, for the reason that, while we may be well aware of general differences in the way in which various languages and foreign dialects 'sound,' it is not easy to analyze these differences in terms of specific factors involved. Although adequate experimental evidence or exact information is lacking with respect to this particular aspect of oral language, we do know that certain factors appear to be involved in this quality referred to as melody. These will be presented briefly in the following paragraphs.

a. ACCENT We know that in a word of more than one syllable one of those syllables is likely to receive more force, or accent, than the remaining syllables. We say that the word is accented on this syllable. For example, the words *measure, calendar,* and *honorary* are all accented on the first syllable. This is one aspect of pronunciation and must be learned when a word is added to a person's vocabulary. The foreigner may learn the words improperly or imperfectly and may get the accent misplaced. Often he attempts to follow the accent pattern characteristic of his own language. If in his language the next-to-the-last syllable is commonly accented, for example, at least two of the words used as illustrations above are likely to be distorted. The general accent pattern of the language contributes to the basic effect known as melody.

b. UNSTRESSING Syllables that are not accented and words in a sentence that do not receive major force because they may be relatively unimportant to the meaning of the sentence as a whole tend to be unstressed and relatively obscure in spoken English. For example, an individual who attempts to accent or stress unduly more than the first syllable of *character,* the second syllable of *phonetic,* or the third syllable of *university* will sound strange and foreign. Spoken English is characterized by a strong pattern of alternating stressed and unstressed syllables, with the latter often becoming noticeably obscured and weak in pronunciation. This pattern does not hold true in many foreign languages, where, more often than in English, there is a more even stress pattern over all of the syllables of the word. When this more even stress is applied to English pronunciation, the result is a heavy, labored effect.

c. INTONATION Even more difficult to categorize and represent than accent and unstressing are the patterns of inflection and vocal pitch change within the sentence that are characteristic of various languages. It is obvious that the general tempo and intonation of Italian is different, for example, from that of German, both of which differ distinctly from the Scandinavian. British English is even different from American English in this respect, the typically rapid, clipped rhythm of the Englishman differing from the comparatively slower, easier intonation of the American. While in spoken English we tend to employ a falling pitch pattern in our sentences, using the upward inflection only when we are in doubt or are asking a question, in the Scandinavian languages the rising pitch pattern is very evident even in the statement of a simple fact. When English is spoken with Scandinavian inflections, it is certain to sound foreign, regardless of what other factors may be involved.

Although there are certain rules that can be applied to problems of accent, unstressing, and even vocal pitch changes within the sentence, they are often involved, difficult to remember and apply, and usually have numerous exceptions. The auditory approach is doubtless the simplest and most effective; the pupil must be taught to listen for these various aspects of spoken language and must learn to identify them, first in the speech of others and then in his own speech. Recordings can be used to good advantage in this type of training, the pupil comparing what he has recorded with some model or 'standard,' perhaps something that the teacher herself has recorded to illustrate the particular point under consideration. If recording apparatus is not available, much can be accomplished through direct imitation of patterns spoken by the teacher. The pupil should be encouraged to listen carefully and analytically to the speech of others who speak English acceptably, such as he would hear over the radio or on television. After he has learned to hear and recognize the various patterns, he is ready to begin to use them in his own speech. The thoroughness of the first step will in large measure determine the ease and effectiveness with which the second can be mastered.

3. *Sentence structure, word order, and idiom* When an individual says, 'I am here now seven years,' his speech is going to sound strange, regardless of what other qualities it may have. Each language has its own grammatical and idiomatic structure, and when that structure is carried over from one language and superimposed on another, there is little likelihood that the old pattern will fit the new language. A foreign student who had recently arrived in this country from Turkey was telling his instructor about a mutual acquaintance whom the student had seen on the campus, remarking about the acquaintance that 'his head was open.' The instructor, having horrible visions of the poor chap going about the school with a hole in his skull, finally discovered the Turkish student was trying to say that the acquaintance had his hat off. In other words, he was bareheaded, according to the expression we use in English.

Fortunately, this is a problem that is not confined to spoken English but is one that can be attacked from many angles, including the written language. Speech training, in this respect, merges with the larger problem of language training as a whole, the only special requirement being that the teacher should make sure the pupil has ample opportunity for oral expression, as well as written, in controlled situations where the teacher can observe and offer such assistance as may be required. Suggestions for co-ordinating the various aspects of language training are presented in some detail in Chapter XII.

Deviant American Dialects

It is obvious to anyone who is at all speech conscious that we have in the United States distinct dialects that are largely independent of foreign language influence. The typical individual from Boston, for example, 'talks differently' from one who lives in Iowa, whose speech in turn is still different from that heard in Georgia or Louisiana. These different patterns of pronunciation are known as regional dialects, the country as a whole being divided into three major divisions or regions—the Eastern, composed largely of New England; the Southern, roughly the Confederacy; and the remainder of the country, referred to as General American. Various attempts have been made to set up a standard American English for the country as a whole,[3] but none of them has been entirely successful, partly because no general agreement could be reached about what constituted a suitable standard. Others have suggested that there is little choice among the three major dialects, the speech of one region being just as 'correct' as that of another, provided it is truly representative of the most acceptable usage of that region. This point of view has given rise to the concept of regional standards, and rather careful analyses have been made of what is accepted as standard in each of the major dialect regions.[4]

Within these major areas there exist numerous subsidiary local dialects confined to more restricted localities; these differ to a greater or lesser degree from the generally accepted standard of the larger region. Some of them are more or less direct offshoots of foreign language influence, such as the Pennsylvania German dialect or the Mexican (Spanish) dialect of the Southwest. The degree, if any, to which these local dialects or ways of speaking can be considered substandard depends on a number of factors too involved to be discussed in detail at this point. Perhaps the safest course for the teacher is to apply the definition of a speech defect as set forth in Chapter II. Accordingly, when dialectal speech calls adverse attention to itself or interferes with the individual's ability to communicate, to that extent it should be considered substandard and therefore defective.

While the factor of communication may be paramount in speech, language of which speech is an integral part is far more involved and important. Language functions as one of the

---

3. Claude E. Kantner and Robert West, *Phonetics*, rev. ed., Harper and Row, New York, 1960, pp. 295–305.
4. Giles W. Gray and Claude M. Wise, *The Bases of Speech*, 3rd ed., Harper and Row, New York, 1959, pp. 264–313.

principal means of man's thought, memory, learning, imagination and problem solving and, in fact, is related to all mental activities. It can thus be seen how important a child's language is to his mental growth, his learning development, and his ability to solve the problems of life. Therefore, it is fairly obvious that if a child is to grow out of what may be a limited and confining environment, it is essential that his language competency provides him with an adequate basis for his development.

As Shriner expresses it,

Specifically, with respect to the disadvantaged child, it must be remembered that any child's language is related not merely to the way he speaks but also to the way he thinks. Low-status dialect may hamper the child's social mobility, but a restricted language development may limit his intellectual potential as well.[5]

There is developing at present an active interest and a large body of literature relating to the deviant forms of speech and language in the United States, variously referred to as the language of the impoverished, the ghetto, the disadvantaged, the economically deprived, the minorities, and the inner-city. There is one group, especially, the Negroes, whose language called by some black English, has evoked special attention and has stimulated a considerable body of literature, controversy, and, to a somewhat lesser extent, research. A number of students of the subject contend that Black English has a substantial historical background and that it is a linguistically rich and complete language of its own with its unique syntax, grammatical rules, et cetera. They also contend that it is an outgrowth of, and hence reflects, the cultural development of the blacks in this country, and they also believe that no effort should be made to deprive the black child of this cultural heritage. They would have him retain and use this natural language, and some have even ad-

5. Thomas H. Shriner, 'Economically Deprived: Aspects of Language Skills,' in Lee E. Travis, ed., *Handbook of Speech Pathology and Audiology*, Appleton-Century-Crofts, New York, 1971, p. 1143.

vocated that black English might well be used as the medium of instruction for blacks in the schools, especially in the early grades. If English is to be introduced into the picture, it should be as a second language to be used for special purposes. One clinician, for example, works with his black pupils on the basis of 'home talk' (black English) for the child's normal communication with family and friends and 'school talk' (Standard English) for classroom and more formal use.

On the other hand, there are those who believe that black English is not just a deviant language but is basically a deficient language and hence is defective and substandard. The black child is retarded in his language development and hence is likely to be backward in his school work and general mental development. He is at a social disadvantage because his dialectal speech lacks the prestige of accepted Standard English of the larger community in which he lives. The solution obviously is to teach him to abandon his black dialect and acquire Standard English as his habitual medium of communication.

At the time of this writing, there is sharp conflict between these two points of view and the future resolution of the problem remains uncertain, although there appears to be increasing acceptance of black English as a respectable linguistic reality. Standard English, then, would be taught as a second language which perhaps the child will come more and more to accept as he progresses educationally.

In view of these conflicting points of view and the uncertainty as to what the future may bring, it seems unwise at this time to offer any authoritative recommendations to the teacher as to a course of action. Then, too, local situations over the country as a whole are sufficiently varied as to render any specific advice unwise and perhaps unfeasible. Therefore, it is urged that the teacher follow the recommendations in her own school system course of study. She is also reminded that many local school districts, especially in the larger cities, and a number of state departments of Education or Public Instruction have also prepared special publications dealing with educational policy relating to the speech and language of the blacks and other minorities that may be represented in any significant number in the schools. These publications, plus the references listed at the end of this chapter, should provide the teacher with the guidance she will need to handle this problem in her classroom.

References

American Speech and Hearing Association, *Language, Speech and Hearing Services in Schools, Special Issue: Language and the Black Urban Child*, vol. III, October 1972.

Baratz, Joan C., *Teaching Black Children To Read*, Center for Applied Linguistics, Washington, D. C., 1969.

Bereiter, C., and S. Engelmann, *Teaching Disadvantaged Children in the Preschool*, Prentice-Hall, Englewood Cliffs, N. J., 1966.

Black, John W., *American Speech for Foreign Students*, Charles C. Thomas, Springfield, Ill., 1963.

Bronstein, Arthur J., *The Pronunciation of American English*, Appleton-Century-Crofts, New York, 1960.

Carrell, James, and W. R. Tiffany, *Phonetics: Application to Speech Improvement*, McGraw-Hill Book Company, New York, 1960, Chap. 14.

Chreist, Fred M., *Foreign Accent*, Prentice-Hall, Englewood Cliffs, N. J., 1964.

Gordon, M. J., and H. Wong, *A Manual for Speech Improvement*, Gallaudet College Bookstore, Washington, D. C., 1961.

Joseph, S. M., *The Me Nobody Knows: Children's Voices from the Ghetto*, Avon, New York, 1969.

Labov, W., *The Social Stratification of English in New York City*, Center for Applied Linguistics, Washington, D. C., 1966.

————, *The Study of Nonstandard English*, National Council of Teachers of English, Champaign, Ill., 1970.

Michel, Joseph, *See and Say*, W. S. Benson and Company, Austin, Texas, 1965.

Riley, Glyndon D., 'Language Problems of Culturally Disadvantaged Children,' in Morris Val Jones, ed., *Language Development*, Charles C. Thomas, Springfield, Ill., 1972, Chap. 6.

Shriner, Thomas H., 'Economically Deprived: Aspects of Language Skills,' in Lee E. Travis, ed., *Handbook of Speech Pathology and Audiology*, Appleton-Century-Crofts, New York, 1971, Chap. 44.

Stewart, W., *Urban Negro Speech*, National Council of Teachers of English, Champaign, Ill., 1964.

Thomas, Charles K., *An Introduction to the Phonetics of American English*, Ronald Press, New York, 2nd ed., 1958, Chaps. 21–24.

Williams, R. and R. Ham, eds., *Speech and Language Problems of the Urban and Rural Poor*, Ohio University, Athens, Ohio, 1972.

Wise, Claude M., *Applied Phonetics*, Prentice-Hall, Englewood Cliffs, N. J., 1957, Parts ii, iii.

VII

Nasal Speech

Three of the speech sounds of English, [m], [n], and [ŋ], are emitted through the nasal passages and hence are known as the nasal consonants. There are no other strictly nasal sounds in English, although the best evidence indicates that there is a small amount of nasal resonance on most of the vowels as they are pronounced in the speech of the average American. Whether or not this nasal resonance on vowels is judged to be good or bad by the hearer will, for the most part, depend on two factors: (1) the amount of nasal resonance present in the vowels, and (2) the section of the country from which the hearer comes. With respect to the first item, experience has shown that voices judged to be decidedly nasal have been found to exhibit more nasal resonance on all vowels than superior voices. In other words, if nasal resonance is allowed to increase beyond a certain amount, the average listener will identify the voice as being nasal and he will find it unpleasant.

In regard to the second item mentioned above, it should be observed that our attitude toward nasality, whether we find it pleasant or unpleasant, or are unaware of it, is determined to some extent by our linguistic background and training. If we come from certain localities where more nasal resonance is commonly heard, as, for example, sections of the Middle West and the South and parts of New England, we do not find it unpleasant or think of it as being a fault of voice production—all of which suggests that the term nasality is, within limits, a relative one, having a rather pronounced subjective basis. When a voice exhibits nasality beyound the limits accepted as normal in any section of the country, however, there is no question of its status—it is distracting to the hearer and should be investigated and eradicated if possible.

Types of Nasality

There is considerable confusion about the use of the term *nasality*, which must be cleared up if the teacher is to understand this problem and recognize the various symptoms when she hears them. As has already been seen, the three nasal consonants must be resonated and emitted through the nasal passages. If certain conditions there restrict the nasal emission or render it impossible, as happens when a person develops a bad head cold, for example, the nasal consonants will be missing or greatly reduced, and the voice will sound muffled and 'stuffy.' If, on the other hand, an excessive amount of the resonance and air stream involved in speech is allowed to intrude into the nasal passages, the consonants will be greatly reduced in clarity, many of them being missing or escaping through the nose as puffs of air, and the vowels will have a hollow, 'nosey' quality characteristic of cleft palate speech.

The first of these conditions, in which there is too little nasal resonance on the sounds that should have complete nasal emission, [m], [n], and [ŋ], is called negative or closed nasality, or denasalization. When there is too much nasal resonance on the sounds that should be predominantly oral, the condition is known as positive or open nasality, or nasalization.[1] In a sense, therefore, from the point of the mechanism involved, the two conditions are opposite. Because both are associated with the nose, however, the layman often refers to both simply as nasality without attempting to differentiate them or to identify the different symptoms in the two cases. Such differentiation is necessary, though, if the teacher is to deal successfully with this type of speech disorder, since causes and methods of retraining differ markedly in the two conditions.

If the instructor is to understand nasality of either type, it is necessary to gain a minimum working knowledge of the essential mechanism involved. The amount of tone that will issue through the nasal passages will normally depend on the extent to which those passages are open and offer free egress for the tone. In a normal structure the amount of nasal emission will be determined basically by the size of the posterior opening into the nasal cavity formed by the movement of the velum (soft palate), with its pendent uvula attached, either toward or away from the posterior pharyngeal wall (fig. 5), assisted in closure by some inward movement of the surrounding structures at the back and on each side. When the velum is raised up against the back of the throat (fig. 6), nasal resonance is reduced to a minimum or eliminated altogether, because the mouth has been effectively closed off from the nasal chambers. But when the velum is relaxed and open (fig. 7), tone is allowed to pass up into the nasal chambers. And when the mouth is closed, as in the formation of the nasal consonants [m], [n], and [ŋ], the sound is emitted wholly through the nose. If any nasal obstruction prevents that emission or interferes with it, a degree of denasality will result. Conversely, if habit or some physical con-

---

1. The terms hyponasality (*hypo* meaning too little) and hypernasality (*hyper* meaning too much) have also come into common use to designate these two conditions, and it should further be noted that the simple terms nasal, nasality, and nasalization are commonly used for the open type, in contrast to denasal, denasality, and denasalization for the closed type.

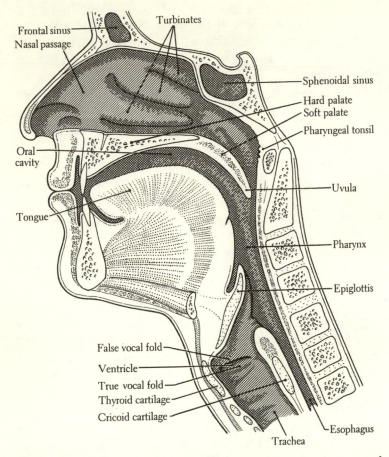

FIGURE 5. Sagittal (midline) section of the nose, mouth, pharynx, and trachea. Only the right half of the nasal passage is illustrated; the thin bony partition known as the septum, which divides the right from the left, lies directly in the line of section and is therefore not shown.

dition prevents the hard and soft palate from closing off the nose from the mouth to the extent needed to produce a good oral consonant or vowel sound, then a degree of nasalization will be present. The factors responsible for these two opposite conditions will be discussed in more detail in the following paragraphs.

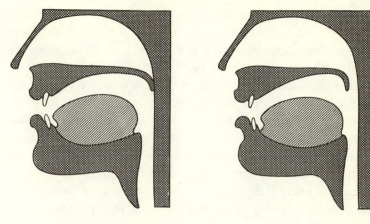

Fig. 6   Fig. 7

FIGURE 6. Diagrammatic outline of the mouth, nasal passage, and pharynx, with the velum raised as in the production of an oral sound.

FIGURE 7. Same as figure 6, except with velum lowered, creating an opening into the posterior nasal passageway.

Denasality

As was stated previously, in denasality there is a reduction of resonance on the [m], [n], and [ŋ]. In extreme cases where the nasal passages are completely blocked, as in a bad head cold, no nasal emission at all is possible on these consonants. Then their oral equivalents are substituted for them, [m] becoming [b], [n] turning into [d], and [ŋ] changing to [g]. In the speech of such an individual, the expression *good morning* would sound like 'good bawdig' [gʊd bɔdɪg]. It is not just the nasal consonants that are involved in denasality, however; in cases that are at all serious the whole speech, especially the vowels, will sound 'dead' and 'stuffy' with that well-known cold-in-the-head quality which is not difficult to recognize.

Causes of Denasality

Denasality is almost always traceable to some type of nasal obstruction. In some cases such an obstruction may not be found upon examination, but the history of the child's health may reveal that such a condition was formerly present, having been alleviated through surgery or other means. In these instances the child will often continue to talk as if the condition were still present because such vocal habits, once formed, tend to be continued, despite changes in the mechanism. (It should be noted that a similar situation can also result in nasalization in some cases, as will be explained in a subsequent section.) Usually some voice and speech training is needed to help the child break up the old habit patterns and establish new ones in their place. There are many conditions that may function to occlude the nasal passages, either temporarily or permanently. Only a few of the more common ones will be described briefly.

1. *Adenoids* One of the more common causes of nasal obstruction in children is a condition referred to as adenoids, in reality an enlargement of the pharyngeal tonsil (fig. 5). This tissue may become so enlarged that the entire posterior entrance to the nasal passages is obstructed. In addition to the speech characteristics already mentioned, certain other physical symptoms usually accompany adenoids. The adenoidal tissue may develop to such an extent that the opening into the Eustachian tube becomes blocked, with the result that the child's hearing will be temporarily impaired. Or an inflammation of the middle ear known as otitis media may develop. (This will be discussed in more detail in Chapter xi.) This loss of hearing, coupled with the 'vacant' look commonly associated with mouth breathing, gives the impression that the child is mentally deficient. As a matter of fact, because of the hearing impairment the child may actually fall behind in his work in school. This is a temporary condition, however; after removal of the adenoids, the hearing returns to normal, provided, of course, there is no other hearing disability or continuing complication involving the middle ear.

In all cases of denasality, especially when it is associated with mouth breathing and a general lassitude and unresponsiveness, the teacher would be well advised to see that the child has a physical examination. If adenoids are found to be responsible, they should receive medical attention without delay, for general health reasons as well as for the sake of the child's speech.

2. *Nasal obstructions other than adenoids* There are many conditions, in addition to adenoids, that may obstruct the nasal passages either partially or completely on one side or both. It is necessary to mention only a few of the more common ones:

a. BROKEN NOSE The bones of the nose are very delicate; injury can easily shatter them, with the result that the normal arrangement of the nasal chambers is altered. Some of the passages may be closed off, or adhesions and scar tissue may develop that will effectively diminish their size. Then there will be a reduced capacity for nasal breathing and very likely some denasality. Surgical repair may or may not be feasible, but the possibility should at least be investigated.

b. GROWTHS IN THE NOSE While not so likely to be found in young children, many types of growths are common to the nasal passages. One type is referred to as polyps, a fleshy tumor-like growth in the mucous membrane of the nose. All of these are troublesome, but fortunately most of them can be dealt with successfully through surgery or some other means.

c. ANATOMICAL IRREGULARITIES One of the most common of these conditions is known as deviated septum, the presence of which is often betrayed by an asymmetry of the exterior of the nasal structure. If the septum is badly deviated, one side of the nasal passages may be more or less permanently closed. Usually speech will be affected if the condition is at all marked.

3. *Nasal infections* The most widespread example of such infections is, of course, the common cold. The mucous membranes become inflamed and swollen and there is a marked nasal discharge, often resulting in complete obstruction of the nasal passages. Fortunately the condition is usually temporary, and there should be no permanent effect on the speech unless the

colds are abnormally frequent, in which case the child may develop the habit of talking always as if he has a cold. Somewhat the same condition results from sinusitis, a sinus infection which may become chronic. In all cases where the child is subject to frequent or prolonged nasal infections, an examination by a physician should be recommended.

4. *Allergies, hay fever*   The allergic condition known as hay fever can produce symptoms very similar to those of the common cold. The effect on the voice will also be similar—a stuffy, stopped-up quality. Some individuals suffer from hay fever so frequently and for such long periods of time that they have developed a permanent denasality, which persists even during those periods when the nasal passages may be free. Again, medical attention should be recommended to determine whether the allergy is of a type that can be controlled through diet, immunization, or some other means.

Removal of the Cause

As long as there is any serious stoppage of the nasal passageway, speech training to overcome denasality will be slow and difficult and the result uncertain, not to mention the continuing threat to the child's health. Therefore it is important to explore the possibility of removing or alleviating the basic cause. Many physicians agree that the child with the recurring or seemingly chronic 'runny' nose presents a worrisome medical problem. Too often, unfortunately, the condition is ignored and the careful study that may be required to uncover the cause is never undertaken. This does not relieve the teacher, however, from doing what she can to insure that the child with a nasal condition receives proper attention. Fortunately, in a number of cases relief is not complicated or difficult.

The removal of the cause, however, will not of itself necessarily solve the speech problem. If the cause has been serious or of long standing, one of two conditions, or perhaps a peculiar combination of both, is likely to result, so far as the speech is concerned: (1) the speech habits may persist, and the individual may continue to talk much as he did before the cause was removed, or (2) the former denasality may change to open nasality, since the nasal passages that were previously stopped up are now open and the velopharyngeal closure mechanism has not adjusted itself to the new condition. (This problem will be discussed in more detail in a later section.)

When a combination of both conditions results, there is inadequate resonance on the nasal consonants and a nasalization of the vowel sounds and perhaps some of the oral consonants. In such instances a rather involved program of speech training must be undertaken that will provide more nasal resonance for the [m], [n], and [ŋ] but more careful control of the soft palate in the production of the rest of the sounds.

Speech Training for Denasality

Even though it may not be possible or feasible to remove the basic cause of the denasality, speech training can still accomplish worth-while results, provided the condition is not too serious. As in the case of many other types of speech disorders, ear training is of first importance in the correction of nasality of either type. The individual must learn to identify the quality to be avoided and must be taught to recognize the desirable quality he is attempting to achieve. Here a recording machine becomes invaluable. Other voices, perhaps that of the teacher, can be used to establish a basis for comparison, so that the child can hear the difference between the desirable and undesirable qualities. The teacher's ability to imitate the defect can also be used to advantage in furthering the ear training of the child.

In addition to learning what it sounds like to produce speech correctly, the child must also learn what it feels like. He must learn to associate the feeling of vibrations in the nasal passages with the production of the nasal consonants. He can even detect those vibrations with his fingers if he holds them lightly against the sides of the nose as he hums [m] or [n]. He must be taught to stress and prolong the nasal consonants, through special humming and reading exercises at first and later whenever he encounters them in ordinary speech.

Exercises to Develop Nasal Resonance

1. Hum [m] on various pitch levels up and down the scale. Feel the tingling on the lips and the resonance throughout the nasal passages.
2. Hum [n] similarly; the lip sensation referred to above, of course, will not be present.
3. Repeat rapidly: me[mi]—me-me-me-me-me, etc.
4. Repeat: me, may, mie, moe, moo, stressing and prolonging the [m].
5. Repeat exercise 4, substituting [n] in place of [m].
6. Sing or read the following, substaining the [ŋ] for increased nasal resonance:

    a. Running; coming; going; ting-a-ling; ding-dong.
    b. Ring and swing. (Repeat, singing on a monotone.)
    c. Ringing and swinging. (Repeat as above.)
    d. Sing me a song.
    e. As I was going along.

7. Read the following carefully, emphasizing all nasal consonants:

    a. Eenie, meenie, minie, moe.
    b. Mumbo-Jumbo is my name.
    c. Many men make much money from mines.
    d. 'Good morning, Mother,' said Mary.
    e. Mary made some muffins.

    f. Come in the evening, or come in the morning;
       Come when you're looked for, or come without warning.

    g. As I was going along, long, long,
       A-singing a comical song, song, song;
       The lane that I went was long, long, long,
       And the song that I sang was long, long, long,
       And so I went singing along.

h. I saw three ships come sailing by,
    Come sailing by, come sailing by;
    I saw three ships come sailing by,
    On Christmas day in the morning.

i. Milkman, milkman, where have you been?
    In Buttermilk Channel, up to my chin.
    I spilled my milk and spoiled my clothes,
    And got a long icicle hung to my nose.

j. The blacksmith hammers the whole day long,
    His hammer is heavy, but his arm is strong.
    Here comes a horse—what will blacksmith do?
    He will hammer out a strong iron shoe.

k. The king was in the counting-house,
    Counting out his money;
    The queen was in the kitchen,
    Eating bread and honey.
    The maid was in the garden,
    Hanging out the clothes;
    Along came a bumble-bee
    And stung her on the nose.

l. Little Miss Muffet,
    Sat on a tuffet,
    Eating some curds and whey.
    Along came a spider
    And sat down beside her
    And frightened Miss Muffet away.

m. Evening red and morning gray
    Will set the traveler on his way.
    But evening gray and morning red
    Will bring down rain upon his head.

Positive or Open Nasality

Positive or open nasality is a much more involved and complicated disorder than denasalization. The most obvious type of open nasality is associated with a cleft palate condition in which air and sound can not be prevented from entering the nasal passages. Vowels take on a distinctly dull, 'nosey' quality, usually accompanied by some nasal emission of the oral consonants which lose their distinctive characteristics and may become simply nasal 'snorts' or puffs of air blown out through the nostrils. Such speech often becomes very difficult to understand, since both the vowels and consonants are affected. As we shall see later, conditions other than a cleft palate can also produce these speech symptoms.

A second type of nasality much more difficult to explain and less understood, is sometimes described as nasal twang. This is more likely to be functional rather than organic and is characterized by a flat, strident, twangy quality. The consonants may be properly formed and intelligibility may be satisfactory; there may or may not be some demonstrable nasal emission. Nasal twang may be associated with too much opening into the nasal passages at the back, and it also seems to be related to a tight jaw, as well as tensions in the throat and mouth and possible formation of air pockets along the vocal tract in which sound becomes trapped. The use of too-high pitch in speaking seems to heighten the effect of nasal twang.

While other factors are also doubtless involved in producing excessive nasality, there is little doubt that the chief cause is related to the size of the opening between the mouth and nasal passages. It is believed that in the normally pleasant voice there is a slight opening between the velum and the pharyngeal wall that allows a controlled amount of nasal resonance in the production of the vowel sounds; this is deemed to contribute to the richness and pleasantness of the voice. The moment this opening becomes too large, however, an excessive amount of tone is allowed to pass into the nasal passages, and a recognizable nasal quality results.

Causes of Nasality

As we have seen, any condition that interferes with adequate closure between the velum and the pharyngeal wall or in any other way makes the effective separation of the mouth from the nasal cavities impossible will almost certainly result in a noticeable nasality. Unlike denasality, the present condition may be unrelated to any abnormality or deficiency of structure but rather may result merely from general habits of speech, in which case it is said to be functional. The most important causes of nasality can be grouped under the categories listed below.

1. *Cleft palate* Probably no structural deformity of the entire speech mechanism has as disastrous an effect on articulation and voice quality as does cleft palate, which may or may not be associated with cleft lip, also known as harelip. In cleft palate conditions there is a cleft, or opening, through the roof of the mouth, which may involve only the soft palate at the back of the mouth or which may extend into the hard palate as well. In some cases the cleft may be complete, extending from the soft palate through the hard palate and upper gum ridge and through the upper lip on one or both sides of the midline. Since there is no way of shutting off the mouth from the nasal passages in these cases, all of the speech sounds that should normally be made in the mouth, such as the vowels and most of the consonants, will be emitted through the nose, at least in part. Vowels will thus be nasalized and many of the consonants will pass through the nose as mere puffs of air, or nasal snorts. The effect will be decidedly unpleasant, and intelligibility may be seriously impaired.

No one knows with certainty the specific cause, or causes, of cleft palate, except that it results from some failure of the embryo to develop properly during the first 12 to 15 weeks. Fortunately it is relatively rare, in comparison with other types of speech defects at least, occurring approximately once in 750 live births. The child with a cleft palate is more susceptible to colds and throat infections than is the normal child and, because these infections can more easily get into the middle ear, he is more likely to suffer from some loss of hearing.

Surgery can do a great deal to alleviate the physical disability of cleft palate. Where the lip is involved the cleft will be closed during the first few weeks of the child's life, and the first, or primary, operation on the palate will typically be performed by the time the child is 20 months old. There are several reasons for this early surgery on the palate, including the facilitation of feeding and prevention of middle ear infections, but the principal reason stems from the surgeon's desire to close the cleft before the child has begun to talk very much. In this way improper speech habits which might be difficult to alter later can be prevented. In those instances where the primary surgery was successful and was completed early enough that the child learned to talk with an essentially normal mechanism, no later speech attention may be required.

In a significant number of cases, unfortunately, the original surgical correction does not provide an adequate mechanism for speech, and later secondary operations are necessary to improve the structure. Such procedures do not always insure, unfortunately, that the mechanism will be as good as normal, especially in the case of the soft palate. Here it may be impossible to replace missing muscle tissue, and the presence of extensive scar tissue may render the palate stiff and inflexible. In some instances there just is not enough palate left to close off the opening into the posterior nasal chambers effectively. Sometimes surgery is replaced or supplemented by a plastic and metal device known as an obturator which fits into the cleft, thus closing it up. Such devices are more effectively used with the hard palate than with the velum where movement is involved, often playing an important role in the rebuilding of the front teeth and gum ridge in those severe cases of complete cleft.

In a large number of instances where secondary procedures are undertaken when the child is five, six, seven, or older, a more or less protracted period of speech training will be necessary to prevent a serious disorder, even if the later procedures result in an essentially, 'normal' mechanism. Experience over the years with a defective speech structure develops habits which too often render it difficult, if not impossible, for the child to take full advantage of the improved structure without some outside help. Even with speech training there is no complete assurance that the child will ever develop entirely normal speech and voice quality, if the condition was severe to begin with. Since the retraining program is time-consuming and involves more or less highly specialized techniques, in most instances it will not be practical for the classroom teacher to undertake the major responsibility of training the child. For this she will need the services of the trained speech specialist. Therefore, no detailed program of speech rehabilitation has been included for cleft palate speech, although it was felt that the teacher should know something about the basic condition.

The teacher may well have one basic responsibility toward the cleft palate child, however. If she has such a child among her pupils and his speech is unacceptable, she should determine whether he has been seen recently by a medical specialist and/or a speech clinician. Too many cleft palate children have not had an examination since their first operation at the age of two years or less. They may be in serious need of further surgery, of being fitted with an obturator, or they may have dental problems or be in need of orthodontia. The best place for a complete examination of such a child is a cleft palate team, or panel, typically located in a medical clinic or center or in a hospital. Such a team is composed of a number of specialists who are concerned with the many problems often presented by the cleft palate child. The group may include a pediatrician, plastic surgeon, prosthedontist, orthodontist, speech and language specialist, audiologist, children's dentist, otolaryngologist, radiologist, and perhaps other specialties as well. Such a team is in a position to give a cleft palate child a complete appraisal and recommend the most effective treatment procedure.

2. *Velar insufficiency* In some children, although there is no actual cleft, the velum, or soft palate, is unable for one reason or another to make contact with the back wall of the throat to close off the opening into the posterior nasal passages. These

are referred to as cases of velar insufficiency. In some instances the basic cause may be structural—the soft palate is simply too short to function effectively or the space to be closed is too deep. In these cases it will be observed that even when the palate is fully elevated, there is still a noticeable space between the palate and the posterior pharyngeal wall. This condition may be so pronounced that the individual will sound very much as if he had a cleft palate. Such a situation sometimes develops in a seemingly normal child following removal of tonsils and adenoids. Evidently in these instances the child was depending on the adenoid mass to assist in velopharyngeal closure, perhaps because of a congenitally short palate, abnormally deep velopharyngeal space, or for some other reason. When this tissue is suddenly removed the child cannot immediately adjust.

In other cases the soft palate may be structurally normal, but its movement may be restricted. Such a condition would indicate paralysis, as would an asymmetrical movement or position of the velum. The presence of scar tissue might also impede its movement. In all instances where some structural or physiological deficiency is suspected, the child should be examined by a physician, preferably a plastic surgeon.

3. *Functional causes*　In many cases of nasality, even when it is quite pronounced, no structural or physiological cause can be found. We must conclude that in such instances a nasal voice may merely reflect bad speech habits, which the individual has often acquired as a result of imitation. If a child develops speech in an environment where nasality is common, it is only to be expected that his own speech will resemble that of his elders in this respect. Then, there is a kind of nasality often associated with poor articulation in general, especially of the lip-lazy and tongue-lazy type referred to as oral inactivity. In these cases the velum is as sluggish and unresponsive as are the other articulatory organs, hanging open and relaxed during the production of sounds that should be primarily oral in quality. The result is a considerable amount of nasal emission.

General Procedures in Correcting Nasality

Naturally, the very first step in rehabilitation involves removing or remedying the cause, if such is possible or feasible. Where surgery is indicated, it is usually a waste of time to attempt any speech training until the surgical repair has been completed. In those cases of structural deficiency where surgery is not feasible, the only possible hope for improvement lies in helping the individual make the most effective use of an imperfect mechanism. Often a great deal can be done to improve its functioning. Perhaps the pupils most likely to profit from speech training are those in whom the nasality is of the functional type, although a great deal can often be done for the cleft palate child as well. Basically the process of speech improvement involves substituting new habit patterns for old ones, not always an easy process, to be sure, but one having vast potentialities.

1. *Ear training* Nasality is a defect of vocal quality; often an individual with a nasal voice is totally unaware of this quality difference. But little can be done to improve his voice until he has learned to identify the quality that is to be changed. Here again a recording machine will be found to be invaluable. The majority of such devices will record nasality quite faithfully, and even the individual exhibiting this defect will have no difficulty hearing it when the recording is played back to him. If no recording device is available, the teacher is thrown back on her own resources and must reproduce the defect as best she can in her own voice, alternating between nasality and good oral quality so that the difference will be clearly demonstrated.

2. *Establishing velar control* In pronounced cases of nasality, especially where there is some structural or physiological deficiency, some attention to control of the soft palate may be needed as a prelude to later more formal speech training. In this connection, blowing exercises have considerable value. If the child is young, these can easily be motivated through the use of whistles, toy boats, pinwheels, balloons, and soap-bubble

pipes. In these exercises the objective is to promote as much movement in the velum as possible so that it will rise up and back against the wall of the throat, which should pull in somewhat in a constrictor fashion to meet it. If the child can blow soap bubbles, or keep a candle flame steadily bent to one side as he blows on it, without any loss of air through the nose, then he is achieving effective velar closure for these activities. Loss of air through the nose can be detected by placing a light feather or fluff of cotton on a card and holding it directly under the nostrils and above the mouth. If air is leaking through the nose, the feather will be blown off the card. Older children and adults can also engage in blowing exercises with profit, although here a somewhat different selection of blowing devices will need to be made. Much of the tediousness can be removed from such exercises if the individual can become interested in learning to play some simple musical instrument, such as a harmonica or recorder.

It must be remembered, however, that blowing exercises have certain limitations in a program of speech improvement for nasality. After all, blowing and speaking are two quite different activities, and demonstrated ability to direct the air stream out of the mouth in blowing may not automatically carry over into speaking. An individual can learn to blow a whistle, for example, much more readily than he can learn to control nasal emission in speaking. On the other hand, if the child cannot develop velophrayngeal closure in blowing, it is highly unlikely that he can ever achieve it for speaking with his present speech structure. Thus, blowing exercises may have some diagnostic and predictive value in addition to establishing basic conditions for subsequent speech training.

Other methods of promoting velar control involve such activities as yawning, inhaling through the nose and exhaling through the mouth with the mouth held open in both cases, and also puffing out the checks as pressure is built up in the mouth and then releasing the pressure through the nose by relaxing the velum. Practicing the open vowel sounds, such as [ɑ] or [o], pre-

ceded by a plosive consonant such as [p] or [b], will tend to re-
duce the nasality on the vowel, because the velum, which must
be closed off in order to build up pressure for the plosive, will
tend to remain relatively closed for the vowel that follows. Conversely, vowels preceded or followed by one of the nasal consonants, [m], [n], or [ŋ], will in all probability exhibit more
nasality than usual because of the carry-over effect of the nasal
sound. This is known as assimilation nasality. More specific
exercises for the control of the velum will be found at the end
of this section.

3. *Correcting nasality by promoting good habits of voice production* It has been observed that many cases of nasality are
associated with faulty habits of voice production in general,
such as improper breathing, tenseness of the throat and mouth
region, and the use of an improper basic pitch. Tenseness will
often produce a strident, nasal voice, and nasality of the nasal
twang variety tends to become much more conspicuous as the
pitch of the voice rises. It is clear, therefore, that the approach
to many cases of nasality will be through the establishment of
good vocal habits. The individual must learn to remain relaxed,
and every effort should be made to utilize the most favorable
conditions for voice production, including the discovery and cul-
tivation of the individual's optimum pitch. For a suggested
method of achieving these objectives, the teacher is referred to
the program of training in the latter part of the following
chapter.

4. *Correcting nasality through training in good articulation* It
must be remembered that the velum, along with the tongue,
lips, and jaw, is part of the articulatory mechanism and, as such,
contributes to clear, intelligible, and pleasant speech. If the
individual is in the habit of speaking with a lazy tongue and
immobile lips, there is no basis for supposing that his velum is
any more active or responsive than are the other articulatory
organs.

It can be seen, therefore, that a very important avenue of approach to the correction of positive nasality lies in the development of good, clear articulation generally. As the individual learns to speak distinctly, the velum will be drawn into the articulatory pattern of good speech, reducing or eliminating the nasality. Therefore, a general program of re-education aimed at the improvement of general diction should be followed. This should include: (1) Basic articulatory drills and exercises (vocal gymnastics) to limber up the speech organs and make them more active. (2) Exercises to get the mouth open for the full emission of tone. Those individuals who talk between clenched teeth are the ones most likely to exhibit nasality, for if the tone cannot get out of the mouth easily, it will tend to come out of the nose. (3) Clear, precise formation of the vowels and consonants that make up speech, with the primary emphasis on the role of the mouth in achieving *orality*, rather than dwelling negatively on nasality.

Many of the drills and exercises designed to promote clear speech and included as a part of the training materials in Chapter v are also recommended for use with cases of open nasality.

Exercises to Eliminate Nasality

Openness and Relaxation of the Pharynx
One of the practices most disastrous to good voice quality is the habit of elevating or humping up the back of the tongue too high in the mouth during voice production. The effect is a considerable narrowing of the vocal outlet, or speech 'megaphone' —which is likely to produce a nasal quality. The following drills are designed to help guard against this difficulty.

1. Practice the yawn. Feel the tongue as it is depressed in the back, and the velum as it rises. Your throat is now fully open.
2. With the aid of a hand mirror and a good source of light, explore as much as can be seen of the mouth and throat during the process of yawning. Notice the position of the tongue and the velum and observe how the throat opens.

Still using the mirror, but without actually yawning, duplicate these same conditions. Practice until you are able to
do this readily.

3. Observing with a mirror again, pronounce [ɑ] with the
   throat open as it was in exercise 2.

4. Duplicate the feeling of the yawn as nearly as you can and
   sing (prolong) [o], keeping the throat as open as possible. Do
   not allow it to close with the beginning of the tone; keep the
   feeling of openness as much as possible.

5. Assume the open throat position again and sing [u] for a
   short time. Then carefully merge this vowel into [ɑ], keeping
   the feeling all the while of the open relaxed throat. The transition from the one vowel to the other should be gradual and
   continuous with no break in the flow of tone.

6. Apply the same technique to the three vowels [u], [o], and
   [ɑ], beginning with [u], changing to [o], and then to [ɑ]. Carry
   the open feeling of the [u] through the [o] and over into the
   [ɑ].

Mouth Opening and Relaxation of the Jaw

1. Relax the jaw, allowing the mouth to fall open. To facilitate
   this process, pull down on the jaw with the thumb and fingers
   as if stroking a beard.

2. Keeping the jaw relaxed and passive, move it around by
   grasping it with the thumb and fingers. Guard against any
   tendency for the jaw to resist these movements.

3. Repeat *ouch* a number of times, opening the mouth wide.

4. Pronounce the following words, exaggerating the mouth
   opening for the initial vowels: *open, almond, army, oddly,
   habit, action, offer, outfit, alder, oxen.*

5. Repeat rapidly the two vowels [u] and [ɑ], merging them
   together until a [w] is clearly distinguishable between them.
   Exaggerate the lip action as well as the jaw opening. Repeat
   a number of times.

6. Repeat the vowels [i], [ɑ], and [u], exaggerating the lip and
   jaw action for each—lips wide for [i], mouth open for [ɑ],
   lips pursed and rounded for [u].

7. Pronounce the following sentences and selections clearly, opening the mouth wide and forming the vowel tones very carefully:

   a. Where are you going and what do you wish?
   b. Humpty Dumpty sat on a wall.
   c. Round and round flew each sweet sound.
   d. April showers bring May flowers.
   e. He laughs best who laughs last.
   f. Bob's watch stopped when it fell into the water.
   g. Around the rough and rugged rock the ragged rascal ran.

   h. All in a hot and copper sky,
      The bloody Sun at noon,
      Right up above the mast did stand,
      No bigger than the Moon.

Distinguishing Between Nasal and Oral Resonance

1. As in a previous exercise, with a small mirror study the action of the soft palate under a number of different conditions. Observe its action in yawning, its relaxation in nasal breathing, and its activity in the production of the vowel [ɑ]. Notice carefully how the soft palate operates, in conjunction with the pharyngeal wall and lateral structures, to close off and to adjust the opening into the posterior nasal chambers.

2. Using the mirror once more, allow the velum to remain relaxed as in nasal breathing while the vowel [ɑ] is produced. Observe the distinctly nasal quality of the sound and with the fingers held lightly against the nostrils, notice the considerable amount of nasal resonance as evidenced by the easily felt vibrations. Now reverse the process; with the velum held high, as for the yawn, again produce [ɑ]. Notice the distinctly altered quality of this sound and the relative absence of nasal vibrations. If this exercise has been performed correctly, this second [ɑ] is a good example of an oral vowel and it possesses a quality that should be the dominant characteristic of all of the vowel sounds.

3. Alternate the sounds [ŋ] and [ɑ] a number of times. Observe carefully the difference in resonance between the two and feel the difference in the position of the velum. Strive to make the [ŋ] a strong nasal sound, but the [ɑ] should come out of the mouth.

4. Pronounce the following pairs of sounds, sustaining the vowel tones for a short time. There should be no perceptible difference between the quality of the vowel following the nasal consonant and the quality of the vowel following the oral consonant. Practice this drill until the vowels in each pair sound exactly the same.

[bo]–[mo]	[do]–[no]	[go]–[ŋo]
[bu]–[mu]	[du]–[nu]	[gu]–[ŋu]
[bɑ]–[mɑ]	[dɑ]–[nɑ]	[gɑ]–[ŋɑ]
[be]–[me]	[de]–[ne]	[ge]–[ŋe]

Development of Oral Resonance, Reduction of Nasality

1. The lips play a very important part in shaping the tone to form the vowel sounds. Study the shape and position of the lips in the production of the vowels [u], [ɔ], [ɑ], [æ], and [i].

2. Repeat the phrase, *we are, too*, a number of times, noticing the position of the lips in the careful formation of the three different vowels. Repeat it rapidly as a drill, exaggerating the action of the lips.

3. Repeat [ho] a number of times on a monotone, prolonging the vowel. Notice that [o] is a round vowel; observe carefully the rounded position of the lips. Project the tone out of the mouth, keeping an open throat and avoiding excess nasal resonance.

4. For achieving so-called 'frontal placement,' sing the vowels [i]—[ɑ] a number of times, carefully merging the first into the second. Keep the tone out of the nose and strive to concentrate it in the front of the mouth.

5. Experiment with some negative practice on the following sentences, which contain no nasal sounds. First place a feather or fluff of cotton on a card, as explained earlier in this

chapter, and hold it under your nostrils as you pronounce each of the following sentences. First read the sentence exaggerating nasal emission to the point that the feather or cotton is blown off with each consonant, especially the plosives, such as *p, b, t,* et cetera. Then repeat the sentence, carefully controlling each sound so that the feather is not disturbed and all of the sound comes out the mouth. Note carefully the *feel* of the sounds as they are first produced nasally and then orally through the mouth. Listen to the difference in the way they sound too.

   a. This is the house that Jack built.
   b. This is a beautiful day.
   c. That is a pretty picture.
   d. Jack and Jill walked up the hill.
   e. Peter Piper picked a peck of pickled peppers.

6. The following sentences and selections also contain no nasal sounds. Check carefully to guard against excessive nasal resonance on any of the sounds, and watch especially for any evidence of nasal emission on the consonants. Try the feather on the card technique again if there is any doubt. Open your mouth well and work for full oral resonance.

   a. Who are you? (Repeat, varying the emphasis from word to word)
   b. How are you? (Repeat, as above)
   c. How do you do? (Repeat as above)
   e. We are all very well.
   f. Heigh ho! heigh ho! it's off to work we go.
   g. The little dog barked at the big frog.
   h. Peter decided to stay at the park all day.
   i. Ted was the best kicker of all the squad.

   j. Hard by the shores of far Brazil,
      We rode for pleasure, years ago;
   Led forward ever by the will
      To brave each risk, to fight each foe.

k. The little boy sat at the table with the little girl. They refused to say a word as they ate their breakfast. I asked why they were so quiet. They replied that they were sad because their dog had died. I assured these little tots that I would buy a bigger, prettier dog at the store. I hoped this offer would cause the sparkle to creep back to their eyes, but it failed utterly because I could hardly replace the pet that they had loved.

7. Read the following selections, rounding out the vowel tones very carefully with a relaxed and open throat. Pay careful attention to lip action to insure ample oral resonance. Be careful to avoid nasality on all of the vowel sounds and, again, guard against nasal emission on the consonants.

a. A kitten with a black nose
   Will sleep all the day;
   A kitten with a white nose
   Is always glad to play;
   A kitten with a yellow nose
   Will come out when you call;
   But a kitten with a gray nose
   I like best of all.

b. Tick, tock, tick, tock,
   Merrily sings the clock;
   It's time for work,
   It's time for play,
   So it sings throughout the day.
   Tick, tock, tick, tock,
   Merrily sings the clock.

c. A Snow Man stands in the moonlight gold
   Smoking his pipe serenely,
   For what cares he that the night is cold,
   Though his coat is thin and his hat is old
   And the blustering winds blow keenly.

d. A tutor who tooted the flute
   Tried to tutor two tooters to toot;
   Said the two to the tooter,
   'Is it easier to toot or
   To tutor two tooters to toot?'

e. Peter, Peter, pumpkin eater,
   Had a wife and couldn't keep her;
   Put her in a pumpkin shell
   And there he kept her very well.

f. Hark! hark! the dogs do bark,
   The beggars have come to town;
   Some in rags, and some in tags,
   And some in velvet gowns.

g. Peas porridge hot! Peas porridge cold!
   Peas porridge in the pot nine days old!
   Some like it hot; some like it cold.
   Some like it in the pot nine days old.

h. If wisdom's ways you'd wisely seek,
   Five things observe with care:
   Of whom you speak, to whom you speak,
   And how, and when, and where.

i. Whisky Frisky hippity hop,
   Up he goes to the tree top!
   Whirly Twirly, round and round,
   Down he scampers to the ground.

   Furly Curly, what a tail!
   Tall as a feather, broad as a sail!
   Where's his supper? In the shell.
   Snappy, cracky—out it fell.

References

Anderson, Virgil A., *Training the Speaking Voice*, Oxford University Press, New York, 2nd ed., 1961, pp. 116–22, 128–44, 288–98.

Greene, Margaret C. L., *The Voice and Its Disorders*, Lippincott, Philadelphia, 2nd ed., 1964, Chap. 12.

Luchsinger, Richard, and Godfrey E. Arnold, *Voice-Speech-Language*, Wadsworth, Belmont, Calif., 1965, pp. 658–89.

Massengill, Raymond, *Hypernasality*, Charles C. Thomas, Springfield, Ill., 1972.

Morley, Muriel E., *Cleft Palate and Speech*, Williams and Wilkins, Baltimore, 7th ed., 1970.

Van Riper, Charles, *Speech Correction*, Prentice-Hall, Englewood Cliffs, N. J., 4th ed., 1963, Chap. 13.

———— and John V. Irwin, *Voice and Articulation*, Prentice-Hall, Englewood Cliffs, N. J., 1958, pp. 239–51; 388–95.

Wicka, Donna K., and Mervyn Falk, *Advice to Parents of a Cleft Palate Child*, Charles C. Thomas, Springfield, Ill., 1970.

(See also References following Chapter VIII.)

VIII

Voice Disorders

The teacher has good reason to be concerned about the voices of her pupils, especially if they attract attention because they differ noticeably in quality, pitch, or other characteristics from the voices of other children of like age and sex. Aside from the vital role which the voice itself plays in oral communication, it has been found to be one of the most sensitive barometers of an individual's general health and well-being, both physical and emotional. While a pleasant, properly used voice can do much to enhance a person's effectiveness, a distracting or unpleasant characteristic is not only a social liability but may also be a symptom of a physical or personality disorder that could be serious.

Fortunately, voice disorders are considerably less prevalent than defects of articulation among school children, although recent surveys provide startling evidence that there are far more children with hoarse or otherwise abnormal voices than has ever been suspected previously.[1] Results of special surveys and voice

1. Robert A. Baynes, 'An Incidence Study of Chronic Hoarseness Among Children,' *Journal of Speech and Hearing Disorders*, May 1966, pp. 172–76.

clinics recently conducted in several areas of the country indicate an incidence of voice problems among elementary school children ranging from 0.5 per cent to over 7 per cent of the school populations covered, which in one instance amounted to almost 6000 children.[2] In this latter study the incidence was found to be 2.6 per cent of the school population.

These percentages are alarmingly high, especially in view of some of the additional findings from these clinics, conducted by laryngologists assisted by speech therapists and classroom teachers. As an example, the medical examination of the children, referred originally by the classroom teachers primarily because of chronic hoarseness, revealed medically significant conditions in approximately 70 per cent of those examined, and other observable structural deviations in an additional 20 per cent. In other words, in only one child out of ten was there no observable organic cause found for the hoarseness.

Vocal nodules, especially among the boys, and a more generalized inflammation or thickening of the vocal folds were the most frequent conditions discovered, but examples of more serious, though less common, disorders were also found, including polyps, partial paralysis of the vocal folds, papilloma, and keratosis. Several of the children were in immediate need of medical attention. One additional finding was also of interest—the studies revealed that often there was not a close relationship between the degree of hoarseness and the seriousness or extent of the observed organic condition causing it. In several instances the child with the milder voice symptom was found to have the more serious organic problem.

Several observations seemed warranted in regard to the findings just cited: (1) None of these children was obviously sick—only hoarse. The point here is that chronic hoarseness is not to be treated lightly, since it is likely to indicate some organic condition in the larynx that warrants attention. Hence if the child

2. Jane Taylor Goraj, 'E. N. T. Clinics for Voice Disorders in Los Altos School District,' *The Voice*, May 1965, pp. 23–26.

is hoarse for any extended period, as for example four to six weeks, a medical examination should be strongly recommended. (2) A look at typical case loads of public school speech clinicians over the country indicates that apparently only about one child in ten with a voice problem is receiving any attention, assuming an incidence of approximately 2 per cent of the elementary school population, as the results of the voice clinics indicate. For the most part, then, this child's problem is being ignored. (3) If we assume that it is one of the teacher's responsibilities to be sensitive to signs of health problems in her pupils, then she cannot afford to be oblivious to hoarseness as a likely significant symptom of disease or organic abnormality.

(4) A large proportion of the voice problems found among school-age children are traceable to voice strain and vocal abuse. Such conditions begin as functional over-use or misuse of the voice and later develop into organic changes in the larynx, such as nodules, thickening of the vocal folds, or roughened edges. (5) While, as we have seen, the vast majority of children exhibiting hoarseness have some physiological or structural condition causing it, there are also other kinds of voice disorders, many of which have no observable organic basis. The only safe procedure, however, is to have an examination by a laryngologist of every child whose voice is sufficiently deviant in pitch, quality, or other characteristics as to cause concern on the part of the parent, teacher, or speech clinician.

All of this is not meant to imply that the classroom teacher should become an expert in voice or attempt serious retraining of an individual with a marked vocal disturbance. It is important, however, that the teacher and the parent become familiar with causes and symptoms of the more common types of voice problems found among children of school age. In the first place, through the application of a few rules of good voice and speech hygiene, the teacher may be able to prevent the child from developing more serious problems later. Secondly, it is important that she be able to recognize a voice problem when she hears it and that she know where to turn for help with those children who need medical attention or other specialized treatment beyond her capacity to give.

Types of Vocal Disorders

In Chapter II defects of voice were classified under three types: (1) intensity, (2) pitch, and (3) quality. Since the various symptoms that relate to each of these types were described and discussed in some detail in that chapter, only a brief summary will be included here.

Disorders of Intensity and Pitch

As was pointed out earlier, disorders of intensity and pitch are more or less readily identifiable. A voice is lacking in proper intensity, for example, if it is so weak that it cannot be heard comfortably by the person to whom the speech is addressed. Likewise, the pitch is too high or too low if it differs significantly from what is considered normal for the age and sex of the individual speaking. It is monotonous if it lacks the variation in pitch ordinarily found in the normal speaking voice. Pitch levels can easily be identified with the aid of a musical instrument, and a simple formula, to be explained later in this chapter, will disclose whether the habitual level which an individual is using is the one best suited to his voice.

Disorders of Quality

It is when we come to disorders of vocal quality that we are likely to encounter symptoms very difficult to identify, classify, and diagnose. Here, as was pointed out in Chapter II, there are no standards that can be used as points of reference and, for the average teacher at least, no objective methods for checking the reliability of what the ear hears, or thinks it hears. Moreover, there is no precise terminology to describe what is heard and can be identified. Therefore, the teacher or speech clinician would probably be well advised to confine herself to the quality defects that can be most reliably identified and explained. There are probably only four general types found among children that come within these qualifications: breathiness, hoarseness, stridency, and falsetto, excluding, of course, nasality, which, strictly speaking, is not a vocal disorder.

1. *Breathiness* An individual's voice will have a breathy, aspirate quality if for any reason more breath is allowed to escape between the vocal folds than is needed to maintain them in vibration at the intensity level being used. This undesirable quality is usually not difficult to identify. Many factors can interfere with the proper alignment of the vocal folds and hence can contribute to this quality disorder, including organic malformation of the folds as well as muscular imbalance and poor vocal habits.

2. *Hoarseness* A voice will exhibit hoarseness if for any reason the free and even vibration of the vocal folds is interfered with. This condition, as we have seen, is almost always traceable to some abnormality in the structure or condition of the vocal folds, such as swelling of the tissues from laryngitis, or to interference with the proper functioning of the larynx, often by surrounding structures. Therefore, in all cases of prolonged, recurring, or unexplainable hoarseness, a physician should be consulted before any vocal therapy or speech training is attempted.

3. *Stridency* This sharp, metallic quality indicates strain and tension, which in all likelihood extend to the larynx itself, as well as to the resonators of the throat and mouth. The pitch of the voice is likely to be higher than normal and the intensity may also be increased—both of which indicate muscular tension. There is a greater probability that stridency may be merely functional, resulting from poor vocal habits, than there is in the case of either breathiness or hoarseness.

4. *Falsetto* This is perhaps more a disorder of pitch than of quality, although falsetto is also characterized, in addition to the

high pitch, by a sort of hollow, thin quality. Almost anyone, especially a male, can produce a falsetto tone by using his vocal mechanism in a certain special way which, unfortunately, may become habitual with certain individuals under certain conditions to be discussed in more detail later under the heading of juvenile voice. This disorder is more likely to have a psychological basis than a physical or structural one.

The categories of symptoms just described are not mutually exclusive ones. A defect primarily of quality, for example, may involve pitch and intensity as well, as was remarked in the case of stridency. Hoarseness is likely to be identified with lower than normal pitch, while falsetto involves a high pitch. It is well, in making a diagnosis, to attempt to break down what is heard into components of intensity, pitch, and quality, to the extent that this is possible, in order to arrive at an accurate appraisal of the problem rather than a vague, general impression of unpleasantness or inadequacy.

Causes of Vocal Disorders

It is important for the teacher to be aware of the probable causes of vocal disabilities, for a number of reasons. In the first place, it is essential to discover the cause so that it can be removed, if that is possible, as a preliminary step to further correction of the difficulty. Also it is important to know which causes are preventable, so they can be removed or alleviated before any real damage is done. The teacher, in co-operation with the parent, can often do a great service to the child in this way. The principal causes of voice disorders can be grouped under the categories that follow.

Structural and Physiological Causes

There are many conditions affecting the structure of the larynx itself that render it incapable of producing a normal vocal tone or otherwise seriously interfere with its proper functioning. For example, the swelling of the vocal folds and the increased secretion of mucus resulting from laryngitis produce a change of quality we identify as hoarseness. Laryngitis may be caused by an infection in the throat or other areas of the respiratory tract, as in the case of the common cold, or it may result from allergic inflammation of the respiratory tract tissues. Many of the conditions affecting the nasal passages mentioned in the preceding chapter produce a discharge that often drops down on the vocal folds, causing a secondary inflammation in the larynx. Temporary, or acute, laryngitis may be induced by an episode of strenuous vocalizing, as when a person 'yells himself hoarse.'

Many growths and structural changes of a non-malignant nature, having such names as polyps, cysts, hyperkeratosis, and papilloma, found in children are not too well understood as to causation, although it is suspected that a virus may be involved in some of them. Such more common conditions as nodules and vocal fold thickening are more or less directly traceable to voice strain and abuse discussed in more detail in the following section. Many types of structural defects are apparently congenital, such as vocal folds with irregular edges, folds that are poorly matched, muscular imbalances that prevent the folds from lining up properly, and malformed epiglottis.

While the most common vocal symptoms of structural or physiological conditions are hoarseness and breathiness, only a properly conducted laryngeal examination can determine the exact nature of the condition present. Such an examination should be obtained in all cases where these symptoms are present to any marked degree, especially if they are of long standing, and in all other cases where there is any reason to suspect that some organic cause may be present.

The voice is so closely related to general health and wellbeing that almost any condition that has an adverse effect on the functioning of the body as a whole may also be reflected in some vocal deviation. Many forms of paralysis fall into this category. The paralysis may arise from a central lesion in the nervous system, as in the case of cerebral palsy, or it may be more localized, as when there is some injury to the nerves that supply the larynx itself. Except in the highly localized cases, there will usually be motor symptoms involving activities of a more wide-spread nature than voice and speech, for example, paralysis of the arms or legs, loss of control in co-ordinated movements, or loss of balance in walking. A physical examination should be recommended in all such cases or when there is any reason to suspect from the history that some form of neurological disability may be present.

General health and vitality bear a close relationship to voice pitch and quality, the voice tending to become weak, thin, and either too high or too low in pitch in those cases where health is poor or general vitality is low. The pale, thin, anemic-looking child with a voice to match should be given a physical examination to determine the status of his general health. Such symptoms can be brought on by anemia, improper diet, endocrine imbalance, and many similar ailments requiring proper medical attention to diagnose and treat. Likewise, a high-pitched voice with a tense strained quality when associated with restlessness, hyperactivity, and nervous tension should make the teacher suspect that there may be some basic physiological explanation. It is futile and unwise to give voice and speech training in these cases where medical attention is needed instead. In general, it should be remembered that a healthy body is needed to produce a healthy voice.

Vocal Strain and Abuse as Causes

There is little doubt that the most important single cause of voice problems among children is strain and over-use of the voice. Loud talking, yelling, and even screaming are prolonged and common accompaniments of almost any type of group activity among children, especially where action or competition is involved. The situation can become especially traumatic to the voice where organized groups compete as in a school athletic event or Little League baseball. For the average child such vocal strain appears to have no harmful or lasting effects on his voice, save perhaps for some temporary hoarseness following an especially stimulating occasion. For some children, however—and this is likely to be more true of boys than of girls—the hoarseness does not clear up, and if the strenuous vocal activity continues over a period of time certain structural changes may take place in the larynx. These changes may show up as little knobs or corns called nodules on the edges of the vocal folds where they rub together during vibration. Or the folds may become thickened or rough along the edges.

It is difficult to explain why Johnnie develops nodules, while Billie across the street talks more incessantly and yells even louder with no apparent ill effects. For some reason, often not at all clear, Johnnie's vocal organs just 'can't take it.' Perhaps some allergy or structural weakness renders his larynx more susceptible to damage from strenuous use, or even from vocalization that would ordinarily be considered 'normal' for his age. Or it may be that a combination of factors, some of which are referred to in the following sections, are involved.

Psychological Factors as Causes
Not only is the voice a reflection of the physical health and well-being of the individual, but it is also closely related to his personality and mental health as well. Clinical experience indicates, for example, that an excessively high pitch and a thin, falsetto quality are often found in shy, inhibited, submissive individuals. Effeminate traits as well as feelings of inferiority also contribute to this ineffective, weak type of voice. Among children especially, shyness and lack of social adequacy are often reflected in a voice so weak in intensity that it is quite ineffective in many communicative situations.

On the other hand, the blustering aggressive individual may talk too loudly with a raucous, gruff tone that is unpleasant. Here the voice may be merely a part of a general mechanism of maladjustment; for example, it may be the chief medium through which aggression is being expressed. Clinical experience further indicates that many of the same factors that are believed to contribute to the development of stuttering in the child can also set the stage for the appearance of voice problems. Various factors in the environment, especially at home, that tend to keep the child anxious, under tension, or 'high-strung' appear with significant frequency in the backgrounds of children who develop voice disorders. As is true of adults also, the vocal mechanism is placed under added strain when talking is done under conditions of stress and tension. It is enough to say that little permanent or otherwise satisfactory progress can be made with the voice in instances where there is evidence of psychological causal factors unless something is done to relieve these at the same time. On the other hand, speech training itself may constitute the most effective approach to psychotherapy in some of these cases, as will be pointed out in Chapter ix. In any event, both voice and personality must be taken into account.

Developmental Causes
The voice of the adolescent, especially the boy, undergoes a marked change in pitch and quality as he passes through the period known as puberty. The vocal symptoms are merely a part of his general physiological development at this time, and the voice change is usually made with little difficulty. If, during this period, however, certain psychological or social factors are unfavorable, or if any condition interferes with the normal sexual development of the individual, a vocal defect known as juvenile voice may result. This problem will be discussed in more detail in a later section of this chapter.

Disorders of Hearing as Causes
The close relation between hearing and speech has already been pointed out in previous chapters. In certain types of hearing loss the voice is likely to be louder than normal, while in other types it may be excessively weak. Lacking the constant auditory awareness that good hearing provides, the individual may develop a disagreeable vocal quality without being aware of it. A certain type of hearing deficiency known as tone deafness may give rise to a vocal monotone if the condition is at all severe. Exaggerated

or bizarre pitch changes in the voice may also be an indication of a hearing disability. The relationship of hearing to speech, and additional speech symptoms of a hearing loss will be discussed at greater length in Chapter XI.

Miscellaneous Causes

A deviant voice may well result from unfortunate imitation of poor speech models. Characteristic vocal qualities tend to run in families, and, to some extent, in communities and even larger localities. The process of imitation may be more indirect, however, as when tense, nervous mannerisms influence others in the environment to a similar pattern of behavior, resulting in a characteristic strident quality of voice. Vocal strain and abuse are likely to result in poor quality and pitch characteristics, which may culminate in permanent damage to the voice if allowed to continue over a period of time.

Need for Medical Diagnosis

Proper diagnosis is of paramount importance when dealing with vocal disorders for reasons that have already been mentioned. In those instances where pathology is present, the remedy involves medical procedures rather than speech or voice training. Indeed, vocal training may be the very thing that should be avoided; in laryngitis, for example, complete vocal rest, rather than exercise, is indicated. Any use of the voice merely aggravates the basic condition. The vocal symptoms of hoarseness and breathiness, therefore, are especially important danger signals that call for an examination by a throat specialist before any other procedures are undertaken. A complete physical examination should be recommended if frequent colds, excessive fatigue, or similar symptoms suggest that the problem may be one involving the general health of the child. Voice training should be undertaken only in those cases where it is clear that it will do no harm and where adequate attention has already been given to such remediable ailments as may have been discovered.

Juvenile Voice

One important type of vocal problem, sometimes referred to as juvenile voice, which the teacher in the upper grades may encounter might be described as a developmental hazard because it arises from the changes which the laryngeal structure undergoes at the time of puberty. Such changes, particularly in the male, are quite profound because they involve a radical alteration in the size and structure of the larynx in general and the vocal folds in particular. At this time the framework of the larynx enlarges and the vocal folds become longer and heavier. Such changes present a real problem, especially to the male, because they necessitate a completely new vocal technique as well as new auditory concepts of pitch, quality, and loudness. The pitch, during this so-called 'change of voice,' normally falls approximately an octave, the quality becomes deeper and richer, and the voice 'fills out' and increases in force. In the girl the changes in pitch and quality are less radical, the voice dropping only two or three steps in pitch but taking on a more mature quality.

Normally the voice change at puberty is negotiated without incident, save for a few embarrassing breaks in pitch now and then and perhaps a short period of mild self-consciousness. There will be exceptions to this norm, however, and it is these exceptions that furnish the teacher with the troublesome cases of juvenile voice. Two sources of possible vocal difficulty confront the boy who is passing through this phase of maturation: (1) He must learn to use a changed vocal mechanism, a process which necessitates the development of new kinesthetic and auditory impressions and different motor patterns. It is comparable to the situation that would confront an individual who, after playing the violin for a number of years, suddenly had a viola thrust into his hands. The two instruments are similar except that the viola is larger and hence requires different bowing and fingering. It is to be expected that the violin player would, at first, play out of tune and elicit strange sounds from the viola until he had accustomed himself to the new instrument and learned how to play it properly. In a similar way, the adolescent boy must learn to manage a new and enlarged vocal mechanism.

(2) The pubescent boy also has a psychological problem to deal with. The new voice does not feel right and it does not sound right to him, and he finds it a source of embarrassment. His first reaction is to attempt to maintain the old, pre-adolescent pitch and quality because it sounds and feels natural and comfortable and because, at first at least, it does not attract attention to itself. For a while this is relatively easy to do but as the physical mechanism continues to mature, it becomes increasingly difficult for the boy to maintain the old pitch and quality. Finally, the only way he can do it successfully is to adopt a falsetto quality, a type of voice characterized by a high pitch and a thin, husky, hollow, faraway quality. This he may continue to use indefinitely until and unless he finds someone to help him with his vocal problem. Fortunately, such help is not too difficult to give, and the majority of these cases respond to assistance with gratifying, and astonishing, results.

Diagnosis of Juvenile Voice

How can one tell, for example, whether a boy of sixteen or seventeen years of age, whose voice sounds unnaturally high and thin, is a case of juvenile voice or merely a 'budding' tenor with a normally high pitch? In the first place, the quality should be carefully observed. A natural tenor voice, although it is high in pitch, has a true quality about it and, aside from the high pitch, should be relatively free from the common types of vocal defects described earlier in this chapter. The juvenile voice, on the other hand, will sound rough, husky, and thin—qualities very difficult to describe with words, but not difficult to recognize, once they have been heard and identified.

There are other diagnostic aids that can also be used. Have the boy laugh; it has been found that these individuals will sometimes laugh in the normal low register. Coughing or clearing the throat may reveal a pitch considerably lower than he is using for speech. Have him sing down the musical scale beginning with middle C or whatever tone is easiest for him. It may be that on sung tones he can go right on down into the lower range, even though he does not use it for speaking. Boys have been known to have two voices—the old pre-adolescent falsetto voice which they considered the 'normal' one to be used for all speaking purposes, and the lower 'trick' voice, really their normal voice, which was used only for singing or demonstrating curious vocal effects for the amusement of friends. In the usual case of juvenile voice, however, there is only the high, falsetto quality, and the boy is unaware that he can produce any other type of voice, and usually he cannot without some assistance and training.

Although we are prone to suspect arrested sexual development in some of these cases that might be related to malfunctioning of the endocrine glands, especially the gonads or the pituitary, evidence of such has been found in surprisingly few instances, perhaps partly because in most cases there has not been a specific or thorough search for such factors. In a significant number of cases, however, there are observable evidences of some maladjustment in the form of introvertive tendencies, effeminate characteristics, attitudes of inferiority, excessive shyness, or unsocial forms of behavior. Whether these may have resulted from the effects of the abnormal voice or whether they may have functioned as causal factors is not always clear or easy to determine. In any case, some attention may need to be given to the personality if satisfactory or lasting results are to be gained from the vocal therapy.

Therapy for Juvenile Voice

The key to therapy in these cases is ear training, the first step of which is to make a recording of the voice and let the individual hear himself. If this recording is properly handled, it may be all that is needed to motivate the boy to make the change to his new voice without delay. One such fifteen-year-old, whose pre-adolescent voice had persisted four or five months beyond the time when it should have changed, listened to his recording and then remarked with concern and disdain, 'Gee, that sounds like a girl!' After fifteen minutes of work on scales, singing several tones down into the lower range and establishing a pitch approximately an octave lower than the voice that sounded 'like a girl,' a second recording was made of the new voice, which both pleased and startled the young fellow. And that was the end of his problem; he never reverted to the high, boyish quality again. Unfortunately, not all cases can be dealt with as quickly and easily as this one was, often because they are of longer standing and may have become complicated by feelings of self-consciousness and embarrassment.

After the voice has been recorded, it may be necessary to orient the boy by comparing his recording with another recording of a male voice of normal pitch and quality. This 'reference' recording becomes especially important where the clinician or teacher helping the boy is a woman. Since the basic pitch of her voice will be about an octave above that of the average male speaker, she will not be able to furnish a very useful model for the young man to follow. If it is necessary to work the pitch down through successive steps or stages, frequent interim recordings will not only provide motivation but will furnish a basis of comparison and an indication of progress for both pupil and teacher. The auditory impressions should be supplemented and reinforced by kinesthetic impressions as well; the boy must not only learn what his voice sounds like on the lower pitch levels, but he must also learn what it feels like when he is producing the lower tone. At first both of these sensory impressions will seem very strange to the boy as he hears and 'feels' his new voice. These reactions must be discounted in the beginning of therapy and later dispelled altogether through practice and use of the new voice.

There are several techniques or devices that often prove useful in assisting the boy to discover his normal voice. One device that may help is to have the young man 'count down' beginning with 'one' on a very high pitch and lowering the pitch with each count down to 'ten.' The count should be vigorous, and the vocal and auditory aspects of the exercise can be reinforced by an imitation of the teacher whose hand is held very high on 'one' and then lowered dramatically with each successive count. If this exercise is successful, the young man will count right on down into his lower natural range without realizing what is happening. The teacher, however, should be listening for the break or shift that usually occurs when the boy breaks through into his normal voice from the higher falsetto.

Another device that can be tried is to have the boy clear his throat or sigh audibly. If these are done on a lower pitch, as they may well be, the sound produced by the low-pitched sigh can be held and gradually merged into a vowel sound—[ɑ] or [o]. It is only a step from this to the production of real words at the same pitch level—*one, two, three,* et cetera—beginning from the sigh.

A more reliable method is to use the sung vowel in conjunction with the musical scale. If the teacher possesses a fairly good sense of pitch, perhaps she will need only a pitch pipe to establish appropriate pitch levels from which to work. In most cases, however, some musical instrument that will provide the complete scale, such as a piano, will be found very helpful, if not indispensable. Begin with a tone that is easy for the pupil, perhaps in the neighborhood of middle C, and have him sustain some vowel sound, such as [ɑ] or [o]. Then gradually work down the scale on sung vowel tones until the quality begins to sound guttural and forced; then go back up the scales. With repeated trials and some amount of practice, the range can gradually be extended lower and lower until a point is reached that seems to represent the lower limits of his natural range. From this point on the scale his optimum pitch can be calculated, as will be described shortly.

How can one tell when the proper new pitch level has been attained? A rule-of-thumb is to remember that the average pitch level of men's voices is not far from low C, one octave below middle C. The most likely pitch level of the pre-adolescent boy's voice is near middle C; therefore, when it changes, it will need to fall approximately one octave in pitch. However, it is not just the drop in pitch that provides evidence of a real shift into the normal 'register'; there will be a change in quality as well if the young man has been successful. The 'new voice' may sound rough and uncertain at first but it will have a solid, 'natural' quality, quite different from the thin, far-away 'false' quality of the juvenile voice. After the lower tones have been explored and experimented with until the teacher is satisfied that the boy is vocalizing as low as he can go with comfort, the more reliable technique of the 'pitch profile,' explained in the following section of this chapter, should be used to establish the most likely optimum pitch in each individual case. This will vary somewhat from individual to individual, depending on the natural range of his voice.

Carry-over into speaking should be encouraged as each new gain is made in lowered pitch and improved quality. This can be done, for example, by selecting an arbitrary pitch level and having the individual begin counting in a monotone. This monotone is gradually varied until the natural inflections of speech have been introduced, without, however, any change in the basic general level of the pitch, which represents an average, more or less, from which the voice varies up and down as natural inflections and pitch changes become a part of conversational speaking. From counting, the pupil can progress to the speaking of phrases and sentences, such as 'How are you?' 'Where are you going?' or 'I think I'll go downtown.' When a basic pitch level has been quite well established through such exercises, the pupil can progress to the reading of prose and finally to the carry-over into natural conversation, perhaps at first on a selective basis, using the 'new voice' only at home, then with a few close friends, and finally at all times as self-consciousness wears off. Once the most natural and desirable optimum pitch has been found and established, results are gratifyingly permanent.

Determining the Basic Pitch

The technique known as the 'pitch profile' is useful in determining the basic speaking level, or key, that is best for each individual voice, a level also referred to as the optimum pitch. Have the individual sing down the scale, using a sustained [ɑ] or [o], beginning with a tone that is easy for him, until he reaches the lowest note that he can sing comfortably and with some degree of true quality. This can be accepted as the lowest limit of his singing range. Then have him sing up the scale, beginning with this lowest tone, until he reaches a point some three or four full steps above this lower limit. This should be close to his optimum pitch, the level at which each voice is believed to perform the best with minimum effort and maximum effectiveness. This level should then be cultivated as an average basic pitch for speaking purposes, in the manner suggested in the preceding paragraphs.

Two or three further observations should be made regarding the method just described. In the first place, it is not an absolute process, and the results obtained are therefore only approximate. Nevertheless, it is one of the best methods we have of estimating the preferred natural pitch level of a voice. Secondly, it should be taken into account that the average speaking level is not in the middle of an individual's total range, as the layman is likely to believe, but nearer the middle of his lowest octave. This means that in developing the expressive qualities of the voice, particularly variations of pitch, there are greater possibilities among the upward inflections and pitch patterns than among the lower, since the individual is closer to the lower limits of his range to begin with.

Finally, the pitch-profile technique is probably more applicable to the post-adolescent voice than to the voice of the child. As was pointed out previously, the pitch change that takes place at puberty, especially in the case of boys, is so complete that the pitch of the pre-adolescent voice, and to some extent its quality as well, have little predictive value in determining what the adult voice will be like. It is doubtful, therefore, whether any particular concern need be felt about the mere pitch of the child's voice, provided there is no indication of pathology or structural abnormalities, and also provided there is no imminent danger of permanent injury to the vocal mechanism as a result of the way it is being used.

Helping the Child Keep a Healthy Voice

Since the prevention of disorders is more important than their cure, and often much easier, perhaps it is in the field of vocal hygiene that the teacher can make her greatest contribution to the developing voices of her pupils. The vocal mechanism of the child is apparently quite rugged but also decidedly unstable with respect especially to pitch and quality changes. In any case, it is well established that the child's voice cannot safely be taken for granted. His chief vocal organ, his larynx, is much like any other organ in his body—his heart, his liver, or his eyes. It can become diseased or it can be harmed by strain or misuse, and serious damage can and does result from certain unwise vocal practices during childhood and adolescence. It is well, therefore, for the teacher and the parent to be aware of these dangers so that they can be avoided or their effects minimized.

The following suggestions for keeping the child's voice strong and healthy, some of which have already been implied under causes of voice problems, will be found helpful:

1. Since it is generally agreed that misuse of the voice is the most common cause of voice problems in children, it is well to be aware of some of the forms this abuse can take:

a. Yelling and excessively loud talking do not seem to harm most children, and a certain amount of yelling appears 'normal' in children at certain ages. However, if this seems to have a harmful effect on an individual child's voice, at least part of his leisure time should be spent in more quiet activities, such as model building, reading, playing certain games, listening to phonograph records, or watching television.

b. Such 'unnatural' uses of the voice as imitating motor boats, airplanes, or machine guns seem to be found with significant frequency among children who develop voice problems. Such activities place an unusual strain on the voice and may result in hoarseness.

c. Cheer leading, singing, 'rooting' at athletic contests, and taking part in public performances can produce strain that may be harmful to the voice and should be carefully watched and supervised. Cheer leading and 'rooting' can be especially hazardous, since they take place under conditions of excitement and strain. If the child becomes hoarse as a result of such activities, this is a sign that he has strained his voice. If the hoarseness persists, it should never be ignored; the child should be examined by a laryngologist, and his advice followed.

d. All vocal activities, including talking, must be reduced to a bare minimum, or discontinued altogether, if the child has a sore throat, or is already hoarse from a cold or excessive use of his voice. Such a child should be excused from singing, reciting orally, or participating in any public activities where loud or strenuous use of the voice is involved.

e. Special precautions should be taken when children participate in dramatic activities, particularly when they are cast in roles for which they are vocally not suited. The wicked old witch, the menacing giant, and the tough Army sergeant are roles which may well strain the vocal powers of the girl or boy who takes his part seriously and attempts to be adequate and convincing. The teacher must be constantly alert for evidences of vocal strain and fatigue. Much the same precautions hold true for singing, as in a school chorus, for example. The child must not be forced beyond his natural range, either higher or lower than he finds it comfortable to sing. Such caution becomes especially necessary in the case of the boy approaching the change of voice at puberty, who may have been singing in the soprano range but whose voice may drop to a bass after the change. This natural change must not be interfered with.

f. Other precautions should also be exercised when the boy

is undergoing the voice-change, usually between the ages of thirteen and fifteen. The voice may sound uncertain during this period and may waver and crack, often resulting in self-consciousness on his part. Be patient and sympathetic with him and never laugh at or make fun of his squeaky voice. In fact, pay no attention to it, but treat him in a perfectly natural and unself-conscious manner. In no case should he be encouraged to maintain his high, little-boy voice in either singing or speaking. The likelihood is that within a few short months he will have negotiated the change successfully with no problems and no help needed.

2. Good physical health is essential to a sound, healthy voice. Following are some conditions that may contribute to, or result in, voice problems:

a. All upper respiratory infections or inflammation, such as a running nose, 'sinus trouble,' colds, sore throats, or bronchitis, especially if they occur often or have become chronic, pose a serious threat to the voice. If the child has repeated bouts of what seems to be a cold, or if such a condition fails to clear up promptly, the child should have a medical check-up to determine the cause.

b. Coughing, especially if severe or prolonged, places a great strain on the larynx, as does repeated clearing of the throat, which can also become a nervous habit.

c. Allergies pose a special threat to the voice, as was mentioned earlier in this chapter, because such tissue reactions tend to weaken the larynx, making it more susceptible to damage from vocal use or misuse. If the child shows signs of being allergic in any way or if it is suspected that his repeated 'colds' are not true infections, then it would be wise to have an examination by a physician specializing in allergies, or at least bring the problem to the attention of the child's pediatrician.

d. The tonsils may be at the seat of his trouble if the child has had attacks of tonsilitis. The infection may have spread to the larynx.

e. A generally weak and 'run-down' physical condition, of

whatever cause, can, and often does, contribute to a weakened vocal mechanism that tends to 'give out' if subjected to any strenuous use. If the child seems listless and excessively fatigued, a medical check-up is indicated.

3. Emotional and contributing environmental factors may be important in bringing on voice problems, as was mentioned earlier. Some of the factors and conditions that bear careful scrutiny in the environment of the child who develops a voice problem are listed in the following paragraphs:

a. Excessive sibling rivalry may be an important factor. If the child is trying to keep up or compete with an older brother or sister who may be more talented or more aggressive, he is always under a certain amount of tension.

b. Closely related to sibling rivalry, and often contributing to it, is parental favoritism. Although the parents may try to be fair and impartial, if one child *feels* that a brother or sister is more favored than he is, we have a prime source of tension and possible maladjustment.

c. A number of additional adverse environmental influences will be discussed in Chapter ix, which may operate to keep the child tense and anxious and thus contribute to voice strain. These include such undesirable practices as parental quarreling or arguing in the presence of the child, excessive criticism or nagging, unwise or unrealistic standards of behavior, unwise or inconsistent discipline practices, and a general atmosphere of nervousness and frantic uncertainty in and around the home.

d. Above all, the child should be treated as a developing personality—given proper respect, attention, and opportunity to be heard, but at the same time with certain standards and responsibilities expected of him commensurate with his age and abilities.

4. Why some children can yell, talk excessively, and otherwise strain their voices with no apparent ill effects, while other children engaging in similar activities and under seemingly similar circumstances develop vocal nodules or thickened vocal folds has never been fully explained. Children differ apparently

in the ruggedness of their vocal mechanisms, some being more susceptible to damage than others. In this way one may have to think of a certain child as having what might be called a 'weak' larynx, in the same way that some individuals have weak hearts, weak lungs, or poor digestion. Such individuals may lead happy, useful lives so long as they recognize their limitations and learn to live within them. Similarly individuals whose vocal mechanisms begin to show signs of trouble will need to curb their yelling and loud and excessive talking and take better care of their voices to avoid hoarseness, discomfort, and possible damage to the larynx. Vocally, they may have to learn to 'take it easy' perhaps all of their lives. If they do, they may never have any trouble.

References

Anderson, Virgil A., *Training the Speaking Voice*, Oxford University Press, New York, 2nd ed., 1961, Part 1.

Boone, Daniel, *Voice and Voice Therapy*, Prentice-Hall, Englewood Cliffs, N. J., 1971.

Eisenson, Jon, *The Improvement of Voice and Diction*, Macmillan, New York, 2nd ed., 1965.

Eisenson, Jon, and Mardel Ogilvie, *Speech Correction in the Schools*, Macmillan, New York, 2nd ed., 1963, Chap. 2.

Fairbanks, Grant, *Voice and Articulation Drillbook*, Harper and Row, New York, 2nd ed., 1960, Chaps. 10–15.

Fisher, Hilda B., *Improving Voice and Diction*, Houghton Mifflin, Boston, 1966.

Greene, Margaret C. L., *The Voice and Its Disorders*, Lippincott, Philadelphia, 2nd ed., 1964.

Hanley, T. D., and W. L. Thurman, *Developing Vocal Skills*, Holt, Rinehart and Winston, New York, 2nd ed., 1970.

Johnson, Wendell, et al., *Speech Handicapped School Children*, Harper and Row, New York, 3rd ed., 1967, Chap. 4.

Moore, G. Paul, *Organic Voice Disorders*, Prentice-Hall, Englewood Cliffs, N. J., 1971.

Ogilvie, Mardel, and Norma S. Rees, *Communication Skills: Voice and Pronunciation*, McGraw-Hill, New York, 1970.

Pronovost, W. L., and Louise Kingman, *The Teaching of Speaking and Listening*, Longmans, Green, New York, 1959, Chap. IV.

Travis, Lee E., ed., *Handbook of Speech Pathology and Audiology*, Appleton-Century-Crofts, New York, 1971, Part III.

Van Riper, Charles, *Speech Correction*, Prentice-Hall, Englewood Cliffs, N. J., 4th ed., 1963, Chaps. 7 and 8.

Wilson, D. Kenneth, *Voice Problems of Children*, Williams and Wilkins, Baltimore, 1971.

IX

The Child and His
Personal Problems

Students of speech pathology are generally agreed that there is a positive relationship between defective speech and the presence of socially unacceptable personality traits. Moreover, there is some evidence to indicate a direct relationship between the severity of the speech disorder and the seriousness of the accompanying personality maladjustment, although evidence on this point is far from conclusive. Trapp and Evans, however, did find a higher anxiety level among children with severe articulatory disorders than among normal-speaking children—a discrepancy that did not exist when normals were compared with children exhibiting only mild disorders.[1]

Solomon, also, in a study of 49 elementary school children with articulation disorders matched with a control group of normal-speaking children, found significantly greater tension and anxiety and poorer over-all adjustment among the children with articulatory problems, although this was not universally true of all members of the group. Solomon goes on to say, that

1. E. P. Trapp and Janet Evans, 'Functional Articulatory Defect and Performance on a Non-Verbal Task,' *Journal of Speech and Hearing Disorders*, May 1960, pp. 176–80.

speech problems of this type apparently are not isolated phenomena but part of a total adjustive pattern. It is suggested that an underlying stress may be common to the diverse symptomatology here presented and that infantile and non-assertive behavior could very well serve as anxiety-reducing devices to meet environmental pressure.[2]

Stuttering especially has been much studied for its personality concomitants among both adults and children. One of the most significant earlier investigations was conducted by a panel of four researchers headed by Dr. J. Louise Despert of the Cornell University Medical School. Fifty stuttering children, ranging in age from six to fifteen years, were chosen from the speech correction classes of the New York City public schools. Rather detailed studies were made of these children; case histories as well as such testing devices as a laterality (hand-preference) inventory, a battery of motor-skills tests, an intelligence test, and the Rorschach projective test of emotional and personality adjustment were used.

Despert reports, among other significant findings from this study, persistent feeding difficulties among these children, with frequent vomiting as a somatic symptom of frustration or maladjustment to a situation. There was a very high incidence of thumb sucking in the histories and, later, nail biting. She states further that the stuttering children exhibited more fears and anxiety symptoms, obsessive-compulsive tendencies, and hostility, and a greater incidence of such symptoms of instability and neurotic tendencies as emotional blocking and emotional immaturity, repression, and excessive timidity than would be expected of normal-speaking children. She adds that a majority of the children were believed to have made a poor social adjustment even before the speech handicap developed.[3]

A number of studies have also been made of the parents of

2. Arthur L. Solomon, 'Personality and Behavior Patterns of Children with Functional Defects of Articulation,' *Child Development*, 32, 1961, pp. 731–37.
3. J. Louise Despert, 'A Psychosomatic Study of Fifty Stuttering Children,' *American Journal of Orthopsychiatry*, 16, 1946, pp. 100–113.

speech handicapped children. The results of one such study involving parents of stuttering children were reported by Goldman and Shames. They found that these parents tended to set more unrealistic goals for their children generally and higher speech goals specifically than parents of non-stutterers.[4] The effect on the children could well be frustration and feelings of insecurity. Other studies tend to confirm these findings and add to unrealistic goals, such practices as over-protection, dominance, and disagreements between the parents with respect not only to goals, but also to discipline, standards of conduct, et cetera.

In addition to what objective evidence is available, the weight of logic, as well as clinical experience, would support the view that the child with a communication problem is less likely to be well adjusted than the child with normal speech. The limitations of space do not permit a full discussion of the relationship of speech to personality, but any serious study of the subject will disclose that the two are so interdependent that any serious or pronounced disturbance in the one is very likely to be reflected in the other.

This prevalence of emotional problems among certain classes of speech defectives, especially stutterers, has led some writers in the field of speech pathology to believe that a significant number of speech disorders, including stuttering, are largely, if not wholly, psychogenic—the product of emotional disturbances and personality maladjustments. This is an easy conclusion to reach, since in many instances it consists of mere assumption based on the presence of the two together—the speech disorder and the emotional maladjustment.

Possible Relationships Between Speech Disorders and Accompanying Personality Disturbances

The danger of assuming that a speech disorder has resulted from psychogenic factors in every instance where some evidence of

4. R. Goldman and G. H. Shames, 'A Study of the Goal-Setting Behavior of Parents of Stutterers and Parents of Non-Stutterers,' *Journal of Speech and Hearing Disorders*, May 1964, pp. 192–94.

emotional trauma or maladjustment can be found is seen when the various ways in which the speech and emotional problems may be related are considered. Aside from the possibility that the two may in reality be totally unrelated, there are still three other possible relationships between speech disabilities and accompanying disturbances: (1) the two may both result from a third factor but may be causally unrelated; (2) the emotional maladjustment may have been caused by the speech disorder; (3) the speech disorder may have been caused by the emotional maladjustment.

Speech Disorders and Emotional Maladjustments May Both Result from a Third Causal Factor

There is always the possibility that there may exist a common etiological factor that explains both the speech problem and the emotional aberration without the two being directly related. For example, an individual with ugly irregular teeth might well develop marked feelings of inferiority and self-consciousness as a result of this physical defect. At the same time, the inadequate dental equipment could easily produce certain specific defects of articulation in the sounds that depend on the proper alignment of the front teeth for their production. Again, a child suffering from a brain injury often exhibits marked aberrations in behavior, as well as speech and language disorders, both conditions traceable to a common cause.

While it would be a mistake in these cases to think of the maladjustment as causing the speech disorder, or vice versa, it would be just as wrong to consider the two completely unrelated. The individual's embarrassment and self-consciousness will not benefit his speech, and certainly his conspicuously defective speech can only add to his emotional problems. Thus, there will likely be set up a kind of interaction between the two, the one contributing to the aggravation and perpetuation of the other. Accordingly, any attempt at therapy for either the speech or the personality disturbance must take into account the necessity of dealing with the other problem as well, if any permanent results are to be achieved. However, the method of approach would be different in either case from what would be used if the personality and speech problems were causally related.

Emotional Maladjustments May Result from Speech Disorders

Individuals who work with adult stutterers know how rare it is to find one whose personality remains entirely untouched by the speech disability. Be it mild or serious, there is usually some trace of the emotional struggles he has undergone and the adjustment mechanisms he has built up in his efforts to relate to his handicap. This is readily understandable and is to be expected. If the individual stuttered when he first started to school, as is often the case, other children may have mocked him and made jokes about him. When his turn came to recite in class, there would be long, embarrassing periods during which he struggled to get the word out while his teacher and classmates waited in silence, prompted him, or turned away in pity, or let out a muffled snicker from the rear of the room. Soon he learned which speech situations caused him the most trouble, and these he began to dread and to avoid whenever possible. In his efforts to break through the blocks which seized him, he fell into the use of accessory movements and postures that involved jerking the head, twitching the jaw, or producing such unpleasant facial grimaces as opening the mouth wide or protruding the tongue between the teeth. Of these he was painfully self-conscious at first, but they quickly became automatic and more or less an integral part of the whole distorted and labored speech pattern. As he grew older, he came to realize what a handicap his speech would be to him as an adult and how many vocations and professions would remain unattainable as long as his speech problem persisted. In his own mind he became labeled as a speech failure. Is it any wonder that such an individual could well develop attitudes of shame, frustration, and inferiority? The wonder is that stutterers are not more disturbed than available evidence indicates them to be.

Moreover, this tendency toward maladjustment is not confined exclusively to stutterers; the same factors operate to a greater or less degree in the case of other speech disorders as well. The child with delayed speech or language who must start to school while his oral proficiency is still noticeably below the accepted standard for his age, will soon discover that he is different from other children when his 'funny' speech becomes the target of teasing by his playmates. At this age, as, indeed at any age, to be different from the norm accepted as standard by one's contemporaries is a misfortune to be met with all sorts of adjustive mechanisms, many of which may seriously warp the personality. The child whose faulty English betrays his foreign environment may feel keenly the stigma of his dialectal speech when his classmates shun him, laugh at him, or imitate him.

The psychology of the speech defective is essentially the psychology of the handicapped and, as Johnson[5] has pointed out, one of the basic factors in the psychology of the handicapped person is his reaction to frustration. This reaction is especially critical in certain types of speech disorders, such as stuttering, where the crippling inability to communicate, often on the most simple and intimate level, can become a decidedly frustrating experience. Since communication forms the very basis of most of our social relationships, a disability in this function can vitally affect social adequacy and orientation. The stutterer feels keenly his inadequacies in doing what he sees others doing with such apparent ease and naturalness.

As important as is the factor of frustration in the adjustment problems of the handicapped individual, it is not the only bugaboo with which he must contend. Most individuals suffering from a disability that is at all serious sooner or later develop the conviction that they are somehow different and set apart from other people and that other people are painfully aware of that difference.

This feeling of being different can soon become a self-per-

5. Wendell Johnson et al., *Speech Handicapped School Children*, 3rd ed., Harper and Row, New York, 1967, p. 74.

petuating affair because it is not so much the actual reactions of others toward the handicapped person's condition that matters, although they may be bad enough; the important thing is what the handicapped individual believes, or imagines, them to be. If he believes that other people are shunning, pitying, or criticizing him he will react exactly as if they were behaving that way, whether they are or not. Moreover, once this conviction has taken hold and the handicapped individual begins to reflect his self-consciousness, suspicion, and mistrust in his behavior toward his fellows, their reactions toward him in turn cannot but be influenced to some degree by these attitudes. Thus because of this reciprocal influence, the sufferer may actually come to find in the behavior of others toward him more objective evidence than would otherwise be the case to substantiate further his conviction that he is conspicuous and different, that he does not belong.

While the likelihood of occurrence of such unfortunate attitudes increases directly with the severity and obviousness of the handicap, it is surprising to discover what seemingly trivial things in the individual's make-up or background are also capable of inducing self-consciousness, embarrassment, and attitudes of inferiority which may remain with him for years. It has been found, for example, that such comparatively mild misfortunes as being too tall or too short, too thin or too fat, or having freckles or a prettier sister can produce long-standing feelings of resentment, frustration, or inferiority that may be the decisive factor in preventing the individual from realizing his full potentialities as a person. Because of the key role which speech plays in most of our social relationships, it can easily be seen why a speech disability may very often be a potent source of emotional and social maladjustment.

Speech Disorders May Result
from Emotional Maladjustment

The reality of psychogenic speech disorders has never been doubted; there are unquestionably certain types of speech disabilities which can, in individual instances, be traced definitely to factors in the personality make-up or the social environment of the individual. Because of the close and intricate inter-relationships involved, speech and voice are very sensitive barometers of personality and emotional functioning. It is a matter of common experience that we are able to tell something of an individual's state of mind from certain characteristics of his speech and voice. Our friend *sounds* tired, elated, depressed, worried, or angry regardless of what the content of his speech may indicate to the contrary. How do we know? By the tone of his voice—its pitch, quality, and intensity—and the rate and general pattern of his speech.

We are rarely mistaken in these observations. The tremulous quality of sorrow or fear, the sharp 'edge' of anger, or the breathiness and rapid tempo of excitment are all well-known and easily recognized symptoms of what is taking place within the individual, so to speak. The common vocal symptoms of stage fright, as another example, are painfully familiar to most individuals. The relation of the pitch of the voice to various emotional states was the subject of an early experimental study by Fairbanks and Pronovost, who discovered that certain types of common emotions, such as anger and fear, tended to be accompanied by characteristic pitch levels and inflection patterns during the expression of the emotion.[6] Psychiatrists depend heavily in their diagnosis of mental illness on the quality and quantity of the patient's verbal output.

We can only conclude that since voice and speech provide the medium through which personality finds its most potent and intimate expression and by which the individual's adjustment to his social environment is effected for the most part, it is only logical to expect that any malfunctioning of the personality or any warped attitudes toward the social environment will be reflected in the individual's oral communication. When these

6. Grant Fairbanks and Wilbert Pronovost, 'An Experimental Study of the Pitch Characteristics of the Voice during the Expression of Emotion,' *Speech Monographs*, 6, 1939, pp. 87–104.

attitudes and behavior patterns are reflected in speech symptoms that differ sufficiently from the norm to call adverse attention to themselves, we label the speech as defective.

What sorts of speech problems might we expect to be psychogenic? Theoretically, almost any kind of speech abnormality might conceivably have a psychological cause. However, the more common types can be grouped under the following categories:[7]

1. *Defects of vocal pitch, quality, or intensity*   Many types of emotional problems, such as anxiety states, fears, and pronounced feelings of embarrassment or self-consciousness, are typically accompanied by a marked increase in the general muscular tonicity of the body. Individuals with these problems are tense and fidgety and find it difficult to relax. This tenseness is reflected in vocal pitch and quality, giving the voice a high pitch and a tight, strained quality. The voice may be metallic and have a sharp 'edge' to it. A higher than normal pitch in the male, coupled with a falsetto-like quality, has sometimes been found to be associated with a shy, effeminate, asocial type of personality. Such individuals are obviously not well adjusted to their social environment, and there may be other complicating factors in the personality picture as well.

A voice that might be described as weak and thin may be associated with a personality characterized by shyness, fears, or introvertive and withdrawal tendencies sometimes verging on schizophrenia. The opposite, loud, blustering, 'overbearing'

7. The attempt to link specific speech and voice characteristics with corresponding emotional states and personality characteristics has run into difficulties over the years, largely because of the monumental problem of identifying specifically the personality types and traits on the one hand, and the voice and speech qualities to be studied on the other; although more progress has been made in the second than in the first. We still tend to rely heavily on impressions gained merely from personal experience. In the paragraphs immediately following references will be made which tend to associate certain voice and speech characteristics with certain mental states and personality traits. These should be taken for what they are: merely conclusions based upon clinical experience and general observation, although the weight of logic and some experimental evidence lend support.

voice may be a simple bid for attention or it may be a reflection of aggression, a superiority complex, or various other forms of defense mechanisms, many of which may indicate an unsatisfactory adjustment of the individual to his problems. Tremor and breathiness in the voice suggest a type of emotional disintegration and instability, such as is found in a mild form in stage fright and in a more serious form in anxiety states, neurotic behavior, and 'nervous breakdown.'

2. *Delayed speech and language* This problem was discussed in detail in an earlier chapter. It is sufficient here to point out that a delay or a serious retardation in the development of oral communication can often be traced to one or more of a large number of possible causative factors in the child's environment. The possibilities here are virtually legion. Emotional shocks and tensions, feelings of insecurity, fears, regressive tendencies, unusual strivings for attention, and withdrawal behavior are all examples of factors in a child's environment or personality that may result in serious retardation of speech. As was pointed out in Chapter III, speech is wholly a product of the child's environment; if too many factors in that environment are unfavorable, personality and speech development may be seriously affected.

3. *Certain articulatory defects* The extent to which certain specialized articulatory defects, such as lisping or the substitution of [w] for [r], may be psychogenic, has never been conclusively established. A much-quoted pioneer study in this field was conducted by Wood, who found evidence of a greater number of unfavorable home conditions and emotional maladjustment on the part of parents, especially the mothers, in the backgrounds of fifty children with functional articulatory speech defects than would be found among a like number of normal speakers. Wood concludes that, 'We may say on the basis of this study that functional articulatory defects (having no observable structural basis) of children are definitely and significantly associated with maladjustment and undesirable traits on the part

of the parents, and that such factors are usually maternally centered.'[8]

Less evidence is available to indicate actual etiological maladjustment in the children themselves, although observation and clinical experience disclose cases where an articulatory defect such as a lisp or a defective [r] reflects regressive tendencies or serves as an attention-getting device. In other words, immaturity or infantilisms of the total personality tend to be reflected in infantilisms of speech.

4. *Stuttering* The extent to which the speech malady known as stuttering may be traceable to emotional and personality factors has been the subject of much discussion and dispute among speech pathologists for many years. Most are agreed that emotional shocks, fears, anxieties, and tensions, as well as unfavorable environmental factors, play an important part in precipitating stuttering, especially in those children in whom there may already exist some predisposition toward the malady. All are agreed that, once the stuttering has established itself, the accompanying fears, self-consciousness, avoidance reactions, and generally inadequate social adjustment contribute materially to perpetuating the stuttering and making the sufferer's plight worse. It can be said, therefore, that emotional and environmental factors may function as accessory causes, if not to precipitate the stuttering, at least to complicate and perpetuate it.

5. *Cluttering* This disorder of rhythm and articulation, having some characteristics, superficially at least, in common with stuttering, is characterized by a broken, jerky rhythm of speech, with words telescoped and syllables run together, with sounds frequently omitted and many others badly distorted, and with hesitations irregularly scattered here and there—often not coin-

8. Kenneth Scott Wood, 'Parental Maladjustment and Functional Articulatory Defects in Children,' *The Journal of Speech Disorders*, December 1946, pp. 255–75.

ciding with the natural divisions between thoughts. The general tempo is likely to be quite rapid and the intelligibility of the speech may be seriously impaired. Individuals exhibiting such speech patterns are frequently found to be of a nervous, 'high-strung' temperament, tense and restless.

Cautions in Arriving at a Psychogenic Diagnosis

How can we tell whether a speech or language disorder may be caused entirely or in part by psychogenic factors? The safest procedure is to arrive at such a diagnosis through a process of elimination; all other possible causes should be investigated first. Search should be made for such structural deviations as missing or irregular teeth, malocclusion, and cleft lip or palate; for physiological deficiencies such as malnutrition, endocrine imbalance, impaired hearing, or paralysis; for low intelligence; and for the possibility of a similar speech disorder in the environment, which might account for its appearance in the child as a result of mere imitation. It is obvious that the teacher herself will not be able to investigate all of these factors; she will in all likelihood need to enlist the co-operation of the school nurse, school dentist, school physician, or school psychologist or psychiatric social-worker. If these agencies are not available in her particular set-up, the teacher must encourage the parents to secure these services privately.

A few examples will make clear the reasons for this cautious procedure. Persistent hoarseness usually indicates either some structural abnormality in the larynx or inflammation of the tissues. If the child is hoarse, he may be subject to frequent colds for example, or he may be suffering from a secondary infection of the vocal folds caused by bad tonsils, sinusitis, or an allergic condition. In these cases the only safe procedure would be to have the child examined by a physician who can alleviate the underlying condition. Speech training might be the very thing that should be avoided. Again, if the child is listless and unresponsive and his speech is slow, weak, and inaccurate, we must not jump to the conclusion that he is emotionally depressed or in the beginning stages of schizophrenia. He may be suffering from a vitamin deficiency or a malfunctioning thyroid gland, or he may be seriously retarded mentally.

Such hypothetical cases, which can be matched many times from the files of any active speech and hearing clinic, illustrate the danger of arriving at hasty, superficial conclusions about the cause of even a 'simple' disorder. This danger is especially great if the teacher has already concluded that the cause is associated with emotional maladjustment. There are two reasons why such a conclusion should be arrived at only after careful study and consideration. (1) Once the teacher has accepted this explanation, further search for other possible causes usually stops. The teacher is satisfied that she has found the cause and sees no reason to look elsewhere. As a result of this short-sighted procedure, a pathology or some other serious physical disability may remain undiscovered. (2) A psychogenic causation is a dangerously easy and convenient diagnosis to reach, partly because of the readiness with which the teacher can find seemingly significant psychological factors in the developmental history and environment of almost any one of her pupils. Select any child out of a group and begin to explore his background; there are usually many instances of his being frightened, being sent to bed without his supper, being made to feel inferior, given cause to feel jealous, or otherwise subjected to influences that, under certain circumstances, might conceivably have led to maladjustments. Whether they actually *did* lead to maladjustments, and whether such maladjustments as the child's personality may exhibit did in reality cause the speech disorder are questions the overzealous advocate of the psychogenic theory often fails to ponder adequately. It is so easy to take a child with a speech problem, discover that he did have an unhappy childhood, and immediately conclude that the speech problem is entirely explained. It may not occur to such a theorist that he is under obligation to show how and why the particular psychogenic factors in question should have resulted in the observed speech disability. The mere presence of the two together is insufficient evidence of a causal relationship between them.

Fortunately, the explanation for the majority of communication problems the teacher will find in the average classroom situation is not so laborious a process as the foregoing discussion would imply. In many instances the cause will be fairly obvious, or, if not, there may be some rather clear hint of which direction the study should take; or finding the ultimate cause may not even be vitally important to the assistance the teacher is prepared to give. The important thing is that the teacher should be able to recognize which clues to follow, should know when to call in outside help, and should know when it is safe to proceed with speech and language training, even though no clear-cut cause can be discovered.

Diagnostic Aids

What recognizable signs do we expect to find associated with communication disabilities causally related to emotional and personality maladjustment? The first, of course, is the absence of any other likely cause. Also, one of the surest indications of psychological complications in a disorder is the degree to which it varies in severity in relation to the social environment. After discounting the tendency of most normal speakers to feel somewhat tense and self-conscious in difficult social situations, we can conclude that emotional factors are playing some part in relation to the problem when we find that the speech disability grows noticeably worse in situations that place a premium upon effective speaking, and improves or disappears altogether in other situations where social pressure is largely absent. An example would be a child who displays certain speech deficiencies at school but whose speech is normal in the peace and security of his home.

The presence of excessive muscular tension is another symptom to look for. As was mentioned previously, individuals suffering from various types of emotional maladjustments are habitually tense and find it very difficult to relax. As was also pointed out, it is largely through this increased neuromuscular tension that some of the more conspicuous speech and voice symptoms are produced. Also, if the child's history discloses that the speech or language disorder appeared shortly after some traumatic experience or emotional upset, suspicion of a causal relationship between the two would be aroused. At least, further investigation would certainly be warranted. At this point, however, the teacher is cautioned to remember that certain physical conditions can also produce increased muscle tonus, for example, and that a mere time relationship between two events is not of itself sufficient evidence to establish a causal relation between them.

Symptoms of Emotional Maladjustment in Children

In general, we must look beyond the speech symptom itself for corroborative evidence of psychogenic disorders, of which total symptom picture the speech problem may be only a part. How can one tell whether children are maladjusted? As with adults, the child's behavior itself gives the surest indication of what is going on within. The following types of behavior, when present to an excessive degree, are the ones most commonly found to be associated with various forms of maladjustment in the child:

1. *Regressive and infantile tendencies*   The child exhibits evidences of regression and immaturity when he begins to live in the past and assumes certain manners and reactions characteristic of children younger than himself. These may include baby-talk, excessive crying, enuresis, inappropriate fears, and eating and sleeping habits usually associated with younger children.

2. *Excessive daydreaming, phantasy, introversion*   The child who lives in a dream-world instead of reality, who is generally solitary in his habits and prefers make-believe playmates to real ones, is not a well-adjusted child. As he grows older, he may prefer to go to his room and read a book rather than engage in

play or sports with his fellows, or he may merely sit around the house or watch television with insufficient interest or initiative to entertain or otherwise occupy himself. He is likely to be socially inadequate and to appear very shy, and he will usually avoid situations that place him with other people. His feelings will be easily hurt and he will be labeled as a sensitive child, although it is often difficult to know what his real feelings are.

3. *Unusual fears and aversions* A certain amount of fear is a normal and healthy thing, but the generally fearful child who is afraid of strangers or any new situation and who is thrown into a paralyzing fear or state of nausea by things that most children do not find especially terrifying or obnoxious is to that extent maladjusted. Food aversions, for example, if carried too far, can be symptomatic of emotional disturbance. Acute fears may manifest themselves in anxiety attacks or panic states in which certain physiological symptoms appear, such as disturbances of breathing and heart action. Chronic anxieties may also develop in more severe cases.

4. *Unusual sensitivity to emotional stimulation* The child who is too easily moved to pity or who can be thrown into a temper tantrum over a trifle should be considered emotionally unstable. Spells of dramatic weeping and other exaggerated emotional reactions out of proportion to the stimulating circumstance are all symptomatic of instability of either a constitutional or secondary nature.

5. *Tendency toward cruelty* Children are naturally cruel, in some respects at least, by adult standards, but there is a certain norm of behavior in relation to this quality that is characteristic of various age levels and cultural environments. When the behavior of a child departs from this norm significantly, and he appears to derive pleasure from heartless cruelty inflicted on pets or playmates, or when his behavior is characterized by ex-

cessive aggressiveness or chronic hostility, he should be considered maladjusted.

6. *Wanton destruction* Much the same situation holds here as with cruelty. When the child seems unable to restrain himself from tearing things apart to an extent greater than normally expected of a child of his age, then we should look for some underlying environmental factor or emotional problem which the child is attempting to alleviate through this maladaptive behavior.

7. *Tendency to blame others* This is a very common 'smoke-screen' type of defense mechanism often employed by adults as well as children. It is a totally unsatisfactory adjustment to most problems and should not be encouraged. When found to excess in the behavior of a child, it should be considered symptomatic of an undesirable personality.

8. *Negativism and disobedience* While these forms of behavior seem to come very easily to most children, as any parent can testify, they become danger signals when carried to excess. The child who habitually does things simply because he knows that they will be disapproved of and seemingly derives pleasure from such behavior, or who refuses to co-operate for the same reason, or who looks upon each obedience situation as an open contest of wills between himself and his elders cannot be said to be a well-integrated personality. Such behavior is indicative of deeper problems which the child is attempting to solve in unsatisfactory ways.

9. *Excessive manifestations of jealousy* Jealousy, while undoubtedly a natural response of children, becomes symptomatic of unsatisfactory emotional adjustment when present in excess. It may be the outward manifestation of feelings of inferiority or insecurity.

10. *Psychosomatic symptoms* Physical symptoms that may in certain cases have psychological origins range all the way from unexplained allergic manifestations to enuresis. Such symptoms include feeding problems and food aversions, sleep disturbances and night terrors, mutism, nervous headaches, nail biting, thumb sucking, hypochondria, and many others of a similar nature.

11. *Unusual, bizarre, or socially disapproved behavior* There are many forms of childhood behavior which in and of themselves alone do not necessarily furnish evidence of abnormality. However, when they are found to excess or in combination with certain other significant symptoms of maladjustment, they begin to assume diagnostic importance. Such forms of behavior include stealing, running away, lying, excessive fighting, truancy, unusual sex behavior, 'showing off,' excessive hate, quarrelsomeness, and excessive talking or argumentativeness. As was mentioned, such behavior is rarely significant by itself; it acquires meaning only as we delve deeply enough to uncover the underlying conditions that have given rise to these symptoms. Often such behavior is merely a bid for attention, for example, but the fact that the child feels impelled to resort to such means to gain attention is itself related to a still deeper, and usually more hidden, problem.

It should be noticed that the words 'excessive' and 'unusual' were employed several times in the foregoing discussion of behavior that may be symptomatic of maladjustment in the child. It is not always easy to estimate in a given instance whether a certain response is excessive or unusual, or even what would normally be expected of the average child of the age under consideration. Certainly, no child of five or six who 'tells a story' —that his brother took the candy he himself sneaked out of the drawer—or who talks to imaginary playmates upon occasion, or who refuses to obey some request with an impish glint in his eye should be considered maladjusted, at least not on the basis of such evidence. On the contrary, the child who has never done any of these things or who has seemingly never felt the urge to do them is the one who should cause concern lest he be not normal. Only adequate acquaintance with the average behavior of children at a given age level can provide a norm in relation to which significant deviations can be properly evaluated.

Moreover, the classroom teacher is likely to be influenced by a certain bias in her appraisal of childhood reactions, since she will be prone to consider as model behavior that which fits in best with the established rules and procedures of the classroom. Thus, the meek child who conforms and who is either too shy or too listless to cause any trouble is likely to be thought of as the 'good' child, a model of personality and conduct. Actually such a child may be much more seriously maladjusted than the inventive, energetic, extroverted, or even excessively aggressive youngster who causes more trouble in the classroom because he is more difficult to control.

Tests and Other Diagnostic Procedures

The best general procedure is to observe the child's behavior itself at times when he is not aware of being under scrutiny. The teacher in the kindergarten and lower grades has a better opportunity of doing this than the teacher of older children, for in the earlier years of school a larger proportion of the time which the child spends in work and play is under the direct supervision of the teacher. At almost any age level, however, at least through the elementary school, the teacher should be able to gather valuable information about the child's personality by noticing his reactions to various classroom and playground situations. In the child's relation with his playmates, especially, the teacher should watch for evidence of babyish reactions, dishonesty, unusual aggression, withdrawal tendencies, excessive show-off activities, selfishness, quarrelsomeness, cruelty, and various other forms of behavior that might reflect personality maladjustments.

If the child's behavior at school is such as to arouse the

teacher's suspicion that all may not be well with the child's emotional life, she may find it necessary to extend her observations to the home situation. A short visit to the home or an interview with the mother may disclose information that will throw additional light on the child's problems. Such a conference should be conducted with great caution and tact, of course. The emphasis should be directed away from the child's faults and deficiencies and should concentrate on a co-ordinated effort on the part of both teacher and parent to help the child to attain his full potential. Information may also be available at the office of the counselor or the school psychologist, if the school is fortunate enough to have the services of such individuals. The teacher, for example, may want to secure an intelligence rating on the child or may want the psychologist to interview the mother in those instances where it is felt that serious problems may be involved.

Unfortunately, the study of personality through the use of various testing devices is considerably more difficult at the lower age levels than with older children and adults. Some attempts have been made to adapt the so-called projective tests of personality for use with younger children, but the use of these tests requires a rather high degree of specialized skill. As a matter of fact, none of the projective tests is practical for use by the average classroom teacher, since the results are very difficult to interpret and evaluate.

The more highly structured pencil-and-paper type of personality test, in which the individual answers questions with respect to his characteristic behavior and inclinations, is much easier to administer, score, and interpret than the projective tests. All of the tests of this type, however, are open to the criticism that in individual instances they can be highly unreliable and misleading, since they do not test actual behavior, but only the subject's report on his behavior. Moreover, such tests are generally not available for younger children. In general, it is safe to say that the average classroom teacher will have neither the time nor the training to do much by way of formal personality testing. Here is another instance where outside help may need to be solicited in the person of the school psychologist, or the counselor or guidance specialist.

Psychotherapy

The term *psychotherapy* is awe-inspiring, and the classroom teacher may hesitate to become involved in anything so complex and 'professional.' It is true that psychotherapy as practiced by a clinical psychologist or a psychiatrist can well be complex and 'professional,' but it is not the intention of this chapter to make a clinical psychologist out of the classroom teacher or the parent. In its broadest implications, the term simply refers to the process of assisting an individual to improve his emotional attitudes, to adjust himself more satisfactorily to certain problems in his social and physical environment. Whenever a teacher praises a backward child for some pieec of good work in order to bolster up his self-confidence, for example, she is practicing a kind of psychotherapy. There need be nothing mysterious or obscure about the process.

It is not only in connection with a possible speech or language disorder that the maladjusted child should be a subject of concern to the classroom teacher. If she believes that it is the function of the school not just to 'educate' pupils in the narrow sense but rather to develop well-integrated, balanced, effectively functioning individuals, then she must be seriously concerned with the whole child, a concept which includes the environmental influences as well as the abilities and disabilities, the drives and adjustive mechanisms, and the general behavior patterns of the individual person. As was pointed out in Chapter 1, it is impossible to separate the child as a learning, intelligent being from the same child as an emotional being. The chief reason why Johnnie is failing his grade in school may be some upsetting influence at home which is keeping him worried and under tension so that he cannot settle down to apply himself. Under such circumstances, it would be futile to deal with Johnny purely as an educational problem in the classroom concerned only with arithmetic, spelling, and the writing of themes. The reason why he is failing becomes the important issue.

In those cases where there is a communication disability there are additional reasons why the child's personality problems must be taken into consideration if they are found to be at all serious. As was pointed out earlier in this chapter, regardless of the causal relation that may exist between speech and the maladjustment, the two are so closely related that the one tends to reinforce and perpetuate the other. Therefore, if any permanent progress is to be made with the speech-improvement program, all related poor attitudes, social inadequacies, and unacceptable behavior patterns must be dealt with simultaneously. In general, it is safe to say that any speech improvement will be transitory and superficial unless some satisfactory progress can be made in alleviating the other problems as well.

Psychotherapy, as practiced by teachers, clinicians, and school psychologists and counselors, has been defined as simply 'organized common sense.' [9] Before we pass off this definition too lightly, it should be recognized that common sense is not so common as we might think and that it is even more rarely organized. Be that as it may, the fact remains that sound principles and effective procedures of mental health are being practiced every day in many classrooms by conscientious teachers who are simply attempting to apply ordinary intelligence to the solution of the many problems that arise. Such teachers are merely trying to do the best they can; they are doing what seems to them to be the most obvious, the most sensible thing to do under the circumstances. Along this line, Krumboltz and Krumboltz observe:

Many persons have successfully applied a behavioral principle without at the time being able to state that principle. From their point of view they were using common sense. Only later were they able

9. Robert West and Merle Ansberry, *The Rehabilitation of Speech*, Harper and Row, New York, 4th ed., 1968, p. 250.

to recognize that they had applied a basic psychological principle. We like the idea of a 'common sense' approach, especially at a time when common sense is not all that common.[10]

An illustration will serve to show what a classroom teacher did to help a child with a personal problem, not by having any specialized knowledge of that specific problem, but merely by being a good teacher. Her school happened to be in a district where there was no speech clinician available and no one else to whom she could turn for professional advice. She had never had a course in speech correction and knew nothing about stuttering as such, but she observed that a certain boy in her class exhibited rather consistent symptoms of hesitations and blocking whenever he attempted to express himself. She also noticed that his classmates were inclined to be impatient with him, to treat his handicap lightly and make fun of him, and to regard him as queer and different because he could not talk as they did. This she knew was bad for the boy. Consequently when he was absent one day she took the occasion to talk to the class about his problem. She pointed out that he was not queer or different from them, but that he did not happen to have as much skill in his speech as they had. She reminded them that some of them could not run as fast, play ball as well, or make music on the piano as skillfully as some of the others, and that it was no disgrace that they could not. No one expected to be good in everything. The thing this boy did not hapepn to be good in was speech, and it was made still harder for him when they laughed at him or otherwise seemed to notice his trouble.

The class got the point and appeared eager to do what they could to help the boy. Through careful planning, cleverly planted suggestions, and unobtrusive guidance the teacher gradually built up the boy's 'stock' with his classmates until he became one of the most popular boys in his group. The climax came when he was elected president of his class, the duties of which

10. John D. Krumboltz and Helen B. Krumboltz, *Changing Children's Behavior*, Prentice-Hall, Englewood Cliffs, N. J., 1972, p. xvii.

office he was able to discharge with a minimum of difficulty and relative freedom from embarrassment, because he knew that they were all 'with' him. With improvement in personality had come a considerable improvement in speech and, although he still stuttered somewhat, he had become an alert, normally self-confident, pleasant youngster, in contrast to what he might have been had his experiences of frustration, failure, and embarrassment been allowed to continue. This teacher, who knew nothing about stuttering but a great deal about people and their problems, had done a superb job in starting this potentially maladjusted boy on the road to eventual success, happiness, and possible freedom from his speech handicap. She was practicing a high type of psychotherapy, based upon sound common sense.

Finding and Removing Causes of Maladjustment
It is a sound educational principle that before a person is ready to deal adequately with a situation he must be aware of the chief factors contributing to it. Frequently when he is aware of the principal causes contributing to a problem, the proper solution may become fairly obvious. Naturally, the first step, once the cause has been found, is to remove or alleviate it if that is possible or feasible. As any classroom teacher knows, almost any factor—physical, psychological, or environmental—can contribute to personality and emotional maladjustment. Furthermore, there is frequently more than a single cause involved; there may be multiple causes which may or may not be closely interrelated. Some of them may be relatively easy to eliminate; some will apparently defy solution, at least within the limitations under which the teacher and the counselor must operate.

Space does not permit a full discussion of the myriad possible causes of personality maladjustment. Only two of the more important categories can be illustrated with typical examples from each.

1. *Physical disabilities as causes of maladjustment* That the physically handicapped individual faces a difficult task in ad-

justing to his condition is a truism recognized by most teachers. As Symonds long ago stated, 'Any sort of physical atypicality is almost certain to lead to some sort of compensation.' [11] The compensations are not all bad, although many of them must be classed as symptoms of maladaptive behavior. As was pointed out earlier, it is amazing to discover what seemingly trivial factors can become classified as 'disabilities' in the thinking of the individual. Such things as having freckles or red hair; being too fat, too tall, or too short; having irregular or too-prominent teeth; having crossed eyes or other visual defects that necessitate the wearing of heavy glasses; suffering from acne or being otherwise temporarily or permanently disfigured—these are among the many forms of physical deviations from the norm that can easily become categorized as major deformities in the thinking of the individual who is inclined to brood or worry over the problem and become oversensitive about it. Speech disorders can also be placed in this classification, since the psychological reaction of the speech defective resembles that produced by other physical disabilities.

Not all such physical defects are irremediable. Crooked teeth can usually be straightened; obesity can be reduced if the cause is discovered; the homely girl can be taught how to make herself more attractive; disfiguring scars can often be removed surgically; the speech disorder may be corrected; and many other potential sources of maladjustment can thus be alleviated or removed. In cases where the condition is not of long standing, removal of the cause should solve the problem satisfactorily. Where serious maladaptive behavior has already been developed, removal of the cause should be the first step in the program of therapy. The co-operation of the parents will need to be enlisted and perhaps other agencies as well, the director of the school's dental health program, for example.

11. Percival M. Symonds, *Mental Hygiene of the School Child*, Macmillan, New York, 1936, p. 74.

2. *Environmental factors as causes of maladjustment* In the child's environment, at school and at home especially, we have undoubtedly the most potent single source of factors that may influence the child's development, favorably or unfavorably as the case may be. The possibilities here for conditions that may lay the groundwork for later maladjustments in the child's personality are virtually limitless. Any teacher could list off-hand a dozen or more potential sources of maladjustment often found in the home environment of the present-day child. Among the factors and situations she would think of immediately would be parental favoritism, sibling rivalry, unstable marital relationships, overprotection, excessively high standards, inconsistent or oversevere discipline, no discipline at all, rejection, broken home, the presence of extra adults in the home. The reasons why and the methods by which such environmental factors tend to warp the personality and contribute to the building up of unfortunate attitudes and behavior patterns in the child are too numerous and too complicated to permit an explanation here. Whatever the explanation may be in individual cases, it is well known that such conditions do function as contributing and precipitating causes of maladjustments.

Just what can the classroom teacher do toward alleviating some of these unfavorable environmental conditions, once they have been discovered? The possibilities are many, yet at the same time the limitations are severe. The situation may be so bad generally, for example, that the only way to secure relief for the child would be to remove him from his present environment. This may not be at all possible. Again, the teacher may encounter lack of interest and co-operation, or, at worst, open resentment on the part of the parents, whose support and intelligent co-operation is, of course, vital to any serious attempt to alter home conditions.

On the other hand, there may be much that the teacher can do, often with a minimum of time and of interference with the essential routines of the family. What the teacher is unable to accomplish herself may be handled successfully if the case can be referred to a child guidance clinic, for example. If parents are approached in a friendly, diplomatic way, they will be found to be generally attentive and co-operative. After all, their most vital interests are usually centered in their children, and anything touching their welfare is of great concern to them. Later in this chapter some specific suggestions will be given for approaching parents in such a way as to facilitate a favorable response.

In the meantime, an example will serve to illustrate the importance of environmental factors and the possibilities of altering them under certain conditions. A mother brought to the Stanford Speech and Hearing Clinic her young son of four and a half years, who was exhibiting unmistakable signs of primary stuttering, with some of the secondary symptoms as well, a condition very unusual in a child so young. An interview with the mother, whom we found to be intelligent and co-operative, disclosed two items of particular importance with respect to the child's environment. In the first place, a number of the children with whom Norman played were well aware of his difficulty and were missing no opportunities to call it to his attention with the typical statement, 'Norman can't talk; he stutters.' Many times, the mother reported, Norman would come home and, young as he was, tearfully relate to her what the other children had said about his stuttering. This, we explained to the mother, had to be stopped in so far as it was humanly possible to control the situation. After several conferences on this problem, the mother was able to see a number of possibilities for easing this situation considerably. The child's play schedule and routines were altered so that he came in contact with the more desirable children of the neighborhood; the undesirable ones who could not be avoided were 'educated' regarding the harm of calling attention to Norman's speech. Various other factors were adjusted and controlled in such a way that any reference to Norman's speech was largely eliminated from his home and play environment.

The second problem turned up through the interviews seemed

fraught with even more difficulties than the first. The father, a naval officer who apparently operated on the theory that what was good for the Navy was also good for his son, was attempting to impose at home some of the rigorous discipline characteristic of the organization to which he belonged. Unrealistic and unreasonable demands were being made upon the young fellow and, altogether, a type of behavior quite out of keeping with what would normally be expected of a healthy child of four and a half years was being demanded by the father. Obviously the constant tensions arising out of this situation were contributing materially to the perpetuation of the stuttering which had probably originally been precipitated by these same tensions. A conference was then arranged with both the father and the mother during which the rather delicate situation with respect to discipline and the child's speech problem was tactfully explored. After a reasonable amount of explanation, the father saw the point and a modified discipline procedure was agreed upon.

The clinical work with the child, together with these two important modifications of the environment, was continued over a period of approximately six months, at the end of which the stuttering had entirely disappeared. Contact was maintained with the family over an additional three months period, during which there had been no recurrence of the stuttering. At the end of that time the father was transferred to another post. In this instance, the successful outcome was credited almost entirely to the alteration of the crucial environmental factors. Although this problem happened to be handled through a speech clinic, there was little that could not also have been accomplished by a teacher in a school situation applying commen-sense procedures of mental health to the problem as a whole.

It is obvious from this example and many others that the proper growth and development of the child often involve the separate and combined efforts of both parents and teachers. In this connection, Cottingham observes, 'The home and the school have both common and unique responsibilities with respect to child growth. The guidance aspect of education, which emphasizes personal adequacies, would seem to be one of those obligations shared by the school and the home.' [12]

The Role of the Parents and the Home in Guidance

Parents have a natural, and perhaps understandable, resentment against being told how to rear their children. Any advice the teacher feels justified in giving must be very carefully and judiciously presented if this opposition is to be avoided. Many parents are especially sensitive to any suggestion that their child is inferior or abnormal in any way. Mothers may resent the use of the terms 'defective' or 'defect' in reference to their children; therefore, unless the mother has indicated a definitely objective attitude toward her child's problems, it would be wise for the teacher to avoid reference to Johnnie's speech disorder or his defective speech in just those terms. Some more innocuous, and perhaps indirect, way should be chosen to convey the notion that Johnnie could use some special help and that both the home and the school will need to co-operate on the project. The emphasis should be positive rather than negative all the way along the line—not how bad Johnnie is and how detrimental his home environment is, but rather, what can we do to help him and in what ways could he perform to better advantage than he does now?

The teacher should clearly distinguish between the process of gathering information and the formulation of therapeutic measures. Naturally, remediation should be undertaken only after a full and complete picture of the situation as a whole has been gained. Then after the teacher has decided what steps should be taken, the chances of securing the full support of the parent are greatly enhanced if it is made to appear that the solutions and remedial procedures were arrived at by the parent and teacher co-operatively, rather than having it appear

12. Harold F. Cottingham, 'Guidance in the Elementary School—A Conceptual Approach,' in David R. Cook, ed., *Guidance for Education in Revolution*, Allyn and Bacon, Boston, 1971, p. 154.

that the teacher is simply telling the parent what to do. Individuals are always more prone to accept ideas that they appear to have thought of themselves than they are those that are forced upon them, as it were. The role of the teacher will be to direct the interview in such a way that the parent, without realizing it, will be brought to recognize and formulate the points that the teacher herself feels are the crucial ones.

The amount and kind of guidance that the teacher will need to give in specific instances cannot be determined in advance, nor can strict rules be formulated for the solution of specific problems of behavior and environment. Behavior problems themselves are likely to be so complex and the environmental factors contributing to them so involved that the solution to each problem must be an individual matter. The common sense mentioned previously should be applied to such facts as can be amassed in accordance with certain general principles of personality growth and development. When the teacher or the parent is armed with these facts and is conversant with the principles, the proper solution should be fairly apparent. A somewhat different and more direct approach is suggested by Krumboltz and Krumboltz who offer specific suggestions for dealing with a large number and variety of childhood behaviors, some to be encouraged and some to be discouraged or eliminated, employing modern principles and practices of behavior modification.[13]

In attempting to study certain aspects of the child's home environment, one good place to begin is with an appraisal of how adequately it appears to satisfy various fundamental needs or requirements which are generally believed to contribute to good mental health for all children. Cottingham suggests, 'Certain basic needs of the child are paramount in the guidance experience: the meaning and purpose of life, the finding of one's self through personal growth, and the establishment of an identity and autonomy in relation to society.' [14] Cottingham goes on to specify additional basic needs in somewhat general terms.

13. *Changing Children's Behavior*, op. cit.
14. In *Guidance for Education in Revolution*, op. cit. p. 151.

More specifically, the following list might well serve as an aid to the teacher in determining whether the basic conditions in the life of a given child are conducive to his fullest and most satisfactory development.

1. *The need for good physical health*   All psychologists are agreed that sound physical health and hygiene contribute materially to sound mental health. A child who is fatigued, restless, or who cannot hear or see well because of poor health or physical disability may fail to develop the desirable personality traits that he would otherwise have. Factors of diet, rest, and recreation should be looked into, as well as the child's actual physical condition as revealed by a physician's examination.

2. *The need for feelings of security*   Notice the inclusion of the word *feelings;* it is not so much the actual situation, but rather the child's reaction to the situation that is important. The child may actually have security but unless he *feels* that he has, the result can be bad. The environmental factors that may contribute to feelings of insecurity are many and varied. It will be more profitable to consider some of the general conditions that build positive feelings of security. Among the most important are the apparent stability and morale of the home generally; anything that threatens the family threatens the very foundation of the child's security. In this connection, it is important to maintain a workable routine within the home. The child who never knows what to expect from day to day or hour to hour with respect to such matters of routine as eating, sleeping, working, recreation, et cetera, is in danger of feeling that life in general is a very uncertain business. A Bohemian existence, whatever charm it may have for adults, is not in the best interests of the child. Also of first importance, of course, are obvious, overt demonstrations of affection between members of the family, and especially between parents and child, so that he will know beyond any doubt that he is loved and wanted. Whole-

some attitudes on the part of children are often dependent on the skillful handling of such problems as sibling rivalry, the avoidance of seeming favoritism, and the proper preparation of an older child for the appearance of a new baby sister or brother.

3. *The need for social adjustment and recognition* Parents should make a special effort to avoid showing favoritism or discrimination toward any member of the family. Each child must feel that he is receiving his share of attention, respect, and recognition. Discrimination can lead to feelings of inferiority and social rejection as well as to all sorts of bizarre and socially unacceptable behavior which basically stems from the child's efforts to attract the attention and recognition that he feels he does not get through legitimate channels. It is beside the point that the attention thus attracted may be highly unfavorable; any attention at all is better than none. The 'show-off' at school may well be the neglected child at home, or one whose concept of what constitutes adequate recognition and attention has been distorted by unwise parental practices.

4. *The need for feelings of competence* This need, which is related to the one above, must be satisfied at home and at school if the child is to grow up with a just evaluation of his own worth and ability. It may easily become a problem requiring special handling if the child is handicapped in any way that tends to set him apart as being different from other children, which is likely to be interpreted in his thinking as being inferior. If the child suffers from a physical abnormality or from a specific disability such as a speech disorder, retardation in reading, or a hearing loss, a special effort should be made to correct this condition or, failing that, to attempt to find an area in which the child does have some ability and to see that he is adequately praised for his achievements there. Each child should experience the satisfaction of approbation for efforts well expended if he is to avoid feelings of inferiority and incompetence.

5. *The need to accept the realities of his own life*   Even the young child should be expected to exhibit a certain degree of objectivity in his appraisal of his life and the conditions and limitations that affect it. The child who is unwilling or unable to do this may develop all sorts of compensatory devices and escape mechanisms as a substitute, such as daydreaming, regressive behavior, blaming others, or unusual aggression. A child must be led to discover what he can do and what he cannot do, and what the restrictions and opportunities are in his environment. He must learn to accept these conditions and adjust himself accordingly. The capacity to take, and profit from, criticism and the ability to accept failure with a wholesome attitude are important indications of a child's objective outlook.

6. *The need to exercise curiosity and to gain enjoyable profit from new experiences*   It is natural for a child to exhibit curiosity and to desire new experiences. Opportunities for the satisfaction of these drives should be provided by the child's environment. There should be interesting and challenging toys and activities available for the child, places to go, and new things to see. The child should be interested in the things about him and should experience pleasure in learning something new. He should be reasonably successful at entertaining himself and should want to pursue actively one or more hobbies. The child's environment should encourage these aspects of his personality.

7. *The need to be treated as a developing personality*   This is a need which parents may easily overlook. There is a tendency to go to the one extreme of holding up excessively high standards which may be quite out of line with the child's abilities at a given stage of his development or, on the other hand, of becoming overprotective and retarding his development by treating him as if he were younger than he really is. It takes real insight, and perhaps some self-denial, for parents to gauge their child's maturation—physical, mental, and emotional—so that the standards they set for him will be just enough advanced to

provide a healthy challenge and incentive to his development. This is not easy for parents—for one thing, it is difficult enough for some to accept the reality that their child is actually growing up and can't indefinitely remain the sweetly dependent baby that he was only the day before yesterday, it seems. However, it is obvious that the child needs to experience the satisfaction of adjusting successfully to each new stage of his development as it arrives, and in addition he needs the assurance that comes from being treated in a manner commensurate with his state of maturation.

The Role of the Teacher and the School in Promoting Good Mental Health

While it is still true that academic subject-matter is the teacher's principal stock-in-trade, there is a growing concern that the classroom teacher also has responsibilities that transcend teaching in the narrow sense, some of which were referred to in Chapter 1. The guidance movement has grown substantially in recent years until it has come to occupy a prominent and important place in most modern school systems and the school counselor has become its chief representative. However, it is also acknowledged that the teacher has an important role in any guidance program. Munson, in discussing the guidance movement with special reference to the roles of the counselor and the classroom teacher, says, 'Teachers do have very specific classroom opportunities to become engaged with the individual student in ways that not only facilitate the learning process of an individual student but in ways that can be personally relevant and enhancing to him.' [15]

In the first place, the teacher-as-counselor should not forget that next to the home, the school provides the most important environmental influence conditioning the child's development, and the teacher's role in this process is second only to that of

15. Harold L. Munson, 'Guidance and Instruction: A Rapprochement,' in David R. Cook, ed., *Guidance for Education in Revolution*, op. cit. p. 344.

the parents themselves. Nor is there any legitimate way by which the teacher can escape this great responsibility; the child will be what he becomes as an adult partly because of the teachers who guide him during his formative years. One of the first concepts which the teacher must come to understand is that she occupies the status of a substitute parent, more or less, in her relationships with her pupils. This will be especially true in the lower grades. The teacher must understand that the attitudes which the child brings to the school and which color and motivate his behavior toward his classmates are reflections or projections of attitudes and behavior learned at home.

This fact gives the teacher a decided advantage and a serious responsibility at the same time. Since the child's behavior at school does reflect home influences, she has an opportunity to study his basic problems by observing that behavior. Also, since her attachment to the child is not as close as that of the real parent, there is a greater chance that she can be more objective and rational in her appraisal of the child and his problems. The fact that in the eyes of the child she does stand next to the real parent gives her tremendous power to influence him and mold his development.

In this process she should be guided by the same general principles and needs in relation to the child's environment as those previously discussed in connection with the appraisal of the home background. In the first place, since character and personality development are greatly influenced by example as well as precept, she should scrutinize her own characteristic behavior to see that it conforms as closely as possible to what she would hold up as desirable for her pupils. If she is cross, irritable, and short-tempered, she can hardly expect the children in her room to be tolerant, patient, and pleasant. The mere fact that her own tensions are automatically transferred to the children would make a desirable outcome from such an undesirable setting unlikely. As in the case of real parents, she should make sure that no favoritism is practiced, although some children may require more time and attention than others. Success should be rewarded, and every child should have the opportunity to experience the satisfaction of success. The teacher should bear in mind that praise is more effective than blame in securing a satisfactory response. Discipline should be reasonable and consistent, and the teacher should strive for a high type of morale. Rejection and lack of recognition can be just as detrimental in the classroom as at home. Affection must be shown but it should be carefully and judiciously bestowed. These are general principles and conditions that hold for all children and that will make any classroom a better place for personality and character development, as well as for learning.

More specifically, what can the teacher do to assist the child who needs straightening out—who shows symptoms of a real or incipient problem of maladjustment? It is necessary at this point to remind the teacher that she is not, after all, a professional counselor or a clinical psychologist, and cannot therefore be expected to undertake the solution of really serious problems. When a case exhibiting such problems presents itself, it is well that she bear her limitations in mind and seek the assistance of such individuals and agencies as the school counselor, the school psychologist, or a child-guidance clinic. In such cases her most important contribution will come from knowing when to seek help and where it can be found.

There are many situations when the teacher can render valuable assistance to the counselor or other professionals, or, in other instances, can assume responsibility for the type of advice and help which, because of her unique position, she feels qualified to give. In applying 'organized common sense' to the solution to these problems, she may find some guidance and help in the following suggestions:

Methods of Solving Personal Problems

It should be an aid to the teacher who is attempting to help a child with a handicap or any type of personal problem if she is familiar with some of the mechanisms individuals use in their attempts to solve their difficulties. The process of attempting to adjust to the stresses which life presents can be divided into two general categories—the direct approach and the indirect.

The Direct Approach to a Problem

Authorities are agreed that the only final and successful way in which an individual can adjust himself to a handicap, or any type of personal problem, is to develop ultimately what is called an objective attitude toward his whole situation. This involves open recognition of his problem and a rational and unemotional appraisal of the limitations and possibilities involved. He must accept himself as he is and begin his rehabilitation from there. He is crippled, is undersized for his age, has a disfiguring scar on his face, or he stutters—all right. The fact must be faced; there is no use making excuses or attempting to hide it, nor can it be ignored. The first thing to do, after appraising the seriousness of the handicap, is to consider what measures can be taken to alleviate it. If alleviation is not possible or feasible, that fact must be faced too, and the individual must settle himself to live with the handicap and succeed in spite of it. The handicap may impose certain limitations upon him, which must be accepted, but there are still undamaged abilities that can be cultivated; if he can't do certain things, there are still others that he can do, and he can yet make his contribution.

If the teacher is working toward this type of solution—the open, frank attack upon the problem—then her approach to the pupil must also be open and objective. The situation must be recognized and discussed, and ways and means devised for overcoming the handicap or otherwise solving the problem. The classical example, of course, is Demosthenes, who overcame what we are told were very serious speech handicaps to become the foremost orator of his time. Henry Irving, the great English tragedian, began his career under two severe handicaps—a 'halting stammer' in his speech and an awkward lack of control of his bodily movements. By concentrating on these weaknesses he not only overcame them but continued on to achieve world

renown for his skill in the very activities in which he had
originally been handicapped.

Whether or not this immediately objective approach is wise
or feasible in individual instances depends on a number of
factors, the most important of which are the age and intelligence of the pupil. Obviously, it would be unwise to require
a five-year-old boy who stutters, for example, to face his problem objectively. Making him aware of his handicap and its
serious potentialities, even if it were possible at this age, would
only intensify the stuttering symptoms and render the disability
more difficult to correct. The hope for this lad lies in keeping
him naïve and unself-conscious about his problem until it can
be dealt with indirectly by controlling the factors contributing
to it. On the other hand, if the case is a high-school boy who
has stuttered for some time and has already built up a series of
fears, aversions, and avoidance reactions around his handicap,
then the indicated approach would be the direct one in which
the entire problem is explored and the solution arrived at co-
operatively.

It is obvious that the procedure involving a frontal attack
upon the problem is the most desirable course in all those instances where it is possible or feasible. There are certain limitations and dangers, however, of which the teacher and the handicapped individual himself should be aware. It would be unwise,
obviously, to encourage this approach when the handicap is
manifestly irremediable. For example, it would be detrimental
to raise false hopes of recovery in the mind of the totally deaf,
the blind, or the permanently crippled in those instances where
medical science was convinced there could be no recovery.

Then there is the danger of concentrating too much on overcoming the handicap, with two possible bad results: (1) The
individual becomes an extremist, concentrating his entire life
effort on this one task, as if nothing else mattered. The individual who suffers from poor health in early life, for example,
may become a 'crank' on diet and exercise in his single-minded
efforts to build himself up physically. He thus develops a warped

and badly integrated personality. Such behavior is often referred to as over-compensation. Or (2) the individual may suffer feelings of defeat and frustration if he is not able to excel in doing what originally caused him the most trouble. This is frequently not possible or even desirable. A person should be encouraged, certainly, to do what he can to remove his handicaps, but he might also be advised that he may well have other abilities with which he has a better chance of achieving success than those in which he was originally inferior. In this connection parents must be warned against the danger of setting such high goals and levels of aspiration for their children that there is little chance of their being achieved. Only unhappiness and frustration for both parents and children can result from this unfortunate practice.

The Indirect Approach

In certain instances the individual with a problem will attempt to solve it by some mechanism other than a direct attack upon it, described in the preceding paragraphs. These defense, or adjustment, mechanisms may take a number of different forms, some of them desirable, some undesirable, the desirability being determined partly by the degree to which the adjustment procedure is a deliberate, consciously planned process. Many of these forms of behavior unconsciously assumed are merely escape mechanisms or distraction devices which do not successfully solve any problems but only create new ones. A number of these were described briefly in an earlier section as symptoms of maladjustment in children. The more common forms of adjustment behavior will be discussed in somewhat more detail in the paragraphs that follow.

1. *Substitution of some other trait* Here the individual makes up for his deficiencies in one area by excelling in another. The boy who is unsuited for athletics becomes a 'brain' and gets on the honor roll. The girl disappointed in love takes to art and music. The boy who is a dullard in class achieves dubious dis-

tinction by becoming a pest and a nuisance in school. As can be seen, this type of behavior may be good or bad, depending on a number of factors. Frequently it is the only feasible procedure in those cases where a direct solution of the problem is not possible. It can be bad if unconsciously motivated, if carried to extreme, or if the ability chosen for exploitation is unworthy or is one which the individual stands little chance of developing.

2. *Compensation by contrast* This form of adjustment, or more accurately maladjustment, frequently takes on the characteristics of a 'smoke-screen' mechanism adopted by an individual to cover up some weakness. The short man becomes a bully and attempts to impress others with his importance. The coward may be the one who boasts the loudest when there is no immediate prospect of danger. Psychologists are generally agreed that there is no such thing as a true superiority complex; such behavior is usually nothing but a 'compensation by contrast' designed to obscure real feelings of inferiority. Here is a safe rule for the teacher to follow: if any trait is present in the child's behavior to an excessive degree, look for some related weakness—often a trait opposite to that displayed—which he is attempting to cover up.

3. *Desire to reform others* This generally unsuccessful type of adjustment mechanism serves the dual purpose of drawing attention away from the individual's own weakness and also of adding to his feelings of importance and success. It can be seen, however, that unless it is coupled with a direct attack upon the individual's own problems, it is merely a distraction device or escape mechanism which accomplishes nothing of any fundamental importance.

4. *Withdrawal behavior* When things become too difficult, the individual may attempt to solve his problems simply by withdrawing from the competition of life and refusing to try.

Adler contended that this was a common form of behavior among handicapped individuals because they were unwilling to put themselves to the test for fear of failure. So long as they refused to try, they could not fail—a circumstance which gave them a form of satisfaction. It can be seen that this procedure has little to recommend it, especially since it leads very easily into a kind of idle dreaming through which the individual compensates for his unsuccessful real life by indulging in all sorts of imagined conquests and glories. Withdrawal behavior in the child is a potentially dangerous symptom, more to be feared than its opposite—aggressiveness—since it is more likely to indicate serious trouble ahead.

5. *Regression*   One way to meet a problem is to regress to an earlier period of life when the problem didn't exist or was not considered to be a problem. A child of five with defective speech resembling baby-talk, for example, may begin to behave in other respects like a child of two or three, from whom such a type of speech would be expected. If life becomes too difficult for any reason, an easy solution is to revert to an earlier period of childhood, when there were few problems because someone else looked after us and all our wants were supplied. It is obvious that this type of behavior has nothing to recommend it. Indeed, if allowed to persist it may become an habitual mode of response in adulthood resulting in serious maladjustment.

6. *Aggressive or protest behavior*   Misbehaving at school may simply be the individual's protest against what he considers to be unreasonable demands at home. It is common practice for children, or adults, who feel that individuals or circumstances have conspired against them to 'take it out' on other individuals or society in general. Aggressiveness may also be a bid for attention, or it may operate as a defense against fears, lack of self-confidence, or lack of security. The maladaptive behavior may take many forms, but the essential psychological mechan-

ism is not difficult to understand; and, since it evades the real issue, it is a generally undesirable solution to any problem.

It becomes clear that in all those cases where the age and intelligence of the individual, as well as other factors, are favorable, the open, direct approach to any troublesome situation is the desirable one. Except in the case of younger children, whatever other techniques and devices may be employed in solving the problem should be devised with the full knowledge and co-operation of the individual himself, thus preventing the development of undesirable, indirect devices which merely serve to obscure the real issue. This does not mean that some of these forms of adjustment cannot be used to good advantage when they appear to be the most feasible approach and when their application is deliberately and consciously planned, at least on the part of the teacher, or whoever is assisting in the rehabilitation.

What the Teacher Can Do for the Maladjusted Child

Within the limitations of the school routine and with no special knowledge of clinical psychology, there is still much that the teacher can do to assist the child with a personality problem. In addition to general procedures discussed previously, such as searching for the cause of the difficulty and establishing basically sound principles and practices in the classroom to promote good mental health, there are more specific, constructive steps the teacher can undertake. Some of the more practical and obvious of these are discussed in the following paragraphs.

Removing or Mitigating the Social Penalty

As was pointed out previously in this chapter, one of the most important determiners of an individual's personality is his own evaluation of the reactions of others to him. This interaction is especially important in the case of the person with a handicap because he is prone to be hypersensitive, and the reactions of others are more likely to be unfavorable. There is much that the teacher can do, however, to control the attitudes and behavior of the pupils who may be 'picking on' a child because he is shy or different from them in some respect. If not controlled, this can become a very harrowing experience for such a child and may have a permanent adverse effect on his personality. The immediate circumstances will help the teacher determine the way to meet such problems, which are no different from the many others she must deal with constantly. The example of the stuttering boy whose problem a classroom teacher helped solve so successfully, described earlier in this chapter, illustrates one method of coping with a specific difficulty.

Assisting the Individual in Developing
an Objective Attitude
In those situations where circumstances are favorable it is the responsibility of the teacher to help the child develop a wholesome, objective attitude toward his problems. It is so easy for an individual with any type of handicap to develop feelings of failure, inferiority, or self-pity because he loses his perspective, and the handicap looms in his thinking out of all proportion to its actual or potential seriousness. If he has the maturity and intelligence (to make it possible or profitable) he must be taught to face his problems squarely and evaluate them in relation to the total situation. Johnson discusses in some detail certain specific procedures which the teacher could use in the case of a child with a speech problem as an illustration.[16] If at all feasible under the circumstances, the individual must be brought to see that there is still much that he can do either to overcome his difficulty or develop other abilities that will provide him with the experience of achievement and success.

In her efforts to help her pupils achieve better mental health, the teacher must remember that a child doesn't have to be lame or blind to be 'handicapped'; as was already mentioned in

16. Johnson, et al., *Speech Handicapped School Children*, op. cit. p. 101.

this chapter, serious consequences can also result from having too many freckles, being 'skinny' or small for one's age, and getting inferior marks in spelling. It is the individual's own evaluation that determines whether the 'handicap' is trivial or serious. It is from this point of view that the teacher must begin her work of rehabilitation; she must begin where the individual is and go on from there.

Assisting the Individual in Developing His Strong Points
Every child should have the satisfaction of feeling that there is something he can do well, possibly better than the other members of his group. Such ego-satisfaction is necessary to the development of healthy feelings of self-confidence and self-respect. As was pointed out in Chapter 1, it is one of the basic concepts of modern education that children differ considerably in their respective abilities—and disabilities. We cannot expect all children to be equally gifted in all school subjects, in athletics, in art and music, and in social relationships. Few children are all good, or all bad; they tend to be good in some things, poor in others. It is one of the responsibilities of the teacher to assist the child in discovering what his special abilities are and then to provide the encouragement and guidance that will motivate him to achieve some degree of success in the chosen field.

In the case of the handicapped child it will usually be wise to select the ability, or abilities, destined for exploitation from a field other than that in which his disability occurs. In the majority of instances it is as much as can be expected if the child makes satisfactory progress in overcoming his disability, with the hope of eradicating it altogether if possible. That he can then continue until he has won pre-eminence in that particular ability may be too much to expect. In the main, his time and energy will likely have been better spent if they are directed toward developing other abilities in which he enjoys a more favorable advantage to begin with. In many cases, therefore, one of the indirect approaches described previously may well be used, provided the emphasis is not so completely shifted away from the disability that the individual loses interest in doing what he can to overcome it.

Assisting the Child To Achieve Better Social Adjustment

The school enjoys a tremendous advantage over the home in that it is able to provide many opportunities for the child to be a self-respecting and co-operative member of a little community in which he can study, work, play, and mingle in other ways with children of his own age. Moreover, such activities in the school, both curricular and extracurricular, are under a considerable degree of control and guidance by the teacher. This means that they can be organized and exploited in such a way as to contribute maximally to the development of the individuals who participate. Such guided experience in working and getting along with others is exactly what a great many children need most but often cannot get in any situation outside of school.

The teacher, if she is aware of the needs of her pupils, can do much to steer the children who need socialization into the activities most likely to supply those needs. If there is proper direction, it is amazing to discover what mere association with other children can accomplish in the way of 'smoothing off the rough corners' and developing in a child the qualities that make him successful and happy in getting along with others. Moreover, such group contacts provide the opportunities for activities that bring achievement and success to the child and contribute materially to his personality development.

Here again the teacher will need to study the child so that she will know how best to direct him into the activities from which he can profit most. If the child does not have the ability to act in the school play, for example, let him sell tickets, help build scenery, or round up properties. He can still function as a vital part of the organization responsible for the final presentation and can still derive the benefits that such group work affords. If the child cannot participate in athletics directly but is still interested, help him to become athletic manager or give him a place on the athletic committee. There are many such organizations, clubs, and other group activities in almost every school, or school system, that provide excellent experiences and thus contribute to the development of many desirable personality traits.

An example, again from the files of the Stanford Speech and Hearing Clinic, but in this instance largely worked out within the framework of the school situation, will serve to illustrate what can be accomplished to help a child when parents and teachers co-operate toward a common end. Joan, a girl of twelve with a rather pronounced stutter, was brought to the clinic for treatment. She was shy, diffident, and socially immature, a condition aggravated by her speech disability as well as by a somewhat unattractive pre-pubescent chubbiness. We studied her and worked with her for a time in the clinic with some degree of success, and then decided that what she needed most was the development of such traits and attitudes as poise, self-assurance, interest in other people—what we recognize as general social maturity.

Investigation disclosed that she had one or two close girl friends with whom she walked home from school, but that otherwise her social contacts were very limited. We discussed her problem with her mother, a very knowing and co-operative individual, and with her teacher. It was decided that in the little school where Joan was a pupil there were a number of activities in which she could participate and in which she might well become interested. For one thing, plans and rehearsals for the annual spring play to be presented by the school were getting under way. It was arranged that Joan would work on the properties crew and would be a member of the committee in charge of selling tickets, the latter being recommended for the practical application it would provide for the speech training Joan had received in the clinic. This was the beginning of Joan's real rehabilitation; she made new friends, developed new interests, and discovered that she really had a knack for selling tickets and liked the experience. After the ice was broken and her interest was aroused, she tried her hand at other things.

We saw her at intervals over the next two years or so, and each time we noticed a steady improvement in her speech and a progressive development of ease, self-confidence, and friendliness in her manner. The last time the clinic director saw Joan, she was a charming, self-possessed, socially competent young lady who had recently been married. There was no trace of any difficulty in her speech. We attributed much of the credit for Joan's successful recovery—from a handicap which included considerably more than just stuttering—to certain aspects of her personality development that could have been fostered only by participation in such activities as a school can provide, both within and outside of regular academic classroom activities.

Realizing the Benefits of Speech Activities

The teacher may not always realize that speech training itself, whether for the average child or the child needing special corrective attention, is sound mental hygiene and offers many possibilities for desirable personality development. Let us examine some of the benefits that can accrue from speech experiences properly organized and administered.

1. Speech activities can satisfy the child's need for attention. When a child performs in a speaking experience, no matter how briefly or informally, all eyes are upon him; he is the center of attention and activity for the time being. As pointed out earlier in this chapter, a certain amount of this type of attention is essential to the healthy development of the child; and if he fails to get it in some legitimate and approved manner, he may make his bid for it in ways that are highly undesirable.

2. Good speech is a very desirable form of accomplishment in itself and may provide the child with his opportunity to excel. If he shows talent in the school play or the class dramatization or gives an especially good oral language recitation,

speech may become the activity in which he can achieve a degree of pre-eminence, a sound ingredient in any program of mental hygiene. A step-by-step program in oral language development was organized by the Los Angeles City school system, in which many opportunities are presented for studying and promoting the speech abilities of the child from kindergarten through grade six.[17]

3. Many forms of speech activity involve group participation and thus provide opportunity for the child to reap the benefits that accrue from working with others. Among those benefits can be mentioned a healthy interest in other people and a tolerance for their ideas and their foibles, a spirit of cooperation which involves a subordination of self-interest to the interests and welfare of the group, and such qualities as poise, self-confidence, and leadership. Group speech activities offering such potentialities include the various forms of dramatics—from a simple classroom dramatization to a full-scale school or class play—debating in its various forms, and even informal group discussions such as might develop out of a simple classroom lesson project. The teacher must not forget that potentially there is much more to be gained from an oral recitation than merely an opportunity for the child to demonstrate what he has learned about a certain subject.

4. Speech activities provide an excellent medium through which an objective attitude toward self can be taught and fostered. If the child is to progress in his ability to express himself and communicate orally, he must learn to profit from the critical comments of others regarding his performance. Ability to accept criticism gracefully and objectively when it is honestly and sincerely proffered is generally recognized as one criterion of a well-adjusted personality. The speech class or any oral performance offers an excellent opportunity for training in this respect. The skillful teacher can do much to help the child

17. Los Angeles City Schools, Division of Instructional Services, *Language Arts in the Elementary School, Part I*, Publication No. 607, 1961, chap. II.

whose feelings are too easily hurt or who is otherwise so poorly adjusted that he responds to helpful criticism defensively by an assumed bravado or indifference.

5. Since successful oral communication involves a degree of control and mastery over a group situation, speech training and speech activities offer important opportunities for the fostering of such qualities as poise, self-confidence, and other qualities of leadership. The child who learns to express himself well and who is successful in a speech situation acquires thereby a sense of power and self-esteem, which, if not carried to extreme, may contribute very favorably to his personality development.

6. Psychologists are agreed that every well-adjusted individual needs some medium or avenue of self-expression. The individual lacking such outlet becomes shut-in and introverted or frustrated and inhibited, or he may exhibit some other undesirable behavior pattern. There are myriad possibilities for self-expression, ranging from the more obvious forms such as art, music, and writing to the more indirect and less obvious means such as the creative elements of a person's occupation, for example. Speech experiences offer a direct and simple outlet for this natural urge to express our thoughts, our feelings, and our personalities.

7. It is natural for a child to be interested in many things, and this voracious and multi-sided curiosity should be encouraged. Here again, speech activities offer many advantages, for if the child is to express himself orally, he must have something to talk about. Moreover, he should not say the same thing over and over again nor should he talk about something so obscure or bizarre that no one else is interested in it. If he is to perform successfully, he must share his interest with others and must awaken their interest in it too. Such experiences contribute materially to sound mental health.

Assisting the Child in Developing a Hobby

Children must be busy if they are to develop normally. The child who remains all day in a state of listless inaction or who is so bored with life that he cannot be interested in anything is not a well child. The normal child has many interests and seemingly limitless energy to pursue them; if natural, wholesome outlets are not provided for these interests, he will seek his own and may not always display the best judgment in selecting them.

It is in accordance with sound mental health, therefore, to encourage the child to develop and pursue a hobby, which will supply a means of relaxation and recreation for him and will provide a channel through which much of his surplus energy can be funneled. The alert teacher can find many opportunities for discovering and fostering special interests which with a little direction and encouragement may be developed into hobbies. The child can be encouraged to exploit his hobby in class in connection with special projects or oral assignments, for example. Here, again, school and class projects may be utilized to advantage, or the advice and co-operation of the school counselor or the parents may need to be enlisted. All in all, the school has a genuine responsibility to foster the constructive interests of the child and to assist him in finding new ones. The more inclined the child is toward maladjustment, the more he needs this type of help.

Insuring that the Child Is Well and Physically Fit

The importance of physical health to sound personality growth has already been stressed. In those cases where some maladjustment is suspected the teacher may need to delve a bit into some of the more important factors affecting the health of the child, such as his diet, rest and recreation habits, and the general routine under which he lives. If there is evidence of physical disabilities or illness, actual or potential, the assistance of the school nurse or the family physician must be enlisted. The classroom teacher, it should be remembered, is often in the most favorable position to observe obscure or early symptoms of subnormal physical health and vitality in her pupils that may have gone unnoticed by parents and may have been passed up in routine physical examinations. She must not forget that often what appear to be wholly psychological manifestations may have a physical basis.

Assuring the Child that the Teacher Has a Genuine, Sympathetic Interest in Him

Serious consequences can result if a child becomes convinced that no one is interested in him or cares whether he is happy or unhappy, succeeds or fails. Often such feelings arise even when there is no actual basis for them in fact. Parents are so close to their children that they are inclined to take them for granted and hence do not always manifest the overt reactions which tend to reassure the child that he continues to be loved and wanted. Then, too, when there is more than one child in the family it is most difficult, as many parents can testify, to maintain a balance of attention and affection among the several children that will be interpreted by all of them as strict impartiality. It is so easy for feelings to be hurt, for attitudes of jealousy to arise, and for convictions of rejection to develop. The teacher may be the one to save the situation by gaining the confidence and affection of the child and learning thereby of a situation at home that a few words of friendly advice and help can straighten out.

Moreover, if the teacher herself is to be successful in influencing the child along the lines discussed in this chapter, she must first gain the respect, confidence, and friendship of the child through a process that should be well known to every successful teacher. There are many instances in which a child's whole life has been profoundly influenced by his having come in contact with a friendly, sympathetic teacher who made it clear to him that at least one person was genuinely interested in him as an individual and felt real concern that he solve his problems successfully and make something of himself.

If it has appeared to the reader that this chapter has strayed somewhat from the central problem of speech education and rehabilitation, it is suggested that he reread the first part of it in which the close interrelationships between speech and the personality or, more especially, the emotional functioning of the individual are discussed. There the reader will be reminded that factors which influence personality are also likely to have their effect upon speech and that the interaction works both ways. Therefore, speech training alone is often not enough; emotional and personality problems must be taken into account as well if satisfactory results are to be obtained.

References

Adler, Manfred, *A Parent's Manual: Answers to Questions on Child Development and Child Rearing*, Charles C. Thomas, Springfield, Ill., 1971.

Bower, Eli M., *Early Identification of Emotionally Disturbed Children in School*, Charles C. Thomas, Springfield, Ill., 2nd ed., 1969.

Bryngelson, Bryng, *Personality Development Through Speech*, T. S. Dennison and Company, Minneapolis, 1964.

Dinkmeyer, Don, C., *Child Development: The Emerging Self*, Prentice-Hall, Englewood Cliffs, N. J., 1965.

Eisenson, Jon, J. Jeffery Auer, and John V. Irwin, *The Psychology of Communication*, Appleton-Century-Crofts, New York, 1963, Part VI.

Goodman, David, *A Parents' Guide to the Emotional Needs of Children*, Hawthorne Books, New York, 1959.

Gilmore, John V., *Suggestions for Parents*, John V. Gilmore, Boston, 1968.

Ginott, H. G., *Between Parent and Child*, Macmillan, New York, 1967.

Hewett, Frank, *The Emotionally Disturbed Child in the Classroom*, Allyn and Bacon, Boston, 1968.

Kessler, J. W., *Psychopathology of Childhood*, Prentice-Hall, Englewood Cliffs, N. J., 1966.

Krumboltz, John D., and Helen B. Krumboltz, *Changing Children's Behavior*, Prentice-Hall, Englewood Cliffs, N. J., 1972.

Love, Harold D., *The Emotionally Disturbed Child: A Parents' Guide*, Charles C. Thomas, Springfield, Ill., 1970.

McCandless, Boyd R., *Children: Behavior and Development*, Holt, Rinehart, and Winston, New York, 1967.

Montessori, Maria, *The Child in the Family*, Henry Regnery, Chicago, 1970.

Patterson, G. R., and M. E. Gullison, *Living with Children*, Research Press, Champaign, Ill., 1968.

Smith, Judith M., and Donald Smith, *Child Management: A Program for Parents*, Ann Arbor Publishers, Ann Arbor, Mich., 1967.

Travis, Lee E., ed., *Handbook of Speech Pathology and Audiology*, Appleton-Century-Crofts, New York, 1971, Chaps. 8, 32, 35.

Van Riper, Charles, *Speech Correction*, Prentice-Hall, Englewood Cliffs, N. J., 4th ed., 1963, Chap. 3.

Wyden, Peter, and Barbara Wyden, *Growing Up Straight*, Stein and Day, New York, 1969.

X

Stuttering

Stuttering, or stammering (there is no practical distinction between the two terms), is, at the same time, one of the most disabling and baffling of all the speech disorders. Interest in it is widespread both among laymen and among speech clinicians, and considerable thought and research have been devoted to it. During the centuries that men have been studying this strange malady, many attempts have been made to determine its cause, and scores of 'cures' have been proposed, the oldest of which is recorded on a clay tablet excavated from the ruins of an ancient Biblical city. It is in the form of a prayer asking that the sufferer be relieved of his affliction.

Within the past few years a significant body of important information has been added to the impressive total of writings on the subject, but it cannot yet be said that the problem has been completely solved. Enough is known of the characteristics and general behavior of stuttering, however, to provide a basis for a number of useful therapeutic measures. It is not expected that the classroom teacher will become sufficiently familiar with the literature on this subject or will acquire the necessary training to equip her to deal in a major way with all of the cases of stuttering with which she will come in contact. It is quite possible, however, for her to acquire sufficient knowledge to do a great deal of good for the stutterers she finds in her classes, both directly in the classroom situation and more indirectly in the home situation by giving helpful advice and guidance to the parents.

After all, the stutterer does constitute an important group in the public-school population[1] and hence does present problems with which the teacher must deal, for better or for worse, whether she likes it or not, and whether she is equipped for it or not. It is no more difficult to do the helpful and constructive thing for the stutterer than it is to proceed in a way that makes his plight worse than it might otherwise be. It is with the conviction that the classroom teacher would like to be helpful to the stutterer if she knew how to be helpful that the present chapter has been included in this book.

The Development of Stuttering

What is stuttering? Although most people think they can recognize stuttering when they hear it, or see it, a simple, straightforward definition of this complicated disorder is most difficult to put together and may be misleading in some respects. In the first place, many people hesitate, backtrack, search for words, et cetera, in the course of so-called normal speech. Also, true stuttering behavior varies widely not only from individual to individual, but also from one time to another in the same individual. Then, too, the picture tends to change as the disorder progresses from stage to stage.

Many definitions have been attempted, however, and perhaps Van Riper's covers the essential elements as adequately as any: 'Stuttering occurs when the flow of speech is interrupted abnormally by repetitions or prolongations of a sound or syl-

---

1. The most generally accepted estimates place the incidence of stuttering in the public schools at something over 1 per cent of the total enrollment.

lable or posture, or by avoidance and struggle reactions.' ² This definition needs some amplification and perhaps the most effective way to give the classroom teacher some further insight into this disorder is to trace its progress through several related stages of development. The following stages, or phases, were suggested by Bloodstein in a series of three articles he wrote for the *Journal of Speech and Hearing Disorders*.³ It is Bloodstein's contention that stuttering behavior represents an irregular, and at times intermittent, progression of symptoms or characteristics, some of which are present in the earliest stages of the disorder. Although he divides this development or progression into four phases, he is careful to point out that they are not discrete or mutually exclusive, and it is often difficult to categorize a child as being in one phase or another. However, a brief, general description of each phase may give the teacher a better understanding of stuttering behavior, provide her with insight into the child's problems, and suggest ways she may be helpful to him.

Phase I—Generally Kindergarten and the Pre-School Years
Stuttering has been called a disease of childhood because it typically begins at a very early age (Johnson says: 'in the average case, at about the age of three' ⁴) and seldom appears initially in an older child or adult. The first, and most prominent, symptom is what many authorities have called slow, easy repetitions, usually occurring on the first word of sentences and generally confined to short words or syllables, such as articles, prepositions, pronouns, et cetera. The child's speech may also

2. Charles Van Riper, *Speech Correction: Principles and Methods*, 4th ed., Prentice-Hall, Englewood Cliffs, N. J., 1963, p. 311.
3. Oliver Bloodstein, 'The Development of Stuttering: I. Changes in Nine Basic Features,' *Journal of Speech and Hearing Disorders*, August 1960, pp. 219–37; 'The Development of Stuttering: II. Developmental Phases,' *JSHD*, November 1960, pp. 366–76; 'The Development of Stuttering: III. Theoretical and Clinical Implications,' *JSHD*, February 1961, pp. 67–82.
4. Wendell Johnson et al., *Speech Handicapped School Children*, 3rd ed., Harper and Row, New York, 1967, p. 251.

exhibit 'hard contacts' or blocks on certain sounds and/or prolongations of sounds, such as 'I - - - - want to go.' These symptoms are typically intermittent, the child also enjoying periods of free and fluent speech. The stuttering episodes are exaggerated by tension-producing communicative situations, as when a child is being reprimanded by a teacher or a stern parent, and the stuttering becomes worse when the child is excited or telling a long story. During this early stage the child seems unaware of any communicative problem, shows no fear of talking, and does not react to himself as a stutterer.

And is such behavior really stuttering? Anyone familiar with the normal speech development of the child may say that the behavior just described can be found in the communicative efforts of many young children who do not grow up to become stutterers. Johnson especially, among other authorities, points out the prevalence of such speech irregularities among 'normal' children and stresses the danger of labeling such behavior as stuttering.[5] More will be said of this theory in a later section.

Other authorities believe that true stuttering can often be identified, but with caution, at an early age and propose some guidelines to assist in distinguishing it from normal non-fluency found in many children. Bloodstein, for example, suggests three differences between true stuttering in the young child and normal non-fluency.[6] In stuttering we are likely to find:

1. The word and syllable repetitions are far more frequent and more prolonged than those found in the speech of young children generally.

2. Often the parents' and clinician's evaluation of the speech symptoms as abnormal is shared by relatives, friends, and other close associates of the child.

3. There is identifiable evidence of consistency in the non-fluency pattern of the stutterers, and episodes appear in which

5. Ibid. p. 278.
6. Bloodstein, I, op. cit. p. 221.

the child displays some symptoms of struggle behavior during speech in the form of eyes blinking, facial grimaces, breathing disturbances, et cetera.

Whether or not one has faith in his ability to identify stuttering in this early phase, he would be well advised to caution parents and associates not to call attention to the child's speech or otherwise make him concerned or self-conscious about it. Treatment, if any, should be indirect, and emphasis should be primarily upon prevention of more serious or persistent symptoms. Some specific suggestions will be offered in a later section.

Phase II—The First Three or Four Grades

The disorder at this stage is becoming more chronic, the episodes of stuttering are longer and more typical of the child's general speech. He is having trouble with more words, and stuttering has spread to the major parts of speech that carry the principal meaning of what is spoken—nouns, verbs, important adjectives, et cetera. The child experiences more difficulty when he is excited or speaking rapidly, and more tonic spasms, or blocks, are appearing. Most of the time, however, the child seems unaware of his stuttering and generally shows little or no concern about his speech, although some evidence of anticipation of troublesome words is beginning to appear.

Help for the stutterer at this stage must generally be indirect; some suggestions for the parents and teacher are included in later sections of this chapter. Perhaps the safest and most productive procedure at this point involves general speech improvement, but with no direct reference to either fluency or stuttering. Experience in such activities as children's drama, story telling, and general speaking should prove beneficial in aiding the child to develop better fluency patterns. Then, too, an effort should be made to enhance the child's self-confidence and increase his sense of personal worth. His liabilities should be minimized and his abilities maximized through activities in which he can demonstrate success.

Phase III—The Slightly Older Child

The child is now exhibiting more difficulty in certain situations than in others, which doubtless reflects some anticipation based on past experience. He is also resorting to word substitutions in order to circumvent those words and speech sounds he finds difficult to say. Evidence of tension and struggle behavior is beginning to appear in the form of more severe blocks, lip tensions, jaw movements, et cetera. In an effort to avoid these tensions, or escape from them, he may develop facial grimaces, head jerking, or movements of the hands and arms.

Strangely enough, although he is experiencing frustration in an increasing number of speech attempts, he may exhibit few deep feelings of fear or embarrassment, and show no tendency to avoid speaking. At this stage also there may be little motivation for improvement.[7] Direct therapy for the stutterer at this stage is most difficult, and had best be left to the speech clinician, although there is still much that the parents and teacher can do to help the child indirectly. The same applies to Phase IV.

Phase IV—The Older Child and Adult

Stuttering has now become chronic and full-blown. The dominant attitude is fear, and the characteristic behavior is avoidance. Experience has convinced the individual that he is a *stutterer*, and vivid anticipation of stuttering permeates his every effort at communication. He generally knows in advance the words and sounds he is likely to have difficulty with, and experience has shown a close correlation between anticipation and actual stuttering behavior. Research has also borne out this relationship. Much of the stutterer's behavior at this stage results from his efforts to avoid the stuttering, but the harder he tries the more severe the stuttering symptoms become.

7. Franklin H. Silverman, 'Concern of Elementary-School Stutterers About Their Stuttering,' *Journal of Speech and Hearing Disorders*, November 1970, pp. 361–63.

As a part of the avoidance reaction he introduces frequent word substitutions, circumlocutions, and starters, often re-casting an entire sentence to avoid having to use a troublesome word or sound. Consequently, often the most difficult task for a stutterer is to have to give his name, address, or telephone number. With these, he cannot transpose or substitute. The avoidance may also extend to certain speech situations which have caused him trouble in the past, or to individuals with whom he has found it difficult to communicate. As his fear and embarrassment become more intensified, he tends to become shy, isolated, and socially maladjusted. It is obvious that with such an individual, much more needs to be changed than a mere speech pattern, though a frontal approach on the speech symptoms themselves is often used as a beginning technique in therapy. Again, at this stage direct therapy should be left to the speech clinician.

In studying the sequence just presented and attempting to fit any individual stutterer into it, one must remember that it represents only a general progression of symptoms and char-acteristics that cannot readily be segregated into sharply sepa-rate phases or stages. The ages suggested for each stage are es-pecially subject to wide variations, some children starting much younger than others and exhibiting more complicated symptoms at any given age.

Some Characteristics of Stuttering

The speech symptoms which we identify as stuttering can be classified into three general categories: (1) blocks or hesitations while the speaker is preparing for certain speech sounds, during which the flow of speech may be completely interrupted; (2) intermittent interruptions in the form of repetitions of certain sounds, as in 'c-c-c-cat'; and (3) prolongations of certain sounds which the speaker starts and doesn't seem able to finish, as, in a previous example, 'I - - - - want to go.' While the typical stutterer is likely to combine more than one of these symptoms in his speech, it is not uncommon for his speech to exhibit much more of one than of the other two.

Often verbal 'starters' are used in an effort to avoid the stuttering and get speech going. One small boy prefaced every important comment with 'Oh, gee, look'; this was all he needed to get himself started and then he was all right for the remainder of the sentence. An adult stutterer began each major statement with 'Well, now, let me see—let me see—let me see—' which he would repeat, in an undertone and to himself, until he was able to continue with what he wanted to say. While the major spasms of stuttering are associated with the speech mechanism itself—the lips, tongue, jaw, larynx, or muscles of breathing—associated tensions and tics in other parts of the body are often developed to help the stutterer break through his blocks. These vary all the way from facial twitchings and head jerking to such dramatic and distracting gestures as driving the fist of one hand into the palm of the other with terrific force and startling suddenness.

One of the peculiarities of stuttering that has been very difficult to explain is the fact that there are from four to five times as many stutterers among males as among females. Stutterers as a group are not deficient in intelligence; they do not differ significantly from a comparable group of normal speakers. Stuttering has been found to be related to the social significance and the communicative importance of what is being said, as well as the prestige, or 'stature,' of the person or persons to whom the stutterer is talking. Thus, the stutterer can often count quite readily, but cannot use the same numbers in giving his age or telephone number. He can usually talk to animals, to children younger than himself, or to himself when he is alone, or thinks he is. He can usually sing without difficulty, can whisper, and finds speech less difficult when he speaks in a measured, mechanical rhythm, especially if there is some accompanying bodily movement. He may be able to talk quite fluently when he becomes angry. He can read or talk in unison with someone else, even another stutterer. There is also some evidence to indicate that stuttering is more often found in the family history of stutterers than of normal speakers.

Many attempts have been made to study and characterize the personality of stutterers. Woods and Williams report the results of such a study[8] in which 45 speech clinicians were asked to list five or more adjectives which they felt best described the adult male stutterer. From this list they were requested to select the five terms which they felt were the most descriptively relevant and rate them on a scale of one to five. The top five traits chosen by the speech clinicians were: anxious, self-conscious, perfectionistic, apprehensive, and tense. Interestingly enough, Williams comments that very similar results were obtained from another study of traits characterizing school-age male stutterers.[9] Allowing for the possibility of a developing stereotype in the minds of speech clinicians, it is still significant to note that these results correspond very closely not only with opinions expressed by other authorities, but also with the results of many of the personality studies of stutterers using more sophisticated measuring devices.

As we review the symptoms and other characteristics associated with stuttering, we are struck by the complexity and diversity of the many factors that seem to be involved. We are forced to conclude that no simple theory can explain adequately the many aspects of probable causation, manifestations, and indicated therapy involved in this complex problem. Fortunately it is not necessary to have such a final explanation in order to render valuable assistance to the stutterer in a number of common-sense ways. A general survey of some of the more important theories of etiology, however, will provide a basis for understanding the rationale of the therapeutic and preventive measures to be suggested later.

8. C. Lee Woods and Dean E. Williams, 'Speech Clinicians' Conception of Boys and Men Who Stutter,' *Journal of Speech and Hearing Disorders*, May 1971, pp. 225–34.
9. Ibid. p. 226.

Possible Causes of Stuttering

No one knows for sure what causes stuttering. It is quite possible, if not probable, that there is no one cause that is operative in all cases. Rather, it is likely that different factors are responsible in different cases, and there is a further likelihood that there will be a combination of causes, rather than a single cause, operating in any given individual case.

The Emotional-Social Maladjustment Theories

A number of writers on the subject of stuttering have advocated the theory that this disorder is a symptom of emotional conflict or social inadequacy and that the stutterer is basically a maladjusted individual. The emotional shock or mental conflict manifests itself in speech because speech and voice are the natural media of emotional expression and social communication. The stuttering is perpetuated through memories of past failures in speech situations and the fear and dread attendant upon anticipation of similar future situations.

It is true, there is evidence to indicate that the stutterer is more likely to be maladjusted emotionally and socially than is the normal speaker, and that in general he exhibits more fears, tensions, and anxieties, especially in social situations involving speech. It is far from clear, however, whether such conditions operate as causal factors to bring on stuttering, or whether these symptoms of maladjustment have themselves been brought on by the stuttering, and hence in reality may constitute results rather than causes. There is reason to believe that both of these possibilities may be operating, especially in the case of the adult stutterer, who may well develop feelings of frustration, inferiority, and anxiety as a result of contending with his disability.

On the other hand, studies of child stutterers indicate that the malady may in some cases constitute merely one symptom of a rather deep-seated general maladjustment of which there are other symptoms such as feeding problems, temper tantrums, aggression, and similar undesirable behavior. There is evidence that the environments of stuttering children, too, often leave much to be desired when compared with the environments of children who speak normally.

Constitutional Predisposition

There are those who believe that stuttering tends to run in families, and to support their opinion they point to studies that disclose significantly more stuttering in the family histories of stutterers than is found among the normal-speaking population.[10] On the subject of just what it is that 'runs in families' the proponents of this theory are not too clear. It is presumed that the stuttering child may have inherited a predisposition of some sort which renders him more susceptible to the development of the disorder than the child whose heredity is free of stuttering. Environmental factors may thus operate as precipitating causes to bring out the stuttering, which has remained in a latent condition. If the environment is unusually favorable, the actual stuttering symptoms may never appear; they will remain merely potentialities.

To explain the possible nature of this predisposition, the proponents refer to the high sex ratio in stuttering mentioned previously, as well as to certain studies which indicate that the incidence of left-handedness is higher among stutterers and stutterers' families than among the population at large. Some investigations have also disclosed that stutterers are more susceptible to upper respiratory infections than are normal speakers, are likely to be inferior in motor skills, and may also exhibit certain atypical metabolic, vasomotor, and neurological manifestations.

Studies in these areas are not conclusive; there is no one condition that has thus far been found to distinguish stutterers from non-stutterers with any marked degree of consistency.

10. Robert West and Merle Ansberry, *The Rehabilitation of Speech*, 4th ed., Harper and Row, New York, 1968, p. 127.

There does appear, however, to be sufficient evidence to warrant the hypothesis that in certain cases the individual may possess a predisposition for stuttering that is neurophysiological in nature and that may or may not develop into actual stuttering, depending on the favorable or unfavorable balance of environmental influences.

A Developmental Theory

One of the more widely accepted explanations of stuttering sets forth the contention that the stutterer is perfectly normal in every respect except his speech. Supporters of this theory, which is also called the semantic theory, believe that the abnormal speech pattern develops out of the normal repetitions and non-fluencies characteristic of childhood speech. They point out that all children naturally experience periods and situations when it is difficult for them to express themselves because they have much to say and a relatively undeveloped language tool with which to say it. The result is a typical pattern of repetitions, hesitations, and frequent false starts. In most instances these irregularities are ignored by parents who have sufficient patience and understanding to realize that the child will eventually develop adult fluency as his language competency increases. Such a child learns to talk normally, according to this theory.

But there are a few other parents who become concerned over their child's stumbling speech, which sounds so much like stuttering to them that they actually begin to call it that. The accompanying anxiety and tensions attendant upon this parental diagnosis color their attitudes and behavior toward the child. Directly or indirectly they call attention to his speech or attempt to help him with it, make him self-conscious about it, and eventually succeed in transmitting to the child some of their own fears and apprehensions. These only serve to aggravate the irregularities already present in the child's speech, with the result that they become even more pronounced and eventually develop into actual stuttering.[11]

11. Johnson, et al., *Speech Handicapped School Children,* op. cit. chap. 5.

Whether or not this theory presents the whole story with respect to stuttering, the implications for child training inherent in it are essentially sound. Every effort should be made to keep the young child as unself-conscious as possible about whatever deficiencies may be present in his speech. As was pointed out in an earlier chapter, whatever is done for him at this time must be indirect and must be accomplished without making him aware of his problems. Worries and tensions about the child color the parents' attitude and behavior toward him, with the result that these fears are eventually shared by the child himself or react upon him in some other unfavorable way.

Stuttering as Learned Behavior

Somewhat related to the preceding theory is the belief that stuttering is a form of learned behavior and hence can be unlearned or modified according to fairly well-established principles and procedures. Proponents of this theory are not too clear, or too concerned, as to how or under what circumstances this faulty learning may have taken place. Perhaps it is rooted in the early fumblings, repetitions, and hesitations which characterize the typical speech development of the child in its earlier stages. At this time undue communicative pressures may have been brought to bear upon the child by impatient or perfectionist parents, by competitive siblings, or from other demands of the situation. In his attempts to meet these demands and overcome the obstacles, with his as yet immature and incompetent communicative mechanism, the child develops— learns—a style of speaking marked by the repetitions, blocks, and irregularities we call stuttering. As to why some children develop and retain this style of speaking while others do not has never been fully explained.

The importance of this theory lies not so much in any attempt to explain a specific cause or origin of stuttering, but rather in its stress upon principles of learning and the application of techniques of behavior modification to the elimination or reduction of the observable manifestations of stuttering. This is not a new concept or technique, since so-called symptom therapy has been practiced for many years. What has given it new vitality and respectability is the interest in a method of behavior modification known as operant conditioning, which involves, loosely speaking, techniques of reward (reinforcement) and punishment as means of increasing, decreasing, or otherwise modifying desired or undesired responses. More will be said of this in later suggestions for teachers and parents.

Basic Assumptions
Even though the ultimate cause of stuttering is still largely in the realm of theory, there are certain basic conclusions about the nature and behavior of the disorder that are pretty generally agreed on among speech authorities.

   1. Virtually all are agreed that early environmental influences, especially those preceding and accompanying the child's entrance to school, are extremely important in determining whether the child develops normal speech or exhibits the symptoms of stuttering. Many believe that such influences can be adverse enough to constitute the sole and primary cause of stuttering, and few experts doubt that such factors can operate at least as aggravating and precipitating influences to bring out a stuttering condition that might otherwise have remained latent. The child's environment, therefore, is of tremendous concern to the parent and to the teacher, and to anyone else interested in the child's welfare. It must first be such that it insures the development of normal speech, and it must also be controlled and modified in a way that alleviates the stuttering in those instances where it has already appeared.

   2. As we have seen, clinical observation, as well as the results of testing and personality diagnosis, has convinced most speech clinicians that stutterers are likely to be more neurotic, tense, apprehensive, and socially maladjusted than are normal speakers. As was also noted previously, it is not always easy to determine whether such symptoms are results or whether they operate as causes of the speech disorder. There is evidence that

they may be either or both, and it is not always possible to determine the true picture in individual instances. The important point is that where such factors are discovered to be present, they must be dealt with, either directly or indirectly if important and lasting results are to be expected from the speech therapy. As a matter of fact, such procedures as may be required to alleviate the emotional maladjustments accompanying the speech disorder should be considered a necessary and integral part of the speech therapy itself, rather than something additional or peripheral. The stutterer must be rehabilitated as a person.

3. It is obvious that the older, chronic stutterer is basically different from the child who is just beginning to manifest the disorder. While the child may exhibit many of the speech symptoms of stuttering without being aware of any specific difficulties with his speech, the chronic stutterer has developed the *habit* of stuttering, with all of its attendant expectancy reactions, feelings of frustration and inferiority, and fear and dread of speech situations. The former condition is called *primary stuttering*, while the latter is referred to as *secondary stuttering*. It makes a considerable difference which type is being dealt with because the approach to therapy is quite different in the two instances. In the case of primary stuttering, the emphasis must be placed on environmental factors that may be contributing to the difficulty, and the approach must be more general and indirect. Care must be taken not to call attention to the child's speech pattern as such or make him self-conscious about it; such self-consciousness would only intensify his symptoms and tend to put him further along the way of becoming a real stutterer. The speech irregularities may well subside or disappear as he matures if no issue is made of them. In the case of secondary stuttering, the direct approach is usually desirable; the individual must be brought to face his problem squarely and develop an objective attitude toward it. Often a direct attack on the stuttering symptoms themselves is a necessary part of the therapy.

4. Even though there is no final agreement about the cause of stuttering, most, if not all, speech clinicians agree there are certain steps that can be taken to prevent the development of the malady in the first place, or to relieve it or even eradicate it altogether after it has become established. As was seen previously, their procedures are not always the same for all cases; as a matter of fact, there is always the possibility that specific methods that prove successful in one instance may have little or no effect in another case.

Despite the variability found from case to case, however, there are certain fundamental conditions and practices that are applicable in virtually all cases. One of these involves the principle that any factor in the environment producing tensions, fears, frustrations, or feelings of insecurity increases the possibility that stuttering will appear or tends to perpetuate it, once it has begun. Therapy is directed toward the elimination of such factors from the environment and the substitution of constructive, positive conditions that will contribute to the emotional well-being of the child.

The concept of 'environment' as used above must be extended to include the communicative situation itself. Experience and research have shown that stuttering is increased in situations where there is strong need to make a favorable impression, where there is undue pressure to communicate, or where there are, or are likely to be, negative reactions to the speech pattern on the part of the hearer or other individuals. Many obvious therapeutic applications are immediately suggested by these conditions.

Another fundamental principle of therapy is that any factor that 'builds up' the individual, that contributes to his feelings of self-esteem, competence, and self-confidence, will tend to act as insurance against the appearance or growth of stuttering. A third principle on which there is rather general agreement is that some degree of relaxation and composure must be attained if the individual hopes to rid himself of the malady. This does not mean that physical relaxation alone is sufficient, but it does mean that there is little hope of improvement in the stuttering, especially if it is of the secondary type, as long as the individual remains tense and jittery. It will be seen, of course, that physical relaxation and the desirable mental attitudes mentioned above are very closely related, and that they interact, to some degree.

There are definite possibilities, therefore, of doing something constructive for the stuttering child, either directly or indirectly, by applying principles that are sound for bringing up children and furthering mental health. As was pointed out in Chapter IX, it is not necessary to be a specialist in psychotherapy in order to employ sound judgment and good common sense. There is still much that can be done to assist the child in building a stable personality structure and healthy emotional attitudes, an extremely important phase of stuttering therapy. It is probably necessary, and desirable, for the classroom teacher and the average parent to confine themselves to this aspect of the problem. More involved phases of therapy require more specialized knowledge and skill than such an individual is likely to have. The following section presents in some detail a number of suggestions for the kind of assistance the informed parent or teacher can give the child who stutters. It is suggested at this point that the reader also review Chapter IX for a summary of how to build a better life for the normal-speaking child, who might otherwise have become a stutterer.

What the Teacher Can Do for the Stuttering Child

1. One of the factors most important in precipitating the unpleasant, complicating secondary characteristics of stuttering is the real, or imagined, reactions of others to the disability. The stutterer becomes concerned when he notices, or thinks he does, that others are reacting unfavorably toward him when he speaks, and perhaps at other times as well. These responses may take many forms but are most likely to involve such behavior as expressions of pity, solicitude, or embarrassment; at-

tempts at ridicule, humor, or imitation; and well-meaning efforts to assist the stutterer by supplying words for him, telling him to slow down, or avoiding a face-to-face contact with him. Such reactions can be referred to as the social penalties suffered by the handicapped individual. They may be deliberate and well-meaning, deliberate and mischievous, or, as probably more often happens, merely unconscious reactions. In any case, whatever the nature or intent of such behavior, it has the effect of calling the stutterer's attention to his problem and making him feel more ineffective and different than he might otherwise feel.

Within limits, it is possible for the classroom teacher to control some of these aspects of the stutterer's social environment, in so far, at least, as they relate to the school situation. Often individuals behave as they do toward the stutterer because they do not know how else to behave, or they may not understand the nature of the stutterer's problem. A project in education is therefore indicated. The teacher should make an opportunity to talk to the stutterer's associates, as a group, or individually, and explain to them what they can do to help their friend instead of making it more difficult for him. She should proceed as the teacher did whose experience was cited in the previous chapter —explain to them that Billie is just like the rest of them except that he cannot talk quite as well as some of them can. She can point out that some of them, too, cannot do certain things as well as others; perhaps they cannot run as fast, read as well, or play ball as skillfully. They do not feel that it is queer or a disgrace not to be able to do these things; they should take a similar attitude toward Billie's speech. The teacher should explain to them that attitudes of ridicule, humor, or pity are all bad because they only make Billie feel self-conscious and different from them and consequently make it even harder for him to talk well.

The teacher should demonstrate by her own speech and other reactions that the best way to behave toward a stutterer is the same as we behave toward anyone else. Pay no attention to his problem, be friendly, and give him credit for the other things he does do well. When talking with him, do not be bothered or embarrassed by any difficulties he may exhibit; pay attention to what he is saying and not his manner of saying it. For the most part, pupils will be found to be friendly and helpful, once the situation has been tactfully explained to them and their co-operation enlisted.

2. Everything possible should be done to build up the stutterer's self-confidence and his pattern of general success. Every effort should be made to discover what he can do well and what he enjoys doing. Once these abilities have been uncovered, he should he given every encouragement to win success in them. With successful achievement will come a general self-confidence and sense of accomplishment that will have a 'halo effect' on all of his activities, including speech. The average school situation, through its student participation and various activity programs, offers many opportunities for the child to develop qualities of leadership and to experience successful achievement in many areas. The stutterer needs this badly, and the classroom teacher can do much to steer him into the type of situation for which his abilities best fit him, whether it be planning for the new class project, serving on the rally committee, or preparing for the next school or class party. It may not be an activity involving speech to any great extent.

3. Set the stuttering child a good example by being poised and unhurried yourself. Treat him with a quiet, easy friendliness that will be comforting and soothing to him. Make it clear to him by example, as well as precept, that there is no need to hurry, that there is plenty of time to say what we have to say, and that no one is going to interrupt or grow impatient. Tell the stutterer to take as much time as he needs.

4. It may well be that a good heart-to-heart talk with the child will be the best approach to the solution of his problems, provided the child is old enough to have become aware of his difficulty and to bring some insight to bear on it. If such a procedure is indicated, an open, frank attitude should be maintained on the part of both the teacher and the pupil. Some-

what the same point of view as was recommended for his friends should be suggested for him. He has this problem—so what? We all have problems of one sort or another, and his happens to be speech. Explain to him that he should not be ashamed of his speech and that he should not go through life attempting to hide his stuttering. He must accept himself for what he is, not forgetting his assets, which in all likelihood more than outbalance his liabilities. He must expect other people to assume a similar attitude toward him. He will do the best he can in speech, and if that is not good enough, it is just too bad, but he must be determined not to become depressed or apologetic about it.

At the same time, of course, he must be encouraged to follow constructive measures to help himself overcome the speech disability; he should not be allowed to attempt to solve his problem merely by ignoring it. Also he should be discouraged from developing such tricks and devices to help him avoid or get through a speech block as jerking his head, licking his lips, or exhaling a quantity of breath before starting to speak. Such 'crutches' are often found in the older stutterer because he discovered at some time that blinking his eyes or snapping his fingers seemed to help him get started with a sentence or break up a block. The danger is that such devices tend to become integrated into the total habit pattern of the individual's communication and will not only lose their initial success, but may in time become more prominent and disturbing than the actual stuttering itself.

He must be reminded, moreover, that merely trying to keep from stuttering or attempting to cover up when it does occur is generally unsatisfactory and may very well make the problem worse. Remind him that he has the most success when he feels most confident and relaxed and impress upon him that speech situations are not life-and-death matters to be approached with feelings of dread and anticipation of failure. It usually will not make much difference if he does stutter a little; most people 'hem and haw' and are far from being perfectly fluent.

It is quite possible that one of the most beneficial results to come from such a conference with the stutterer will be the feeling of mutual understanding that will be established. He will know that you at least understand his problem and are 'pulling for him'; there will be no need for tension and subterfuge when he is with you. It may well be that his performance in your classroom will improve considerably as a result.

5. One of the most pressing questions facing the teacher of a stuttering child is whether to excuse him from oral recitations in the classroom or put him through the regular routine with the rest of the pupils and make no exceptions for him. The complexities of the problem are such as to make a categorical 'yes' or 'no' answer to this question difficult, if not impossible. There are disadvantages either way, but in general it can be said that some concessions and special arrangements are usually necessary if the peculiar needs and disabilities of the stuttering child are to be taken into account.

Johnson points out that while a stuttering child should generally be encouraged to talk more, he should never be *forced* to recite, speak, or read aloud.[12] He should rather be motivated to *want* to contribute. To make this contribution easier for him, the teacher should remember that stuttering is generally accompanied by feelings of anxiety, which can be increased if the stutterer is forced to wait his turn or is otherwise delayed in reciting. Therefore, allow him to participate early before tensions build up. Also, he should be encouraged to do the things that are most easy for him. For example, some stutterers find it easy to read aloud but difficult to talk spontaneously. With others, the opposite is true. Some slight modification of the assignment to favor the stuttering child way well contribute to a successful performance.

Perhaps the most important single guiding principle for the teacher to keep in mind in deciding what course to follow is that any speech experience the stutterer can handle successfully

12. Johnson et al., *Speech Handicapped School Children*, op. cit. p. 299.

will benefit him and add to his feelings of self-confidence, but any situation in which he fails and stutters badly will only increase his dread of speaking and his anticipation of failure in the future. Therefore, as was mentioned previously, the child should be encouraged to participate in those oral situations which the teacher and the pupil feel will offer the greatest assurance of success. In this the pupil may be a better judge than the teacher and therefore he should be encouraged to volunteer at such times and in such situations as he feels he can manage adequately. Volunteering also has the advantage of shifting the initiative to him, a circumstance that often makes speech much easier for the stutterer. A friendly talk with the pupil in advance may be necessary in order to give teacher and pupil a common basis of understanding and to insure success of the volunteer system.

It is a basic principle of the process of behavior modification known as operant conditioning that rewarding a certain response tends to increase the chances that in a future similar situation that same response will occur again. The response wanted here is fluent speech. While the old cliché that success is its own reward applies to the stutterer's speech, some complimentary words and praise from the teacher can enhance the reward still further, if carefully handled. The compliment must be natural and not so contrived or obvious as to call attention to the stutterer's problem or suggest that he avoided contributing to his hearers' discomfort by not stuttering. A simple 'Very good, Johnnie' is much better than elaborate praise.

There may well be certain oral situations in the classroom that are inherently fraught with difficulty for the stutterer and in which he is not likely to succeed under any condition. Rather than risk the danger of failure and humiliation, it may be desirable to arrange some substitute assignment for the stutterer to take care of these crises. Merely excusing him from the difficult oral assignment is usually not advisable, for the stuttering child may thus come to believe that he can use his disability to avoid unpleasant tasks or to get out of doing his work.

Written work, or some other form of assignment, may be substituted. The undesirable feature of such a procedure is that the stutterer is thus set apart as being different from the others, since special treatment must be accorded him. As was mentioned earlier in this discussion, this is an undesirable attitude for the stutterer as well as for others.

In the end, the common sense and good judgment of the teacher must prevail, rather than a blind adherence to an arbitrary practice. Some modifications in classroom procedure will doubtless need to be made for the stutterer; many types of oral assignments will be difficult or impossible for him. The important consideration is to keep the welfare and abilities of the stuttering child in mind and to do the thing that is most likely to bring him the greatest benefit in the end.

6. Finally, every effort should be made to insure success in the speech situations in which the stutterer does participate. Whenever it is possible, such experiences should be carefully graded to begin with situations easy for him and gradually progress to more difficult ones as his ability to express himself improves. In this way his speech pattern may be modified, the old habit pattern changed and a new one built in its place. Instead of getting practice in stuttering, which he can already do readily enough, he may experience easy, normal speech. The stuttering child thus may come to expect success in speech situations and his self-confidence will be built up. Many of the same principles as are suggested for parents in the following section may also be applied by the teacher—do not supply words for him, do not have him stop and start over, do not show embarrassment or annoyance if he does have some trouble. Give him plenty of time and bolster his confidence by your own calmness and show of friendly interest.

It may well be that by following a program similar to the one suggested here you will be able to do a great deal to help the stuttering child. Progress is seldom steady and miraculous cures are indeed rare. Do not become discouraged if, for a time, the child seems even worse than he was before. Stuttering is characteristically cyclical; it grows better and then worse from time to time, often for no discoverable reason. Of course, if there is a speech clinician available, her help should be sought in dealing with the stutterer, and her advice should be followed about the sort of assistance the classroom teacher can and should give.

If there is no speech specialist, the teacher may still receive valuable assistance from other individuals and services provided by the school, such as the psychiatric social worker, the public-health nurse or school physician, counselors and advisers, and even the home-room teacher. Such assistance becomes especially critical if the child exhibits symptoms of general maladjustment along with the stuttering. Often it will be necessary to assume a broader and longer-range view of the problem than merely alleviating the speech disability, since little progress can be expected until and unless basic and underlying personality disorders associated with it are also cleared up. Not all cases will present this complex picture, of course, but when they do, the teacher may very well need to call upon other agencies for assistance or go into the home for conferences with the parents. For this, some helpful suggestions will be found in the paragraphs which follow.

What Parents Can Do for the Stuttering Child

As has been mentioned, the home environment, of which the parents constitute the major factor, is very important in determining whether a child develops normally in speech as well as in other characteristics or whether problems such as stuttering appear. There is reason to believe that stuttering is likely to be precipitated by environmental factors similar to those that may in other instances give rise to behavior problems and emotional maladjustment in general. It is important, therefore, that fundamental conditions conducive to sound mental health should be established in the home. This becomes especially urgent in the case of a child who is unusually sensitive or nervous or who has already begun to exhibit symptoms of stuttering. The basic needs of the child as well as the factors contributing to the fullest development of his personality were discussed in some detail in the preceding chapter. Further recommendations, with special reference to the prevention or alleviation of stuttering, will be presented briefly in the following paragraphs.

1. Do not nag at the child or call his attention directly to normal irregularities in his speech. Remember that it is perfectly normal for a young child to 'hem and haw' and exhibit certain other non-fluencies in his speech. Do not attempt to correct these directly and avoid referring to them as anything abnormal or to be ashamed of. In general, it is unwise to admonish the child to slow down, take a breath, think before he speaks, or repeat what he has said. Such devices only serve to make the child self-conscious and may operate to fixate or prolong the speech irregularities. If his attention has been called to his problem in any way, reassure him in a calm, unemotional manner that it is nothing to worry about—we all have trouble now and then in getting out what we want to say. All of these instructions do not mean that the parent is to assume a passive, do-nothing attitude toward the child's speech problems. There is much that he can and should do, but it must be done through a general, indirect approach to the child and his speech. Suggestions for such a program will be found in the paragraphs to follow.

2. Set him an example of slow, easy speech yourself; this is most important. Not only does the child imitate directly the speech that he hears most often in his environment, but he also reacts unconsciously to attitudes and states of mind as revealed in the speech and voices of those about him. A mother can scarcely expect a child to speak clearly and slowly and remain calm and relaxed when she herself is tense and jittery and speaks in a rapid, jerky tempo or with a tone that is shrill and scolding. In matters of speech as well as in other aspects of parent-child relationships, like begets like.

3. Go one step beyond the procedure suggested above—make good speech a project in the home. Make it a point to establish some time, or times, during the day when you can chat with your child and he can feel that your time and attention are fully his. During these periods, speak as well as you can and, by your good example, encourage him to do likewise. In this connection, a story hour, preferably at bedtime but at some other time if it is more convenient, can serve a very useful function in speech training, when the story reading, or telling, is properly done. It is here that the pattern of easy, fluent speech can be firmly fixed in the child's mind. Read him the same stories over and over again until he becomes quite familiar with them. Then encourage him to 'take over' here and there and assist you with the narration, but always in the same smooth, easy pattern that you have set for him. Some of the methods described in previous chapters can also be used to good advantage here.

4. Do everything you can to make speech as easy and enjoyable for the child as possible. Do not rush him when he has something to say that he considers important; give him his chance to be heard. Children in the home are often in a serious competitive situation when it comes to speech. No one seems to have any time for them to be heard, each one being so preoccupied with his own affairs that the child can easily come to feel that if he is to have a chance to say anything, he must slip it in quickly before he is interrupted. Such feelings of pressure can easily work havoc with the speech patterns of the child who is experiencing difficulty in expressing himself. The resulting tension is likely to confuse him or get him so upset that he will not be able to say anything. Even though you are busy, take a moment to listen carefully when your child has something important to tell you and make him feel that he has plenty of time in which to tell it.

On these occasions, react to him as you do toward the other children. Pay no attention to any hesitations, repetitions, or other disruptions in his speech. Look him in the eye—not at his mouth—and make him feel that you are interested in *what* he is saying and not bothered by how he is saying it. If he happens to be exceptionally excited or stimulated, try to give him a moment to calm down by having him take off his coat and hang it up, wash his hands, or do some other simple activity that seems natural under the circumstances. Take advantage of his good days when his speech seems to be exceptionally easy and fluent. Those are the times to engage him in conversation, tell stories, discuss pictures, et cetera, remembering that each successful experience will tend to build up his self-confidence and set the pattern for easy, natural speech. Conversely, on his bad days try to keep his talking down to a minimum.

Naturally, we cannot be forever stopping to listen to the chatter of children, nor can they be allowed to monopolize the conversational limelight at the dinner table, for example. It is vital, however, that the child realize he will get his turn and receive an attentive and respectful hearing when that turn comes.

5. Do not interfere with the development of the child's natural hand preference. There is some basis for believing that children who are slow in developing a definite sidedness or who never develop a clear-cut preference for one hand or the other may also suffer some retardation or other disturbance of the speech and language function. During the early years of life most children are naturally ambidextrous, often showing little choice in the use of one hand or the other. But by the time they enter school they should normally have developed some preference for either the right or the left hand in such activities as drawing or coloring. If the child gives evidence of being slow in settling upon a preferred side, his choice may be hastened by encouraging him in activities that involve one-handed skill, such as drawing, coloring, hammering, or using various other tools and toys. There is no inherent virtue in ambidexterity, especially for the child who gives evidence of having difficulty with any of the language skills. For such a child a

definite handedness should be encouraged and one-sided skills built up. It makes no difference whether the side ultimately chosen is the right or the left; the important consideration is that the child must be free to make the final choice for himself. And after the choice has been made and one-sidedness established, no attempt should be made to change it without the advice and guidance of a competent psychologist or speech clinician.

6. Be realistic about the standards you set for your child with respect to his behavior and achievement generally. If standards are set too high, you will only bring disappointment to yourself and a sense of defeat and inferiority to the child when he fails to measure up to them. Every child, and especially one who may be exhibiting symptoms of stuttering, needs to experience feelings of success and achievement. Tasks must be assigned and standards should be set that are commensurate with the child's ability, so that at least a substantial part of the time he can succeed. Failure should be dealt with objectively and 'philosophically.' Be reasonable and consistent in your discipline; do not demand conduct that is out of keeping with his maturity and do not condone it when it falls significantly short of what could normally be expected. Standards can be too lax as well as too high, and if they incline toward either extreme, the result is likely to be unhappiness and a degree of maladjustment for the child. Parents are also enjoined to keep standards and discipline procedures relatively consistent, so the child will know what to expect from day to day and from time to time.

7. Give the child a feeling of security, but avoid an overprotective or domineering attitude or relationship. Be very careful to keep family worries and responsibilities from the child, especially if they are conditions over which he has no control. Remember that anything believed by the child to threaten the peace and stability of the home poses a serious threat to his feelings of security. Family arguments or quarrels, expressions of favoritism, and discussions of financial worries, for example, should be carefully excluded from his experience. A sense of

insecurity can precipitate all manner of problems and symptoms of maladjustment, including stuttering as well as other forms of speech disturbance.

8. Do not attempt to stimulate the child's industry or ambition by comparing him unfavorably with his brothers or sisters or the neighbors' children, especially with respect to his speech ability. Instead of producing the desired effect, such a procedure is just as likely to instill feelings of frustration and inferiority in the child, especially if he happens to have a sensitive, impressionable nature. These practices may very well serve to intensify the weaknesses they were intended to eliminate.

9. Make sure the child is well and strong and has ample rest. Some children need more rest than others, especially if some condition, such as a speech deficiency, keeps them tense and under strain all day. Diet should also be inspected carefully. If the child shows any inclination toward nervousness or excitability, calming influences and activities should be stressed as much as possible. In such cases a quiet bedtime story would be more in order than an exciting murder mystery or cowboy adventure on television. The severity of stuttering characteristically shows a close and positive correlation with the fatigue and tension of the child, becoming more pronounced whenever he is tired or excited. Experiences that are known to excite him unduly should be avoided as much as possible. It should be stressed again that parental temperament and behavior may also be instrumental in determining whether the child remains tranquil or becomes tense and restless. The pattern set by the parent will have a strong influence, either consciously or unconsciously, in determining the behavior of the child.

10. If the speech difficulties persist beyond the normal hesitations and repetitions usually expected from a young child, a serious effort must be made to get expert assistance with diagnosis and therapy. The child may be developing a real case of stuttering, and the parent can no longer remain inactive. The parent should become especially concerned if the hesitations and repetitions persist beyond the time and age when they are

largely unconscious and effortless. The moment they begin to interfere materially with the child's communication or he begins to become aware of them as problems and struggles against them, the passive, 'watchful-waiting' attitude must be abandoned for some course of positive action. If no speech therapist is available or if the parent does not have access to other sources of professional advice, he should at least apply seriously the principles and practices suggested in this chapter, as well as those discussed in more detail in Chapter ix. The aid of the classroom teacher can also be enlisted; the school has a role to play in the prevention and alleviation of speech deficiencies second in importance only to that of the parents and the home. Some suggestions for ways in which the school may assist the child who stutters were discussed in the previous section.[13]

References

Anderson, Elwood G., *Therapy for Young Stutterers*, Wayne State University Press, Detroit, 1971.

Bloodstein, Oliver, *A Handbook on Stuttering*, The National Easter Seal Society for Crippled Children and Adults, 2023 West Ogden Avenue, Chicago, 1969.

Crotty, C., ed., *A Workbook in Speech Therapy for the Child Who Stutters*, Department of Curriculum, Room 822, Chicago Board of Education, 228 N. LaSalle Street, Chicago.

Emerick, Lon L., *Therapy for Young Stutterers*, The Interstate Printers and Publishers, Danville, Ill., 1970.

Fraser, Malcolm, pub., *Stuttering: Its Prevention*, Speech Foundation of America, 152 Lombardy Road, Memphis, Tenn., 1962.

———, *Stuttering: Treatment of the Young Stutterer in the School*, Speech Foundation of America, 152 Lombardy Road, Memphis, Tenn., 1964.

13. For information on possible clinics and individuals available in your area to assist the parents of a stuttering child, write to The American Speech and Hearing Association, 9030 Old Georgetown Road, Washington, D. C., 20014.

Goven, P., and G. Vette, *A Manual for Stuttering Therapy*, Stanwix House, Pittsburgh, 1966.

Hall, Helen, *Help Wanted? A Guidebook for Parents and Therapists Dealing with Young Nonfluent Children*, Northwestern University Speech Clinic, Evanston, Ill., 1966.

Johnson, Wendell, et al., *Speech Handicapped School Children*, Harper and Row, New York, 3rd ed., 1967, Chap. 5.

———, *Stuttering and What You Can Do About It*, University of Minnesota Press, Minneapolis, 1961.

———, *Toward Understanding Stuttering*, The National Easter Seal Society for Crippled Children and Adults, 2023 West Ogden Avenue, Chicago, 1958.

Luper, Harold, and Robert Mulder, *Stuttering: Therapy for Children*, Prentice-Hall, Englewood Cliffs, N. J., 1964.

Pennington, R. Corbin, and Elizabeth James, *The Stuttering Child —in the School and in the Home*, The Interstate Printers and Publishers, Danville, Ill., 1967.

Van Riper, Charles, *Speech Correction*, Prentice-Hall, Englewood Cliffs, N. J., 4th ed., 1963, Chaps. 11, 12.

Williams, Dean E., 'Stuttering Therapy for Children,' Chap. 41 in Lee E. Travis, ed., *Handbook of Speech Pathology and Audiology*, Appleton-Century-Crofts, New York, 1971.

XI

Hearing Impairment

Recently a physician was asked, 'If you had to be either blind or deaf, which would you choose?' Without hesitation he replied, 'I would rather be blind.' When asked to state the reasons for his choice, the physician replied that in his experience the blind were in closer touch with the world about them than were the deaf, and as a result the blind were as a group better adjusted to their handicap and more emotionally secure.

Until faced with impairment of hearing, a person is likely to take this important sensory process very much for granted. Actually, for his development as a social being, man is perhaps more dependent on his hearing than on any of his other senses. Hearing plays an important role in our lives in the following respects: (1) communication with our fellowmen; (2) awareness of our environment; and (3) aesthetic appreciation. An impairment of hearing divests us of enriching experiences in these three areas in proportion to the severity and type of the hearing loss.

The Functions of Hearing

In Communication

The ear is the natural medium through which the infant acquires language. As we have seen in a previous chapter, the development of meaningful speech follows the course of, first, an attempt to imitate the speech and voice patterns that an infant hears, and second, an awareness on the part of the infant that voice patterns and articulated speech do convey meaning. From the time of the first crude attempts of the infant to express himself, the development of speech consists of a refinement of the process of imitation of what he *hears* in his environment. The normal development of speech is dependent, therefore, on a normally functioning hearing mechanism.

In our early years of life, hearing provides our only source of communication with others, except for the relatively crude methods of pantomime and gesture. And even after we learn to read, hearing still plays the most important part in the communication of our daily lives. The relation of teacher to pupil requires that the pupil respond to the teacher's oral instructions and questions. Even in higher education, the lecture method has long been the standard way of presenting the basic material of a course.

Of no less importance in the development of the individual is the part hearing plays in the casual communication of daily living. Our conversational exchanges with members of our family, with our friends, with the postman, with the various other people with whom we come in daily contact, provide us with comradeship and a feeling of belonging which would be jeopardized by any impairment of the hearing function. Much of our lives is consumed in the small talk essential to our modern existence as social beings. A hearing impairment can thus seriously interfere with our social development.

In Making Us Aware of Our Environment

Hearing is also important to us in making us aware of our environment. Our ears are constantly recording the sounds about us, consciously or unconsciously. We heed the sound of an approaching truck when crossing a street, the sound of water boiling on a stove, the ringing of the telephone or the doorbell. Absence of familiar sounds in our environment to which we have reacted unconsciously causes a vague uneasiness which awakens our consciousness, so that we seek to determine the reason for the absence of the familiar sounds. We are suddenly aware that the sound of the refrigerator running is different somehow, and we begin to react consciously to what had been an unheeded part of our auditory background. Thus we are led to investigate, and we discover that the refrigerator motor is in need of repair.

The importance of the unheeded background noises of our environment to our sense of security is demonstrated when we stay away from home overnight in a strange place. The man from the city may have difficulty going to sleep in a quiet country place because of the absence of various sounds characteristic of city living. Likewise, the person from the country or small town who is suddenly transplanted to a hotel or motel room in the heart of a teeming city may find it hard to compose himself for sleep in the presence of so many unfamiliar background noises. Ramsdell has termed our reaction to background noises as hearing on the 'primitive' level, and he attributes many of the psychological problems characteristic of the hard of hearing to loss of hearing on this primitive level.[1]

In Aesthetic Appreciation

In addition to its functions in communication and in making us aware of our environment, hearing serves as a source of

1. D. A. Ramsdell, 'The Psychology of the Hard-of-Hearing and the Deafened Adult,' Chap. 18 in Hallowell Davis and S. Richard Silverman, eds., *Hearing and Deafness*, Holt, Rinehart and Winston, New York, 1970, pp. 437–40.

aesthetic experience. We enjoy a variety of sounds from the simple cracking of wood in the fireplace to the tonal complexities of a symphony. When our hearing is impaired, we are deprived of the full use of this source of aesthetic enjoyment.

Extent of Problem of Hearing Impairment

There has been considerable confusion about the number of school children in the United States with hearing impairments. Estimates have ranged from one million to three million. Part of this confusion results from the difficulty of determining when hearing is sufficiently atypical to be labeled defective, and part is due to a difference in methods used to discover hearing impairment. Various individuals have employed various standards of significance in measuring hearing loss. Since hearing impairment can range all the way from a very slight loss at relatively unimportant frequencies to 'total' deafness, it is a problem to decide at just what point hearing changes from 'normal' to 'defective.' The Maternal and Child Health Service estimates that about 2.3 million children have hearing impairments.[2]

At this point a distinction should be made between the deaf and the hard of hearing. Probably the best definitions are those devised in 1937 by the Committee on Nomenclature of the Conference of Executives of American Schools for the Deaf. This committee proposed that the deaf be defined as those in whom the sense of hearing is non-functional for the ordinary purposes of life, and the hard of hearing as those in whom the sense of hearing, although defective, is still functional with or without a hearing aid.[3] This chapter is concerned with the *hard-of-hearing* child, not the *deaf* child, within the meaning of the definitions above.

2. 'Services for Crippled Children,' Public Health Service Publication No. 2137, U. S. Department of Health, Education and Welfare, Washington, D. C., 1971, p. 11.
3. S. R. Silverman and H. S. Lane, 'Deaf Children,' Chap. 16 in Davis and Silverman, *Hearing and Deafness*, op. cit. p. 386.

Description of the Ear

While, as we have seen in previous chapters, most speech disorders are of the functional or non-organic type, deficiencies of hearing are almost always related to some pathological condition of the hearing mechanism. It is true that some children and adults may exhibit symptoms of impaired hearing for psychological reasons, or to achieve some pecuniary advantage. The great majority of individuals presenting symptoms of hearing impairment, however, do actually have some pathology. Since this is so, it is essential in discussing problems of hearing to have some understanding of the sensory process with which we are dealing.

The ear is a highly complex structure. We still do not know all the answers to the question, 'How do we hear?', and no attempt will be made here to do more than describe briefly the principal parts of the ear and explain the simplest elements of the physiology of hearing. Figure 8 is a drawing of the right ear with labeling of the principal components of the outer ear, the middle ear, and the inner ear. In the description of the ear that follows, the parts of the hearing mechanism labeled in the figure have been italicized.

The Outer Ear

The outer ear consists of the *pinna* (also called the *auricle*) and the *external auditory meatus* or *ear canal*. While the outer ear is the most prominent part of the hearing mechanism, it is the least important. Loss of the pinna results in only a slight diminution of hearing sensitivity. Its function is to channel sound waves into the ear canal along which they travel until they strike the *eardrum*, or *tympanic membrane*, which separates the outer ear from the middle ear. In addition to providing a pathway for sound to reach the middle ear, the external canal contains wax-secreting glands and hairs that discourage insects and dirt particles from penetrating to the eardrum. While the outermost portion of the canal is encased by cartilage, the innermost portion penetrates the mastoid process of the temporal bone.

The Middle Ear

The middle ear is separated from the outer ear by the eardrum and from the inner ear by a bony wall through which there are two openings—the *oval* and *round windows*—separated by a rounded projection called the *promontory*. The eardrum is conical in shape, with the apex of the cone pointing inward and upward. The middle ear is called the tympanum because of its resemblance to a drum. The *tympanic membrane* is of course the drumhead, although in popular usage the term 'eardrum' refers only to the membrane.

The middle ear is filled with air supplied through the *Eustachian tube* that is an extension of the middle ear to the posterior nasal passage, or *nasopharynx*. The Eustachian tube, by serving as an air inlet or outlet, keeps the air pressure in the middle ear equal to that outside. If the Eustachian tube is blocked, air-pressure changes outside the body cause the eardrum to be either distended or retracted, depending on whether the pressure in the middle ear is greater or less than the outside pressure. The middle-ear cavity also connects with the air cells of the mastoid process of the temporal bone.

Bridging the middle-ear cavity is a chain of three tiny bones called the ossicles. The first of these, the *malleus* (hammer), is attached to the eardrum. It extends into the *attic* (*epitympanic recess*) where it articulates with the *incus* (anvil). The incus in turn connects with the head of the *stapes* (stirrup). The two *crura* of the stapes attach to the *footplate*, which is held in the oval window by an annular ligament. The round window, below the promontory, is covered by a membrane.

The middle ear has two opposed functions. One of these functions is to increase the sensitivity of the hearing mechanism. This is accomplished both by a lever action of the ossicles vibrating as a unit to transmit the movements of the eardrum

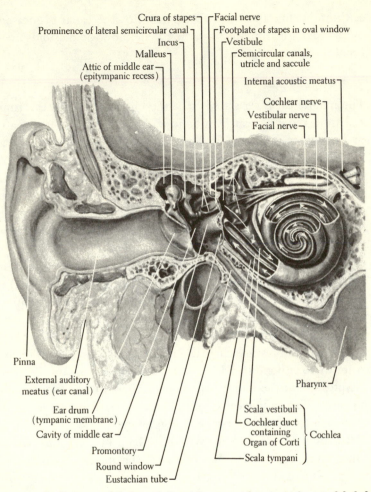

Crura of stapes
Prominence of lateral semicircular canal
Incus
Malleus
Attic of middle ear
(epitympanic recess)

Facial nerve
Footplate of stapes in oval window
Vestibule
Semicircular canals,
utricle and saccule
Internal acoustic meatus
Cochlear nerve
Vestibular nerve
Facial nerve

Pinna

External auditory
meatus (ear canal)

Ear drum
(tympanic membrane)

Cavity of middle ear

Promontory

Round window

Eustachian tube

Pharynx

Scala vestibuli
Cochlear duct
containing
Organ of Corti
Scala tympani

Cochlea

FIGURE 8. Cut-away drawing of the right ear with principal parts labeled. Copyright 1970 CIBA Corporation; reproduced with permission from the *Clinical Symposia*, illustrated by Frank Netter, M.D.

to the footplate of the stapes, and by the differential in the area of the eardrum and the area of the footplate. The other function of the middle ear is to protect the inner ear from damage resulting from stimulation of the eardrum by sounds of excessive intensity. This protective function is accomplished by the reflex action of muscles which impede the movements of the ossicular chain and thus prevent the transmission of vibrations of excessive amplitude to the inner ear.

The Inner Ear

The inner ear consists of a bony labyrinth which encases in fluid the membranous end organs of hearing, and of equilibrium or balance. The end organ of hearing is the *cochlea,* named for the snail shell that it resembles. The end organs of equilibrium are the *semicircular canals* (three of them) and the *utricle* and *saccule.* The part of the inner ear common both to the cochlea and to the organs of equilibrium is called the *vestibule.* It is into the vestibule that the oval window opens. The semicircular canals together with the utricle and the saccule constitute the vestibular portion of the inner ear.

There are two fluid systems in the inner ear. The membranous labyrinth is suspended in perilymph, which is essentially identical to the cerebrospinal fluid that bathes the brain and spinal cord. The perilymph of the vestibular and cochlear portions of the inner ear is continuous. Within the membranous labyrinth is found a fluid called endolymph, which is chemically different from perilymph. Although there is a duct that provides limited communication between the two parts of the membranous labyrinth, the endolymphatic systems of the cochlea and the vestibular mechanism are essentially separate.

There are some practical consequences of the close association between the end organs of hearing and of equilibrium: (1) Certain forms of deafness are accompanied by symptoms of dizziness or vertigo, indicating that an impairment at the cochlea is also producing an abnormal stimulation of the vestibular system. (2) A 'dead' vestibular system may be accompanied by a 'dead' cochlea, so that the absence of vestibular responses—for example, the failure of rapid rotation of the body to produce symptoms of dizziness—may point to a lack of cochlear function as well. (3) The surgeon may bypass a blockage at the oval window produced by a fixated stapes by creating a new window in the bony capsule of the *lateral semicircular canal* that bulges into the wall separating the middle ear from the inner ear. This operation, called fenestration (from the Latin word *fenestra*, meaning 'window'), restored useful hearing to many individuals suffering from the disease called otosclerosis that produced fixation of the stapes in the oval window. Newer operative techniques have now made the fenestration largely obsolete.

Within the cochlea, three 'galleries' or scalae may be identified, extending from the basal end of the 'snail shell' to the apex. The *scala vestibuli* and *scala tympani* are perilymphatic spaces, while the scala media or *cochlear duct* contains endolymph in which is suspended the essential organ of hearing, the *organ of Corti*. The scala vestibuli communicates with the middle ear by way of the oval window, while the scala tympani communicates with the middle ear by means of the round window.

The organ of Corti (located but not detailed in figure 8) consists of thousands of hair cells that are interconnected in a complex fashion by nerve fibers that terminate in ganglia outside the cochlea. From these ganglia proceed neurons that join together to form the *cochlear nerve* which then joins with the *vestibular nerve*, coming from the semicircular canals and the utricle and saccule, to constitute the VIIIth cranial nerve. The VIIIth nerve, in company with the VIIth, or *facial nerve*, proceeds toward the brain stem through an opening in the temporal bone called the *internal acoustic meatus*. Once the neurons enter the brain stem, they proceed to various nuclei and course upward until they reach the cortex of the cerebrum. On their way to the cerebral cortex, some of the fibers of the

VIIIth nerve cross to the opposite side of the brain, so that neurons from both ears terminate in each cerebral hemisphere.

How We Hear

By Air Conduction

The usual way in which we hear is by air conduction. Sound waves are directed into the external canal by the pinna, causing the eardrum to vibrate. As the drum moves, the chain of ossicles moves, resulting in a rocking motion of the footplate of the stapes in the oval window. The vibrations of the footplate are transmitted to the perilymphatic fluid in the scala vestibuli. As can be seen in figure 8, the fluid movement in the scala vestibuli is transmitted to the endolymph in the cochlear duct and then to the perilymph in the scala tympani. The incompressible fluids in the cochlea are able to move because of the reciprocal movements of the oval and round windows. As the oval window bulges into the vestibule, the round window is moved outward toward the middle ear, and vice versa. The movement of the endolymph in the cochlear duct causes movement of the hairs in the organ of Corti which stimulates the hair cells and initiates nerve impulses that are transmitted through the neurons of the cochlear nerve to the cerebral cortex by way of the various nuclei within the brain stem and higher levels of the brain. Sounds of high frequency produce maximum stimulation of the organ of Corti at the basal (middle ear) end of the cochlear duct, while sounds of low frequency cause maximum stimulation toward the apical end of the cochlear duct.

By Bone Conduction

The sensation of hearing can also be produced through what is called 'bone conduction.' Since the inner ear is housed in one of the bones of the skull, sound waves which cause the bones of the skull to vibrate can produce movement of the fluids of the inner ear directly without passing through the eardrum and the middle ear. Compared with the eardrum and the chain of ossicles, however, the bones of the skull are relatively insensitive to sound waves originating from outside the body. Except for the vibrations produced by our own larynx and resonating cavities, therefore, we are not aware of hearing by bone conduction unless some pathological condition is interfering with the normal operation of the outer or the middle ear.

Types of Hearing Impairment

Excluding those of psychological origin, hearing impairments are broadly classified as being either peripheral or central. A hearing impairment is peripheral if the pathology occurs outside the central nervous system, that is, in the outer, the middle, or the inner ear, or in the cochlear nerve between the inner ear and the brain stem. An impairment is central if the pathology occurs anywhere from the brain stem to the cortex, or, in other words, within the central nervous system. A central impairment is characterized by the inability of the higher centers of the auditory system to process information delivered from the sound-receiving part of the system. A central impairment produces what might be termed auditory imperception, rather than a loss of sensitivity to sound. Central impairments, therefore, cannot be identified through routine hearing tests, which measure loss of sensitivity. Many so-called aphasic children have central hearing impairments.

By contrast, peripheral hearing impairments are characterized by loss of sensitivity for some or all frequencies. Peripheral impairments may be unilateral (affecting only one ear) or bilateral (affecting both ears). Peripheral impairments can be identified through routine hearing tests. In this chapter we shall be concerned only with peripheral hearing impairments— the identification of children with peripheral hearing impairments, and the therapeutic and educational management of such children. It is possible, of course, that a given child may present both a peripheral and a central impairment. As indicated earlier in this chapter, we shall concentrate on the hard-of-hearing (hypacusic) child rather than the deaf (anacusic) child, since the concern throughout this book is with children in regular classrooms who present problems of speech, language, or hearing.

Peripheral hearing impairments are categorized as being conductive, sensori-neural, or mixed. A conductive impairment is due to pathology of the outer or middle ear when the inner ear is normal. A sensori-neural impairment is due to pathology of the inner ear or the cochlear nerve when the outer and middle ears are normal. A mixed impairment occurs when both conductive and sensori-neural components are present in the same ear.

Behavioral Characteristics Differentiating Conductive
from Sensori-Neural Impairments

Some generalizations may be made concerning the behavioral characteristics that differentiate those with conductive impairments from those with sensori-neural impairments. There are many exceptions to the generalizations, so they have limited diagnostic significance. Nevertheless, it is useful to understand the ways in which the typical individual with conductive impairment differs from the typical individual with sensori-neural impairment. Some of the generalizations that follow are more applicable to adults than to children.

1. *Loudness of voice* The individual with a conductive impairment is likely to have a voice that is relatively weak, whereas the person with a sensori-neural impairment will probably speak too loudly. The reason for this difference is that we tend to hear our own voices to a considerable extent by bone conduction, the bones of our skulls being set in vibration directly by the vibrating vocal folds and vibrating air in resonance chambers of the head. Since the person with a conductive impairment has a normal inner ear, his bone conduction is functioning

normally and he hears his own voice at all times with what seems to be sufficient loudness. The person with a sensori-neural impairment, however, does not have a normally functioning inner ear. His hearing by bone conduction—as well as by air conduction—is impaired. To hear his own voice with what seems to be normal loudness, he must talk loudly enough to overcome the amount of his sensori-neural loss.

2. *Hearing in noise* An individual with a conductive impairment will usually report that he can follow conversation better in a fairly noisy place than in a quiet one. The person with a sensori-neural impairment is uncomfortable in the presence of noise and cannot hear as well in a noisy place as in a quiet one. The explanation for this difference is that a conductive impairment acts much the same way as ear plugs do in cutting down the loudness of the sounds that reach the inner ear. When we have plugs in our ears, people have to talk more loudly to us before we can hear them well enough to follow what they are saying. In other words, with plugs in our ears, a shout may sound to us as a voice of only average loudness. In noisy surroundings, people have to talk loudly to each other in order to make their voices carry over the noise. Since to the person with a conductive impairment a shout may be equal to average loudness, he is obviously at an advantage in a situation where people have to talk more loudly than they normally would. The ear with a sensori-neural impairment, on the other hand, cannot be compared to the normal ear with a plug in it, since the pathology is not in the sound-conducting part of the ear, but in the sound-*perceiving* part. In the case of most sensori-neural impairments, the ear has lost its ability to respond to sounds that reach the cochlea with relatively weak intensity. The cochlea can respond to sounds that reach it with relatively high intensity, but the perceived sound is then heard as a sound of high intensity. In other words, whereas a shout may be heard by a conductively-impaired ear as a voice of average loudness, a shout will be heard by the ear with a

sensori-neural impairment as a shout. This characteristic of most ears with sensori-neural impairments of responding to loud sounds as loud sounds, though not responding to sounds of weaker intensity, is called 'recruitment.' Recruitment is characteristic of sensori-neural impairments of cochlear origin, but not those due to involvement of the cochlear nerve, which constitute relatively few of the cases of sensori-neural impairments.

There is another factor that operates to make it more difficult for the ear with a sensori-neural impairment to hear in noisy surroundings. Whereas in a conductive impairment the ear usually loses sensitivity to sounds of all frequencies, or pitches, in equal amounts, in a sensori-neural impairment sounds of higher pitch are usually affected much more than sounds of lower pitch. Noise in general is low pitched. Many of our speech sounds, on the other hand, are high pitched. In the presence of noise, then, the person with a sensori-neural impairment may hear the noise relatively well but have difficulty hearing speech intelligibly.

3. *Speech-sound discrimination* This difference in response to sounds of various pitches accounts for another point of rough differentiation between the conductively-impaired ear and the ear with sensori-neural impairment. Since the typical conductive impairment is characterized by fairly equal losses at all pitches, speech loud enough to overcome the amount of the hearing loss will be heard with normal quality—that is, a normal relationship among all the pitches employed in speech. We say that the typical person with conductive loss has good speech-sound discrimination, because when speech is loud enough for him to hear, he can perceive all of the speech sounds correctly. The typical case of sensori-neural impairment, however, is characterized by an unequal response to various pitches. A person with such an impairment usually has much more difficulty hearing high-pitched sounds—for example, [s], [θ], [f], [t], [k], and [p]. Increasing the loudness of speech does

not alter the inequality of pitch response; in fact, increasing the loudness may accentuate the inequality of response, since relatively more energy will go into the low pitches. Therefore, no matter how much louder the voice is made, the person with sensori-neural impairment may have difficulty discriminating between words such as *pass* and *path*, which differ only in their high-pitched final sounds. In comparison with the conductively-impaired ear, therefore, we say that the ear with sensori-neural impairment has poor speech-sound discrimination.

Diagnostic Hearing Tests

Pure-Tone Audiometry

The preferred method of determining whether a particular hearing impairment is conductive, sensori-neural, or mixed is to administer a pure-tone audiometric test, which gives quantitative measures of the amount of hearing loss over a wide range of frequencies or pitches, both by air conduction and by bone conduction. The pure-tone audiometer is an electronic instrument which generates a number of individual frequencies over a wide range of intensities, or hearing levels. An audiometer test determines the intensity at which the tested ear can just barely detect the presence of each of the test frequencies. This intensity is termed the 'threshold hearing level' (sometimes 'hearing threshold level'), or more simply just 'threshold.' Hearing level or hearing loss is expressed in logarithmic units of relative intensity called 'decibels,' abbreviated 'dB.' Frequency is expressed in 'hertz,' abbreviated 'Hz,' which is synonymous with cycles per second. Audiometers are calibrated so that the average threshold hearing level of a group of normal young adult ears is zero dB at each frequency. Ears are tested singly both by air conduction and by bone conduction. The air-conduction test is accomplished by placing a dynamic receiver, or earphone, over the ear. Bone conduction is tested by placing a vibrator on the mastoid process of the temporal bone just behind the pinna, or sometimes by placing the vibrator on the center of the forehead.

The results of a hearing test administered with a pure-tone audiometer are usually graphed on a special form called an audiogram, although some examiners prefer to record the threshold hearing level at each frequency numerically rather than graphing it. A sample audiogram is shown in figure 9.

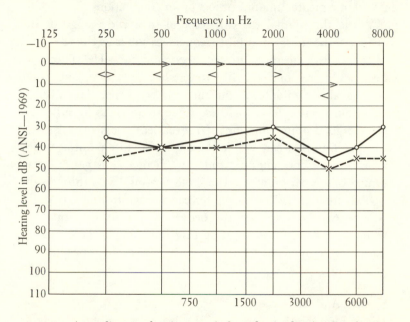

FIGURE 9. An audiogram showing a typical conductive hearing impairment. The vertical lines represent the available audiometric frequencies, not all of which have been utilized in this example. The horizontal lines represent hearing level in dB, measured in steps of 5 dB. Air-conduction threshold hearing levels for the frequencies tested are represented by O's for the right ear and X's for the left ear. Bone-conduction threshold hearing levels are shown by arrowheads pointing to the right for the right ear and to the left for the left ear.

The loss represented by this audiogram is a typical conductive impairment, indicated by the fact that this patient's bone conduction is normal. The air-conduction curve for each ear shows hearing levels that are fairly equal at all frequencies tested. A sensori-neural impairment would be represented by an audiogram showing losses by bone conduction equaling those by air conduction. Also, the typical sensori-neural impairment would show greater losses for the high frequencies than for the low frequencies. The low frequencies might even be within the range of normal. A mixed impairment would be represented by an audiogram showing some degree of loss by bone conduction, but a greater amount of loss by air conduction.

While the normal ear can respond to a wide range of frequencies, the most important frequencies so far as the reception of speech is concerned are 500, 1000, and 2000 Hz. These frequencies correspond roughly to pitches one, two, and three octaves above middle C on the musical scale. The average threshold hearing level for these three frequencies in either ear gives a good approximation of the patient's loss of sensitivity for speech in that ear. While there is no definite point at which a hearing loss becomes a handicapping one, it is generally assumed that a person whose threshold hearing levels through the 'speech frequencies' of the better ear average from 25 to 35 dB will benefit from at least the occasional use of a hearing aid, while a person with average hearing levels in the better ear of 40 dB or more will probably require the almost constant use of a hearing aid.

Speech Audiometry

While pure-tone audiometry is the accepted method of making diagnostic tests of hearing impairment, this test yields only indirect data on how severely the individual is impaired in his hearing and understanding of speech. In recent years otologists (medical ear specialists) and audiologists (hearing specialists) have made increasing use of speech audiometry to measure loss for speech directly. Speech audiometry yields measures of loss of sensitivity for speech (speech-reception threshold) and ability to identify words or sentences at supra-threshold hearing levels (discrimination score). Pure-tone audiometry plus speech audiometry gives a more complete picture of a patient's hearing loss and the true extent of his handicap than can be obtained through a pure-tone test alone. While pure-tone audiometers are generally available in otologists' offices, speech audiometers are usually found only in audiology clinics or hearing and speech centers. No attempt will be made here to explain the methods of speech audiometry. The reader should be aware, however, that in addition to the pure-tone test, a more complete picture of hearing impairment can be obtained through speech audiometry.

Causes of Hearing Impairment

The causes of hearing impairment are manifold. We shall not attempt to chronicle all of them but will be concerned here only with the more common causes of hearing impairment among children of preschool and school age. We shall consider causes of conductive and sensori-neural impairments in that order.

Conductive Impairments

1. *Otitis media* The most common cause of a conductive impairment is otitis media, which means literally 'inflammation of the middle ear.' This condition is usually traceable to an upper respiratory infection, such as the common cold, or one of the children's diseases, such as measles, or it may be related to malfunction of the Eustachian tube because of swollen tissues in the nasopharynx or the presence of excessive adenoid tissue.

In the case of infection in the nose or throat, it is easy to see how the middle ear can become involved secondarily, since the Eustachian tube provides a pathway for the infection to reach the ear (see fig. 8). As the ear becomes involved, the eardrum is distended, or forced outward, by the pressure within the middle ear created by the presence of pus. The drum may be distended to the point that it ruptures spontaneously, releasing the matter into the external canal. A spontaneous rupture may destroy much of the eardrum or create a perforation that is too large to heal by itself. To prevent such an occurrence, the otologist may decide to make an incision in the drum to provide drainage and relieve the pressure within the middle ear. This surgical procedure, called a myringotomy, results in no permanent damage to the eardrum, since the incision heals quickly without a scar.

Presence of pus in the middle ear is dangerous, as well as posing a threat to the hearing. There is always the possibility that the infection will spread to the air cells of the mastoid process, producing a condition called mastoiditis. Such a condition can easily progress to an involvement of the brain which may prove fatal. At the least, the extended presence of pus in the middle ear may cause erosion of the ossicles, resulting in a substantial hearing loss. Thus, whenever the ears present any evidence of infection, a physician should be consulted immediately. Fortunately, prompt administration of antibiotics can usually control an infection before it reaches the point of producing mastoiditis. If a spontaneous rupture of the eardrum is threatened, the physician can perform a myringotomy.

The otitis media associated with Eustachian tube malfunction results in a retracted eardrum—one that is forced inward. The tissues of the middle ear require oxygen. When the supply of air through the Eustachian tube is cut off, the oxygen in the middle ear is quickly absorbed, creating a condition of reduced air pressure. The drum is then forced inward by the greater outside pressure. The tension on the drum reduces its sensitivity to slight pressure changes induced by sound waves, resulting in a loss of hearing sensitivity. If the reduced pressure in the middle ear persists, fluid is 'milked' from the tissues which will partially or completely fill the middle ear cavity. Since this fluid is serum, the condition is called 'serous otitis media.' Serous otitis media may also occur following a case of acute infectious otitis media that has been treated with antibiotics. While the drugs neutralize the infection and thus remove its active threat, the middle ear may remain partially or completely filled with fluid that has now become sterile. If allowed to remain, this fluid may thicken and cause increasing interference with the operation of the ossicular chain with a resulting decrease in hearing sensitivity. Thus the physician should seek not only to control infection but to insure proper drainage of fluid from the middle ear. To drain the ear it is frequently necessary to insert a drainage tube through a myringotomy incision to prevent its premature healing.

If properly treated, otitis media should not result in any permanent hearing impairment. Otitis media that persists for any length of time or that recurs at frequent intervals, however, can cause permanent damage to the structures of the middle ear and thus result in a hearing loss of the conductive type.

Special mention should be made of the middle ear problems associated with cleft palate, discussed in Chapter vii. Some of the muscles involved in velo-pharyngeal closure are responsible also for opening the Eustachian tube. Since these muscles are frequently impaired in cleft palate children, the Eustachian tube may not function properly to ventilate the middle ear, leading to an increased incidence of middle ear problems in such children. Moreover, cleft palate children tend to have frequent colds and other upper respiratory disorders, which can cause secondary involvement of the middle ear. Parents and teachers of cleft palate children should be aware of their special susceptibility to middle ear problems and seek the consultation of an ear specialist whenever there is any suggestion of earaches or diminished hearing sensitivity.

2. *Blockage of the external canal* A conductive hearing impairment occurs whenever there is a complete blockage of the canal that prevents sound waves from reaching the eardrum. Usually such blockage is the result of an over-accumulation of wax that is secreted by glands in the skin lining the canal. Some people seem to produce much more wax than is needed to protect the eardrum, so that it is necessary for them to have the

excess accumulation removed at regular intervals. If allowed to remain in the canal, the wax will become hard and 'impacted' and difficult to remove. The only danger of a permanent hearing loss resulting from this condition is that the removal of the impacted wax imbedded against the eardrum may produce damage to the drum. Frequent medical inspections of the external canal should be performed in persons subject to the excessive secretion of wax.

Blockage of the external canal can result from foreign objects in the ear. Children are prone to stick things in their nose and ears, and any object capable of sealing the eardrum from air-borne sound waves can produce a conductive impairment pending its removal. Because of the possibility of damaging the delicate skin of the ear canal or the eardrum, no one but a physician should attempt to remove wax or foreign objects from a child's ear.

3. *Congenital malformations*   Occasionally babies are born with malformations of the outer or middle ear. The pinna may be missing completely, which in itself would not cause more than a mild impairment of hearing. Usually, when the pinna is missing or deformed, however, there are other more serious anomalies present such as an absent ear canal, or defects in the middle ear structures, for example, missing or disarticulated ossicles. If the difficulty is limited to lack of a canal, hearing can be restored by a relatively simple surgical procedure. Even if the middle-ear structures are affected, plastic reconstruction can frequently eliminate or at least minimize hearing impairment.

4. *Otosclerosis*   Although few children of school age have noticeable impairment of hearing as a result of the disease called otosclerosis, some mention should be made of this cause of conductive impairment. Otosclerosis is an hereditary disease which manifests itself in a pathological type of bone replacing some of the normal bone of the inner-ear capsule. When this pathological bony growth results in the fixation of the footplate

of the stapes in the oval window, a conductive hearing impairment results. While otosclerosis may affect the hearing of only one ear, it usually occurs simultaneously in both ears. Most frequently the hearing impairment becomes noticeable when the patient is in his late teens or twenties, although occasionally the condition has been diagnosed in young children. The disease is characterized by a progressive hearing loss that in time may change from a purely conductive impairment to one that is mixed, and in extreme cases may eventually become purely sensori-neural.

Mention has already been made of the fenestration operation for otosclerosis in which a new route for sound to reach the cochlea is provided through a surgically-constructed window in one of the semicircular canals. The most popular current operation for restoring hearing to otosclerotics is the stapedectomy, which consists of replacing the whole stapes bone with a prosthesis connecting the incus with tissue placed in the oval window to provide proper closure.

Sensori-Neural Impairments

Sensori-neural impairments in children may be hereditary, congenital, or acquired after birth. Several kinds of genetic defects associated with varying degrees of hearing impairment have been identified. Some produce hearing impairment from the time of birth, while others may not cause deterioration of the hearing mechanism for several years. Congenital defects that are not hereditary may result from damage in utero because of illness incurred by the mother during pregnancy. The best known cause of congenital hearing impairment is maternal rubella (German measles) which, while usually a mild illness for the mother, can have devastating effects not only on the hearing mechanism but also on the visual system, the heart, and the intellectual potential of the unborn child. Other viral infections incurred by the mother during pregnancy are thought to be similarly dangerous to the embryo or fetus. Blood incompatibilities between the mother and the fetus, most notably

Rh incompatibility, may be responsible for either peripheral sensori-neural impairment, central auditory impairment, or both. Certain drugs administered to the mother during pregnancy may cause harm to the unborn child's auditory system.

Acquired sensori-neural impairments may be due to disease, injury, or to the toxic effects of certain drugs. Meningitis frequently causes a profound sensori-neural impairment. The toxic effects of such common contagious diseases as measles and mumps may produce sensori-neural impairment.

Sensori-neural impairment may result from a blow to the head causing a fracture of the temporal bone, or from exposure to an explosion or extremely intense noise. When the causative agent is an extreme pressure wave, the injury to the ear is called acoustic trauma. It is not uncommon for acoustic trauma to produce a ruptured eardrum and perhaps a disarticulated ossicular chain as well as damage to the cochlea, in which case the resulting hearing impairment will be mixed rather than purely sensori-neural. A long-time exposure to excessive sound intensities will produce in some people a gradually progressive sensori-neural impairment with the higher frequencies affected first and more severely. Such noise-induced hearing impairment would not often be found in young children, of course.

Certain drugs are ototoxic, that is, have harmful effects on the inner ear. Quinine used to be the chief offender. Some so-called 'miracle drugs' used to combat serious infections may cause severe or profound hearing loss. Dihydrostreptomycin, neomycin, and kanamycin are the chief offenders. Physicians now are generally aware of the potential danger these drugs pose to the hearing, so they would be employed only where required as a life-saving measure.

Hearing Conservation

In recent years a great deal has been said and written on the subject of hearing conservation. Just what is meant by this term, and how can it be accomplished? By hearing conservation is meant a program in which parents, speech and hearing specialists, educators, and physicians combine their efforts (1) to prevent hearing impairment; (2) to discover hearing impairment where it exists; (3) to treat the cause of the hearing impairment where possible; and (4) to provide suitable habilitation or rehabilitation and suitable educational procedures for individuals whose hearing is permanently impaired. Usually such a community program is centered in the public schools, where children are readily available for observation, testing, and medical examination. The remainder of this chapter will be concerned with the four main facets of a hearing conservation program, with special emphasis on the role of the classroom teacher in such a program.

Prevention of Hearing Impairment

Probably the most important item in the prevention of hearing impairment is prompt and proper attention to any upper respiratory infections, including the common cold. In an earlier section of this chapter it was mentioned that the most common cause of conductive hearing impairment is otitis media, an inflammation of the middle ear, one type of which may be caused by infections proceeding to the middle ear along the Eustachian tube from the nasal passages. The object in the prompt treatment of an upper respiratory infection is to prevent its involving the ear. In addition to treating the nose and throat symptoms of any such infection, care should be taken in blowing the nose, since improper nose blowing may easily force mucus into the Eustachian tubes. When the nose is blown, as it inevitably must be during a head cold, the nostrils should not be pinched shut with the fingers. Whenever the nostrils are closed off in blowing the nose, excessive pressure built up in the nasopharynx can force the Eustachian tubes open and blow mucus into the lower end of the tubes, causing swelling and paving the way for ascending infection. Teachers can help to prevent middle-ear trouble by instructing their pupils in the proper way of blowing their noses, which is to blow gently with the nostrils open, or with very light finger pressure.

The next most important item in the prevention of hearing impairment is taking proper care of ears in which otitis media has developed. If the otitis media is of the infectious type, medical treatment is indicated. Antibiotics should be promptly administered to bring the infection under control before it can damage any of the structures of the ear or invade the mastoid process. If there is danger of the eardrum rupturing spontaneously from the pressure of fluid in the middle ear, the attending physician will probably perform a myringotomy and also perhaps insert a tube to facilitate drainage. Since infectious otitis media is usually accompanied by pain, the teacher should be alert to any complaints of earache in her pupils, so that they may be properly investigated and treated. Running or discharging ears indicate that the drum has ruptured. A child with running ears should be under the care of a physician. Treatment in such cases is directed toward drying up the middle ear and eventually closing the perforation to restore the useful function of the eardrum and to guard against the entrance of infection into the middle ear from the external canal.

Since a form of otitis media can result from malfunctioning Eustachian tubes, an important step in preventing hearing loss is the surgical removal of excess adenoid tissue around the orifices of the tubes. The child with enlarged adenoids will not only have difficulty in breathing through his nose but may also have occluded Eustachian tubes. The teacher should be alert to detect cases of mouth breathing, or vocal quality of the denasal or negative nasality type, for the cause of these symptoms may very well be a profusion of adenoid tissue in the nasopharynx that might also cause otitis media. Since enlarged adenoids provide a convenient focal point for infection, there is always the danger that an infection originating in the adenoids may reach the middle ears by way of the Eustachian tubes, resulting in an infectious otitis media. Physicians do not always agree on the desirability of performing a T and A (tonsillectomy and adenoidectomy). Since lymphoid tissue is thought to serve as a protective barrier against infection, pediatricians frequently are loath to permit a T and A, preferring instead to treat diseased tonsils and adenoids conservatively with antibiotics. Ear, nose, and throat specialists, however, usually prefer to remove enlarged tonsils and adenoids before any serious infection develops that can involve the ears. In the case of the cleft palate child, who may utilize adenoid tissue to help effect velo-pharyngeal closure, a decision to perform an adenoidectomy should not be reached without considering the possible harmful effects of such an operation on the child's voice and speech patterns. In such cases, a suitable compromise may be to perform a partial adenoidectomy.

Though exposure to intense noise is not a common cause of hearing impairment in children, still the teacher should keep this possibility in mind and do whatever she can to assure her pupils a normal sound environment. She should discourage children from their frequent practices of shouting in each other's ears, shooting off cap pistols close to each other's ears, and from similar activities that involve the danger of injuring the sensitive inner ear. Children must not be allowed to 'box' each other's ears, since the sudden build-up of pressure at the opening of the external canal can cause rupture of the eardrum and possible damage to the ossicles, as well as to the delicate structures of the inner ear.

Discovery of Hearing Impairment

An important element in the success of a hearing conservation program is the discovery of unsuspected hearing impairment. Cases amenable to treatment can thus be given medical attention, and cases of permanent hearing loss can be effectively guided and trained throughout their school experience with the object of minimizing the handicap of their impairment. The heart of a hearing conservation program is thus an effective means of identifying children with hearing losses.

1. *Screening tests* The purpose of school-administered screening tests is to separate those children with hearing impairments from children with normal hearing. This screening can be accomplished either by individual tests or by group tests of hearing which are either pure-tone or speech tests, or combinations of the two. There is disagreement among hearing conservationists as to which type of screening test is preferable. The proponents of group testing maintain that it is more profitable from the hearing conservation point of view to screen as large a segment of the school population as possible each year. Those in favor of the individual method of screening claim that it is more important to obtain accurate test results on fewer children than to secure incomplete data on more children. What is needed, actually, is an inexpensive, easily operated and maintained group test that will perform with the reliability and validity of an individual screening test. Until such an ideal group test is devised, however, the preferred method of screening has to be the individual 'sweep-frequency' test.

In individual screen testing with a pure-tone audiometer, five frequencies are utilized: 500, 1000, 2000, 4000, and 6000 Hz. The screening level employed is 20 dB at 1000 and 2000 Hz, and 25 dB at 500, 4000, and 6000 Hz, assuming a relatively quiet testing environment. Background noise tends to mask low frequencies, so if the screen testing must be performed in a noisy location it may be necessary to increase the screening level at 500 Hz by 5 or 10 dB, or else eliminate that frequency entirely. A child who fails to hear any of the test frequencies in either ear at the prescribed hearing level is considered to have failed the screening test and should then be scheduled for a complete pure-tone test to determine his threshold hearing level at each frequency. The follow-up threshold test should include bone-conduction testing for any frequency that shows a 10 dB or greater deviation from audiometric zero by air conduction. The follow-up test should be conducted in the quietest available location. Children whose threshold test confirms the screening test, that is, indicates that at one or more frequencies in either ear the threshold hearing level exceeds the screening level referred to above, should be considered to have a 'medically significant' loss and be referred for examination by a physician. Children with lesser amounts of loss by air conduction should be referred also, if bone-conduction testing reveals the presence of an air-bone gap, pointing to some conductive problem. Incidentally, all hearing levels referred to in this chapter assume measurements made with audiometers calibrated to ANSI-1969 standards.[4]

Testing in the schools may be performed by trained personnel who are licensed or certified by either the state department of health or the state department of education, by school nurses, or by volunteers working under the supervision of fully qualified personnel. The follow-up threshold examinations by air conduction and bone conduction should be performed by qualified audiologists. If an audiologist is not available through the school system, the testing may be contracted for through a hearing and speech center, or through an audiologist or otologist in private practice. In the primary grades, where the incidence of upper respiratory problems and communicable diseases is high, children should be screened annually. Children in the upper elementary grades and in junior and senior high school should be screened routinely at least every third year. Cleft palate children, other children known to have recurring bouts of middle-ear problems, or those already identified as having permanent, irreversible hearing impairments, should receive annual threshold examinations of their hearing.

2. *Teachers' observations* School systems that do not operate screening test programs will have to depend on the classroom teacher to detect evidence of hearing loss among her pupils. The teacher then refers children with suspected hearing loss to the school nurse or the school physician for testing and physical examination. It is dangerous to rely entirely upon teachers'

4. 'American National Standards Specifications for Audiometers,' ANSI S3.6-1969, American National Standards Institute, New York, 1970.

observations to uncover cases of hearing loss, however, since studies have shown that teachers are able to name only from 20 to 25 per cent of the pupils who will be found through audiometric tests to have significant hearing impairments. On the other hand, teachers will suspect many children of having hearing impairments whose hearing will actually be found to be normal.

Even when the school system has a well-organized program to test hearing, the classroom teacher must be alert to evidence of hearing disability among her pupils, for in some systems it may not be possible to perform screening tests as frequently as desirable, and hearing impairment may occur in the interval between tests. Here are some possible indications of hearing impairment of which the teacher should be aware:

a. The hard-of-hearing child may consistently pay little attention to what the teacher and other pupils say. In order to gain his attention, the teacher may have to address him rather sharply. His usual immediate response to any remark addressed to him may be 'Huh?' A hearing loss should be suspected especially when the child who fails to respond appropriately to oral instructions is otherwise capable of doing good work.

b. As we have seen in previous chapters of this book, hearing is always suspect in the case of a speech disorder that cannot be explained adequately in other ways, although there is no typical vocal or articulatory symptom that points incontrovertibly to defective hearing as being responsible for the disorder (if we except the dull, lifeless vocal quality of the profoundly hard-of-hearing or deaf child). The teacher should keep in mind, however, the distinction made previously between the weak voice accompanying conductive impairment and the loud voice characteristic of sensori-neural impairment, since marked deviations from normal vocal intensity may indicate a hearing loss. Also, difficulty in articulating certain consonants may point to a hearing problem. The hearing-impaired child will almost always demonstrate faulty [s] and [r] sounds. As explained in Chapter v, the [s] is a voiceless consonant that is weak in phonetic power, relatively invisible for the person dependent on visual cues, characterized by a concentration of energy in the high frequencies, and requiring a high degree of precision in articulator placement for correct production. While the [r] is not a voiceless consonant, a sound of weak power, or considered to be a predominantly high-frequency sound, it is invisible and one of the most difficult sounds to produce correctly from the standpoint of articulator placement. In addition to the [s], other voiceless consonants may be faulty, since as a class these sounds have weak intensity and contain high frequencies. While, to repeat, there is no typical or invariable speech symptom of a hearing impairment, a general rule may be stated: the sounds most likely to deteriorate in articulation because of faulty auditory monitoring are (1) those of high frequency and low phonetic power, (2) those requiring most complex adjustments of the articulators, and (3) those least visible when produced.

c. Obvious physical symptoms of ear trouble may, of course, be indications of hearing impairment. If a child has running ears or complains of earache, it is natural to assume that the hearing may be affected. Other physical symptoms that may have an indirect effect on the hearing are chronic nasal congestion, chronic 'sinus' trouble, allergy, and mouth breathing.

d. There may be manifestations of hearing loss in the general behavior of a child. One such indication is a constant restlessness —an apparent inability to 'stay put' for any length of time. This restlessness may very well be connected with the inability of the hard-of-hearing child to pay attention to oral instruction or recitation. While there are, of course, many explanations for the existence of behavior problems, it is true that the hard-of-hearing child may, because of this restlessness and inability to pay attention, be somewhat of a disciplinary problem. On the other hand, the effect of a hearing loss may be in just the opposite direction: the hard-of-hearing child may become shy and introvertive. Therefore, it is well for the teacher to question any deviation from normal behavior as being a possible sign of hearing impairment.

This listing of possible indications of hearing loss is not intended to be exhaustive, nor is it meant to suggest that such indications are always evidence of hearing impairment. Unless other satisfactory explanations of these symptoms are found, however, the teacher should be aware that a hearing impairment may at least be a contributing factor.

Treatment of Hearing Impairment

A hearing survey is useful only if there is an effective follow-up program with the children who are found to have hearing impairments. A necessary part of such a follow-up program is, of course, an ear, nose, and throat examination. The purpose of this examination is to diagnose the hearing impairment and to determine whether there is any physical condition present to cause it. The ear, nose, and throat examination may be performed by an otologist engaged by the school system; there may be otological clinics scheduled by the department of health, by the local medical society, or by ENT residents from a near-by medical school; or the school may simply recommend that the parents of children determined through testing to have medically significant hearing losses make their own arrangements to have their children examined. In any event, the parents should be present during the examination, so that the examiner may obtain a medical history from them that may shed light on the present hearing impairment, and so that he may advise them about his findings and give them his recommendations for treatment. It is the responsibility of the parents, then, to see that the children are given proper medical attention when it is indicated. In most states, the crippled children services (CCS) of the state department of health will underwrite part or all of the cost of diagnosis and treatment for those families who qualify for such financial assistance.

It has already been mentioned that in cases of conductive impairment there may be specific therapeutic steps to take which may restore hearing to normal. The treatment in such cases may consist simply of removing an accumulation of wax in the external canal, or it may involve the surgical removal of excess adenoid tissue from the nasopharynx, or plastic surgery on the eardrum or other structures of the middle ear. The hearing impairment may be secondary to a 'sinus' condition or to an allergy, in which case treatment of the primary condition may improve hearing. The point is that the chances of improving the hearing in cases of conductive impairment are very good, provided competent medical attention is obtained before there is irreparable damage to the middle ear. Thus a premium is placed on the early discovery of hearing impairment.

There is little that can be done medically to treat a case of sensori-neural impairment. Unfortunately, once the nerve endings in the cochlea or the fibers in the cochlear nerve have been destroyed, there is no way of restoring them. In cases of sensori-neural impairments, therefore, medical treatment consists of trying to keep the present loss from becoming more severe. In this connection, the physician will try to build up the individual's general health. He will advise him to avoid noisy environments and to refrain from taking drugs that might have an injurious effect on the inner ear. He may administer vitamins, not so much in the hope that some of the lost hearing will be restored as with the idea of improving the individual's general health.

Rehabilitation of the Hard of Hearing
In addition to providing for medical examination and treatment of cases of hearing impairment, a hearing conservation program must also make provision for the educational guidance and training of children found to have permanent hearing disability. In the larger school systems, trained personnel will be available to administer the special education programs for the hard of hearing. In many schools, however, the classroom teacher will be the only one responsible for helping these children.

1. *Where special education is available* Where personnel and facilities are available, a complete aural rehabilitation program can be undertaken. Such a program should include (a) auditory

training with and without amplification, (b) speechreading (lip-reading), (c) speech correction and language instruction where needed, (d) psychological counseling, and (e) vocational guidance. This special education program must be integrated with the regular school program, so that the hard-of-hearing child is kept with his contemporaries in the regular classroom, and so that he receives special training in addition to his regular schoolwork. In metropolitan centers there are frequently special 'home rooms' for those with severe or profound hearing handicaps. In other school systems, such children must be kept in the regular classroom but are then given aural rehabilitation by speech and hearing specialists in therapy sessions outside the classroom. It should be emphasized again that this chapter deals with the *hard-of-hearing* child—not the deaf child. The aural rehabilitation program outlined above pertains to the child whose hearing can be made functional with or without a hearing aid.

Auditory training refers to teaching the child to make the best use of the hearing he has. The child with a mild or moderate impairment may need a minimum of training of this sort, whereas the child with a severe or profound loss will probably require considerable auditory training. If the child is unable to hear adequately without amplification, he should be provided with a hearing aid, or perhaps two hearing aids—one for each ear. As a matter of fact, from the time a child is discovered to have a handicapping hearing impairment, regardless of his age, he should be provided with a hearing aid and encouraged to use it in all his waking hours. The decision concerning the child's need of a hearing aid and the particular 'fitting' that is most appropriate for him is best handled by audiologists at hearing and speech centers. In the absence of such expert guidance, the child's family must depend on the advice of a physician and the assistance of a knowledgeable hearing-aid dealer to provide the child with the amplification he needs. It is not enough simply to 'hang' a hearing aid on a child, however. He must be taught how to make the most effective use of what he hears. As an adjunct to his own hearing aid—or in the case of a child with a mild to moderate impairment, sometimes in place of a wearable aid—the use of an individual auditory training unit may be helpful in the training program. An auditory training unit provides a wide range of high-fidelity amplification and thus furnishes the hearing-impaired child with the ultimate in acoustic stimulation.

Speechreading is a necessary part of the training of any child with even a mild impairment of hearing, unless, of course, the child has learned by himself to become a proficient speechreader. Not only does speechreading offer him an additional communicative tool for the present, but it acts as insurance against the possibility of an increasing hearing loss which may eventually force him to rely primarily on visual cues. As a matter of fact, training in speechreading would be helpful to children whose hearing is perfectly normal, since there are many listening situations that severely challenge one's auditory abilities. Speechreading is most effective when it is accompanied by auditory training, since an individual can follow conversation better by integrating what he hears with what he sees, rather than by relying on either sensory process to the total exclusion of the other.

Since good speech depends on good hearing, it follows that an impairment of hearing may result in defective speech. Effective communication depends on expression as well as reception. Speech training in cases of serious hearing loss may have to emphasize visual and kinesthetic methods of learning correct sound production, if the individual is unable to monitor his own speech adequately by ear alone. As in the case of instruction in speechreading, training in the correct production of speech may be considered as insurance for the child with a mild but progressive impairment. The time may come when such a child will have to depend primarily on non-auditory methods of monitoring his speech. In addition to instruction in the correct production of speech sounds, the child with a severe to profound impairment may require help with the mastery of language concepts that normal-hearing children acquire with minimal effort.

Psychological counseling is usually desirable in the special education program, for the hard-of-hearing child may have problems of adjustment in school and at home owing to his hearing impairment. The younger a child is when aural rehabilitation is begun, the fewer the adjustment problems that occur. An older child, on the other hand, may refuse to admit the existence of a sensory deficiency for fear of inviting the ridicule of his classmates. Older children who should use hearing aids present especially difficult problems, again for the reason that they fear the ridicule of their contemporaries. Parents are frequently to blame for the adjustment problems of their hearing-impaired children. If the parents accept the sensory deficit philosophically and realistically, the children will tend to do the same. But if the parents feel ashamed of their child's disability and do everything they can to deny it, the child will reflect their attitudes. The program of psychological counseling, therefore, needs to be directed both to the children and to their parents.

Because a hearing impairment may be a handicap in certain lines of work, depending on the extent of the hearing loss and the requirements of the position, it is wise to assist each hard-of-hearing child in a sensible choice of occupation. High-school-age children are eligible for the vocational counseling services of state bureaus or offices of vocational rehabilitation. Special diagnostic and therapeutic services for the physically handicapped are also sponsored by state vocational rehabilitation services, which are funded through the cooperative efforts of state and federal governments. In most lines of work, a mild or moderate hearing impairment need be no handicap, provided the hard-of-hearing individual has been effectively trained through the methods of special education referred to above. The successful rehabilitation of thousands of hearing-impaired servicemen following World War II and more recent conflicts has done much to educate the public to the possibilities of aural rehabilitation. Employers are coming to the realization that a hearing impairment need not disqualify a job applicant who is otherwise well suited to the position.

2. *Where no special education is available* In the absence of special education facilities in the school system, the classroom teacher must assume all responsibility for the hearing-impaired pupils in her class. Just as in the case of children with speech disorders, there are many things the classroom teacher can do in the course of her daily routine to help the acoustically handicapped child. Of course the availability of special education facilities within the school system does not relieve the classroom teacher of all responsibility toward the hard-of-hearing children she may have in her class. The following suggestions to the teacher apply equally, then, to either situation.

a. GENERAL PROCEDURES It is the teacher's responsibility to make sure that the hearing-impaired child is seated to best advantage in the classroom. No definite rule can be stated that would apply to all classrooms or to all hard-of-hearing children. Generally, the child with a hearing impairment needs to be seated near the front of the room and where the light is favorable for him to watch the teacher. The teacher may need to experiment, however, with the child's seating arrangements until the most satisfactory location is discovered. It may be that no one location will prove satisfactory for all classroom situations, in which case the teacher should be guided by the child's reactions and change his seating as often as necessary. Since a hearing loss may be more severe in one ear than in the other, the teacher must take into account any marked difference between the child's ears and seat him so that he can use the better ear to advantage. The teacher should constantly be aware of the presence of a child who does not hear normally and govern her movements about the room accordingly.

In this connection it should be remembered that the hearing-impaired child must depend more on his eyes than do children who hear normally. The teacher must take care, then, to speak from such a position that the hard-of-hearing child can watch her face at all times. She should not talk with her back toward the class, for example, nor should she speak with her hand, or any other object, in front of her face. She should consider the source of light within the room and place herself at all times so that the light is directed on her face, rather than in the eyes of her pupils; for example, she should not stand in front of a window while talking to the class.

Though it is important for the teacher to demonstrate good speech at all times, it is especially important that she speak clearly, distinctly, and naturally to the hearing-impaired child. Many older people who are hard of hearing complain that they cannot hear because other people mumble all the time. Of course such people will not admit that there is anything faulty about their receiving apparatus; the blame for impaired communication is always with others. In speaking to any hard-of-hearing individual, however, child or adult, there is a premium on distinct, natural speech. The importance of speaking naturally cannot be overemphasized, since many people erroneously believe that they are helping the hard-of-hearing individual by exaggerating the movements of their articulators and increasing the intensity of their voices almost to a shout. The emphasis in training the hard of hearing in speechreading and in making the most effective use of their hearing is all directed toward better understanding of normal conversational speech. Exaggerated lip, tongue, and jaw movements make a parody of speech, and in combination with too much loudness, such distortion of the normal movements of speech can make communication virtually impossible.

The classroom teacher can do a great deal to help the hard-of-hearing child adjust to his hearing impairment. A sympathetic attitude on her part, coupled with a positive mental-health approach directed at the child's behavior in the classroom and elsewhere, can do wonders to reinforce the work of the special teachers and to establish a sensible and healthy attitude on the part of the child. The teacher is responsible for molding the attitudes of others in the class toward the hard-of-hearing child. If she can demonstrate to the child that his fears of being ridiculed because of his impairment are groundless, she will go a long way toward helping him make a satisfactory adjustment to his disability.

If there is no special education program incorporating a parent-training feature, the classroom teacher should assume this responsibility as well. If she is informed about the nature of hearing impairments, the causes of hearing loss, and what can and cannot be done medically for those with hearing difficulties, she can help the parents interpret the audiometric and medical findings in the case of their child. Her big job in parental counseling, however, is to guide the parents to an acceptance of their child's disability. Once parents have faced the child's impairment objectively, they are amenable to recommendations for his rehabilitative needs. The teacher will find some of the references listed at the end of this chapter valuable reading material to suggest to parents of children with hearing impairments.

b. SPECIFIC REHABILITATIVE PROCEDURES   The teacher should constantly be aware of the hard-of-hearing child's needs in the way of auditory training, speechreading, and speech and language training, and she should seize every opportunity to add to the child's experiences in communication. It is not the purpose of this chapter to provide detailed lesson plans for an aural rehabilitation program; for these, the teacher can turn to the references at the end of this chapter. Instead, a few specific training techniques which the teacher may be able to work into her regular classroom program will be presented.

The hard-of-hearing child must be made aware of the presence of *sound* in his environment, and he must be taught that sounds have meaning, just as words on the printed page and pictures have meaning. Auditory training is simply a systematic approach to the problem of teaching the child to use his hearing to best advantage.

The child with normal hearing follows a pattern of hearing development that progresses from an ability to distinguish highly dissimilar sounds frequently heard, such as a telephone ring from a door slam, to an eventual ability to discriminate sounds that are highly similar, for example, the words *bath* and *bat*. Auditory training lessons should progress in difficulty, therefore, from simple, gross sound recognition to difficult speech-sound discriminations. The point at which the lessons begin is determined by the present hearing ability of the particular child with whom the teacher is concerned. Most children in the public schools will be capable of making gross auditory discriminations. The teacher's purpose should be to keep the child at the highest level of auditory functioning of which he is capable. She must emphasize the importance of attentive listening at all times.

The teacher should become familiar with hearing aids, so that she can help the child to make most effective use of his aid. She should learn how to insert the earpiece correctly and make frequent checks to make sure the earpiece fits in the canal properly. An improper fit may result in a 'squeal' which is annoying both to the child and to others in the room. The squeal is called acoustic feedback, and it results when amplified sound from the hearing aid's receiver is picked up by the aid's microphone, producing a 'vicious circle' of amplification. Growing children require periodic replacement of earpieces to maintain proper fit. The teacher should be familiar with the controls of the aid, so she can make sure it is turned on and properly adjusted to the child's needs; that is, she should determine that the volume-control setting is appropriate. By listening to the aid with her own ear, the teacher can satisfy herself that it is functioning properly. She should know how to change the battery in case the child needs help. It is advisable for the parents to furnish spare batteries to the teacher, so that the child is not suddenly deprived of amplification at school because a battery becomes lifeless.

Speechreading (lipreading) is a process all of us use, with little conscious awareness of what we are doing. It is a common experience, however, that we 'hear' another person better when we can see him. Many hard-of-hearing individuals develop a high degree of proficiency at speechreading as compensation for their impaired hearing without being at all aware that they are 'reading lips.' Instruction in speechreading consists of teaching the hard-of-hearing individual to systematize the visual observations he is already making. Speechreading should be taught as a means of enlarging communicative ability, and not as an end in itself. It should be taught as a *supplement* to hearing rather than a substitute for hearing. Auditory training and speechreading, therefore, should be integrated, rather than taught as separate skills. The teacher must emphasize at all times the importance of *looking* while *listening*.

The natural way of learning speech is by imitating what we hear. The first step in speech correction, therefore, is ear-training—that is, teaching the child to recognize the correct production of the sound or sounds that are faulty. Frequently, with a child who has normal hearing, it is necessary only to teach him to imitate the correct sound, which he is able to hear, in order to eradicate an error in articulation. The child who has a hearing impairment usually cannot learn to correct his own speech by sound imitation alone. Rather, he must be taught correct sound production through a combination of imitating what he hears as well as what he sees. He should be encouraged to watch the teacher's articulators as she produces a sound and then attempt to duplicate her movements while he observes himself in a mirror. He should be instructed about the correct placement of his articulators for the production of the sounds with which he experiences difficulty. It can be seen, therefore, that instruction in proper sound formation goes hand in hand with auditory training and instruction in speechreading. The reader is referred to Chapter v and to the references cited at the end of the chapter for books that explain and illustrate the articulatory adjustments for the correct formation of the various speech sounds.

There may well be certain sounds the child is incapable of hearing at all. He must be taught to recognize these sounds by speechreading alone, and to produce them correctly by learning to imitate the teacher's articulation movements. In addition, since the child will not be doing all his talking in front of a mirror, he must be taught to monitor the sounds he cannot hear by learning the correct 'feel' of the sound. In other words, he must learn to control the production of certain sounds through tactile and kinesthetic sensations of articulator placement. First he must be taught to imitate the articulator movements he sees the teacher making, and then he must learn to 'remember' the sensations of muscle action that he experiences while correctly imitating those movements.

The classroom teacher should be aware of the importance of integrating auditory training, speechreading, and speech training in the rehabilitation of the hard-of-hearing child. The daily classroom routine presents many opportunities for the teacher to introduce practice materials that will be beneficial to the hard-of-hearing child, and, as a matter of fact, useful to the entire class. For example, lessons in spelling and reading can be utilized as 'look' and 'listen' games for the whole class. The teacher might say, 'I am going to read a list of words which I want you to spell. Pay very close attention to me as I read the words, because the second time I read the words to you, I am not going to make any sound. You will have to decide which word I am asking you to spell by the *look* of the word on my lips and mouth.' Or, in a reading lesson, the teacher can ask questions about the story the class has just read—framing simple questions in a whisper, or with no voice at all. Speechreading is an excellent technique to hold the undivided attention of the class. The children must watch the teacher intently in order to grasp what she is saying when she is speaking in a whisper, or with no voice at all. Such techniques make the whole class more conscious of the relations among the sound, the appearance, and the mechanics of production of a word or phrase. Further suggestions about how the teacher may utilize classroom routine to advantage in emphasizing speech, hearing, and language skills will be found in the following chapter.

In addition to the general emphasis the teacher can give to

sharpen the sensory acuity of the whole class, and thus indirectly improve the hearing and speechreading ability of the hearing-impaired child, the classroom teacher should find some time each day to work individually with the hard-of-hearing child. Lesson planning will, of course, depend on the specific needs of the child. The teacher should, therefore, make an analysis of the child's ability to make auditory discriminations among the various sounds of the language. A convenient way of doing this is to ask the child to repeat, or better yet to write, lists of so-called phonetically balanced (PB) words, which are used in audiology clinics for testing speech discrimination. These are lists of fifty monosyllables each, constructed so that each list contains all the common sounds of our language in the proportion of their occurrence in running speech. Four of these word lists are reproduced in the Appendix to this book. The teacher should read the words in these lists to the child in her normal manner of speaking and at a distance of from four to six feet. Either the child should be instructed not to watch the teacher, or she may hold a sheet of paper in front of her mouth so that the child cannot receive any visual cues. The errors the child makes should be carefully noted and analyzed, for they indicate the particular sounds the child is confusing. Thus if the child repeats *foe* instead of *so*, it is obvious that [f] and [s] sound the same to him, at least at the loudness of ordinary conversation. It may be added that if the child can make correct sound discriminations when the words are spoken only a few inches from his ear in a somewhat louder than normal voice, it is probable that he should be using a hearing aid. If he already has a hearing aid, he should use it at its normal settings while listening to the PB words. There are many other word lists that have been devised for speech-sound discrimination testing, but the PB words should work as well as any to provide the teacher with information concerning the sounds that are most difficult for the child to discriminate.

Once these sounds have been identified, lessons can be constructed utilizing these sounds and words containing them. In the case of the confusion of [f] and [s], for example, the teacher should make every effort to teach the child to differentiate the sounds on the basis of hearing alone, producing first one sound and then the other while the child listens intently and tries to identify which sound he is hearing. Then the teacher should incorporate the sounds in words that are similar, such as:

fit	sit	knife	nice
fine	sign	muff	muss
fee	see	laugh	lass
fold	sold	lift	list

Again the emphasis should be on the child's learning to discriminate the similar-sounding words correctly on the basis of hearing. If the child wears a hearing aid, auditory training of this sort should be undertaken while he wears the aid at the volume and tone control settings he usually employs.

The teacher should next point out the differences in the way the sounds are produced, calling the child's attention to the fact that [f] is formed by bringing the lower lip in contact with the upper incisor teeth, whereas [s] is formed by grooving the tongue and directing a thin stream of air against the cutting edges of the incisors. The child should watch the teacher carefully while she silently produces the [f] and [s] sounds, so that he can learn to recognize the difference in the appearance of the two sounds. When he has learned to differentiate the sounds by appearance alone, he can be taught to distinguish between the words in the paired lists above as the teacher speaks them with little or no voicing.

Next the teacher should encourage the child to utilize both sensory avenues—hearing and vision—to make the discriminations between these sounds. The child should be instructed both to 'listen' and to 'look' as the teacher compares the sounds in isolation, and then in words such as those in the paired lists above. In the same way, the child may be taught to identify words containing the [f] and [s] sounds when they appear in sentences. In the sentences below, words containing both sounds appear frequently. The teacher should emphasize the child's comprehension of each sentence as a whole—which of course means that he will have to recognize each of the important words in the sentence.

1. Father slept soundly after supper.
2. Sally found several flowers.
3. Sandra said she could not fill the basket with food.
4. Frank sold some fish to Sam.
5. Fifty plus fifteen equals sixty-five.

After practice on these sentences, the child should be able to identify the words when the teacher reads them without voice. The teacher should emphasize both the sound and the appearance of the sentences, however, rather than concentrating on appearance alone.

A brief story can be used effectively to climax the teacher's work in teaching the discrimination of speech sounds. For example, in the case of [f] and [s], the following story might be suitable.

Five mice lived in an old house. One mouse, who was stronger than the other four, made himself the king of the mice. The other four mice did not feel that the first mouse would be a good king, so they decided to fix a trap for the first mouse. The four mice found a piece of cheese, which they placed on the top edge of an open glass jar. Then the four mice hid until the first mouse found the cheese on the top edge of the glass jar. The first mouse saw the cheese and wanted it all for himself, so he jumped on top of the glass jar. Just then the other four mice ran out, and the first mouse was so surprised that he fell into the glass jar. 'Get me out of here,' the first mouse screamed, but the four mice shook their heads. 'Not until you promise you will be our friend instead of our king. You are stronger than any of us, but not stronger than all four of us.' The first mouse cried, 'I promise. I have been a foolish and silly mouse. Let me out and I will be your friend and will forget I ever was a king.' So the four mice pushed until the glass jar fell over and the first mouse ran out. The first mouse kept his promise, so the five mice were all good friends forever after.

The story may be used in a variety of ways. For example, the teacher can instruct the child to 'listen' and 'look,' and to raise his hand every time he hears or sees a word with the [f] sound in it. Since the [v] is the voiced counterpart of the [f] and looks the same as the [f], the teacher should allow the child credit for all words he correctly identifies as containing either [f] or [v]. The next time the story is read, the teacher can have the child raise his hand every time he hears or sees a word containing [s]. As in the case of [f] and [v], the child cannot distinguish [s] from [z] by appearance alone, so the teacher should allow credit for every word he correctly identifies as containing either [s] or [z].

The complete story may be used as an exercise in speech-reading, in which case the teacher can read the story with little or no voice, while the child watches and tries to follow the general idea of the story. If the child cannot follow the story in its entirety, the teacher can take one sentence at a time. It may be necessary for the teacher to use drawings or gestures to assist the child in following the story successfully. The use of the story as a speechreading lesson is desirable only if the child can experience success in the situation. The main point in utilizing the story is to emphasize the difference in the sound and the appearance of [f] and [s], when words containing these sounds are used in connected speech. The groundwork in distinguishing [f] from [s] should already have been thoroughly mastered by the preceding drills on the sound in isolation, in words, and then in simple sentences, before the story is attempted.

Since it is likely that the child will have difficulty producing sounds he does not hear accurately, the teacher will need to go one step further in her lesson work. As she teaches the child how the sounds are formed, so that he may recognize them visually, she should have the child imitate the movement of her articulators while she forms the sounds. In the case of [f] and [s], for example, with the help of a mirror the child can readily see the difference in appearance of the two sounds on his own articulators, as he imitates the movements the teacher is making. The articulation of all sounds is not equally visible, unfortunately, so it may be necessary for the teacher to instruct the child in the correct formation of some sounds by describing the position of the articulators, or showing their correct placement in drawings or diagrams. Many helpful suggestions for teaching articulatory adjustments for the various speech sounds will be found in Chapter v, which deals with articulatory problems in general.

The point is, the child should be taught correct sound production at the same time he is taught sound recognition. If the child cannot hear the sounds he is producing, the teacher must make sure that he is taught to form them correctly and must emphasize his remembering the *feel* of the correct formation. As in the case of sound recognition, the work in correct sound formation should proceed from the sound in isolation, to the sound in simple words, and then to phrases, sentences, and finally connected speech, such as is represented by the story given above.

While it is desirable to have aural rehabilitation of hearing handicapped school children in the hands of competent and well-trained special teachers, the importance of the classroom teacher to the rehabilitation program cannot be overemphasized. It is the regular classroom teacher, after all, who has the day-to-day responsibility for the education of the hard-of-hearing child. Her efforts to improve the child's communicative ability may very well be just as important as the work of the special teacher, which, after all, is usually limited to one or two lessons a week. And certainly, where there is no special teacher available, the responsibility for the rehabilitation of the hard-of-hearing child falls squarely on the classroom teacher. To shut her eyes to the needs of these handicapped children would be a denial of her obligation to help every child in her class to his best ultimate attainment.

With even a few minutes a day of individual attention, the teacher can do a great deal to improve a child's use of his sensory facilities and his ability to produce sounds more correctly. Moreover, such individual attention is psychologically beneficial to the child with a hearing impairment. With the realization that someone is interested in helping him with his problems, he is encouraged to apply himself to the limit of his capabilities. When he does apply himself with the help and encouragement of an understanding teacher, he is bound to improve his ability to communicate, and, therefore, his entire adjustment to his handicap.

References

Bender, Ruth E., *The Conquest of Deafness*, The Press of Case Western Reserve University, Cleveland, 1970.

Berg, Frederick S., and Samuel G. Fletcher, *The Hard of Hearing Child*, Grune and Stratton, New York, 1970.

Davis, Hallowell, and S. Richard Silverman, eds., *Hearing and Deafness*, Holt, Rinehart and Winston, New York, 1970.

Harris, Grace M., *Language for the Preschool Deaf Child*, Grune and Stratton, New York, 1971.

Katz, Jack, ed., *Handbook of Clinical Audiology*, Williams and Wilkins, Baltimore, 1972.

McConnell, Freeman, and Paul H. Ward, eds., *Deafness in Childhood*, Vanderbilt University Press, Nashville, 1967.

Myklebust, Helmer R., *Auditory Disorders in Children*, Grune and Stratton, New York, 1964.

Newby, Hayes A., *Audiology*, Appleton-Century-Crofts, New York, 1972.

O'Neill, John J., *The Hard of Hearing*, Prentice-Hall, Englewood Cliffs, N. J., 1964.

Rose, Darrell E., ed., *Audiological Assessment*, Prentice-Hall, Englewood Cliffs, N. J., 1971.

Sanders, Derek A., *Aural Rehabilitation*, Prentice-Hall, Englewood Cliffs, N. J., 1971.

XII

Integrating Speech and Language Training with the School Curriculum

As has often been stressed in this book, the classroom teacher has two basic responsibilities relating to the quality of oral communication among her pupils. The first involves the welfare of the child who suffers from one or more of the communication handicaps described earlier. The second relates to the need to provide opportunities for continued oral language improvement for all of her pupils. The first problem, of course, becomes the primary responsibility of the speech and hearing specialist or clinician, if one is available in the school system, in which case the clinician and the teacher function as a team to give every possible aid to the handicapped child.

The teacher, of course, is aware of which pupils, if any, from her class are receiving special help. She should also become aware of the nature of the child's problem, what the clinician is doing for the child, and in what ways she can co-operate to provide the support and experience that will best reinforce the efforts of the clinician. This includes such motivation-enhancing activities as taking note of improvements the child may demonstrate and expressing pleasure and encouragement at the child's progress. Frequent conferences with the clinician are advised for her suggestions, and the teacher may well want to invite her to provide some demonstration lessons in speech improvement before the entire class. These can be most helpful, not only to the children, but to the teacher as well in suggesting methods, techniques, and materials she herself can use with her pupils.

If there is no specialist available, the teacher is on her own to do what she can for the handicapped child, utilizing the suggestions and within the limitations set forth in this book. If she feels that the problem is beyond her capabilities, she should be sufficiently aware of the school and community resources to know where to refer the parents.

The other responsibility of the teacher, as stated above, is to insure continuing development of all her pupils in the skills of oral communication. At this point it is suggested that she re-read the last two sections of Chapter III—Speech and Language Development as a Continuing Process, and Speech Training vs. Re-training. The teacher can meet the need for speech education and re-education without creating for herself the burden of teaching an additional subject. Instead, speech training can, and often should be, so closely interwoven into the daily activities of the class that it is unrecognizable as a separate subject. The classroom teacher who avails herself of good resource material is able to correlate speech education with nearly every phase of the activities of her planned curriculum. The children benefit greatly through such integration, not only in speech development but in every aspect of language arts, including reading, spelling, and composition.

As was stressed earlier, speech training must not and need not seem artificial, restricted, or divorced from the everyday uses of speech. Many specific techniques that may be used by the classroom teacher have been presented in the preceding chapters. By way of background, the reader is strongly urged to re-read Chapter I where the philosophy and rationale of emphasizing oral communication in the elementary school are explained. More specific suggestions for implementing this training have been included in Chapters IV and V, especially the classroom activities to promote oral language development and participation in Chapter IV, and several sections of Chapter V devoted to ear training, classroom games, and motivational devices, plus the section General Drills and Exercises.

Adequate emphasis on oral communication must result from a special concern on the part of the teacher, since it is the only one of the language arts that does not have formal time allotted to it in the elementary curriculum, in contrast to reading, writing, and spelling, for example. Principal reason for this disparity is probably the notion that the child comes to school already knowing how to speak, in most instances, and how to understand spoken language. What he doesn't know is how to read, write, and spell. Consequently these are the language arts that receive attention; oral communication is likely to be taken for granted and lost sight of. As a result the child's skill in this area too often remains poorly developed and is frequently ineffective. What the teacher needs to remember is that oral communication, including listening comprehension, forms the basis for the development of the other language arts. It is true that oral language experiences are included in certain instructional guides prepared by large urban school systems and by some state departments of education or public instruction. The Los Angeles school system, for example, in their *Language Arts in the Elementary School* (see in References at end of chapter) suggests the following lessons or experiences for kindergarten and the first six grades:

1. LISTENING Beginning with listening to a simple story read to them for enjoyment, the children are taught to listen in order to retell a story, to follow directions, to gain specific information, to evaluate ideas, to increase vocabulary, to enjoy aesthetic experiences, et cetera.

2. CONVERSING Would include such activities as talking on the telephone, exchanging ideas for class projects, learning to speak with ease and fluency, enlarging and enriching vocabulary, using interesting sentences and phrases, et cetera.

3. DISCUSSING Somewhat more formal than conversing. Would

include planning for daily classroom activities or a special class project or establishing classroom standards; learning appropriate vocabulary, sentence structure, and phrasing; listening with respectful attention to others' ideas; evaluating committee work; participating in panel discussion, et cetera.

4. REPORTING May begin with simple show and tell assignments and progress to book reports, committee reports, current events, and extemporaneous speaking. Aims are to provide experience in talking in front of a group, to develop adequate vocabulary for a given subject, to train pupils to organize material clearly and logically, to speak up and be heard, et cetera.

5. CREATIVE ACTIVITIES Aims are to develop richer and fuller vocabulary, appreciation of the aesthetic values in poetry reading, skill in holding the interest of a group, some sense of the dramatic qualities in story telling, skillful use of the voice in conveying mood and feeling, participation in choral reading and creative dramatics, et cetera.

6. SOCIAL COURTESIES Would involve development of pleasant speech habits, remembering to say 'please' and 'thank you,' displaying courteous telephone manners, suiting words and language to a given situation, learning how to make social introductions, et cetera.

While certain of the activities above would require special lessons with appropriate time reserved within the day's routine, it is clear that many of them can become a working part of a basic 'academic' subject. A simple recitation in social studies provides a good opportunity for the child to use adequate vocabulary, speak up and be heard, and demonstrate a degree of interest in what he is saying. For the other pupils, effective listening is in order. The main purpose of this chapter, therefore, is to guide the teacher in making speech improvement and speech correction functional in her program and without becoming a major burden. Classroom teachers with little or no formal training in speech education have successfully carried out in their classrooms the activities to be described, and these techniques have proved to be practical and profitable for the teacher who wishes to plan speech education in an integrated program.

In general, speech education can and should be correlated with large units of study; however, class routine also offers various incidental opportunities for speech improvement. The morning roll call, for example, can occasionally afford some variation. The teacher may introduce this effective speech game: the children respond to their names with the sound of a letter such as *s* [s], *ch* [tʃ], or *sh* [ʃ]. The game may be varied by having every fifth or sixth child initiate a change in sound. Or the child may respond with his name and the statement, 'My name is John,' or 'This is John.' Or the children may greet the teacher with 'Good morning, Miss Smith.' There are many possible variations here.

The teacher may begin the after-recess rest period with certain tongue gymnastics. The children, warm and breathless from playing, will enjoy the game of hanging their tongues out of their mouths and panting like dogs. Then the panting dog puts his tongue in and out of his mouth as he drinks a bowl of cool water. Next, he rolls his tongue all around his lips to catch every clinging drop. The tired little dog now drops his head to relax and rest. This brief interval of tongue exercise is fun. It fits into the day's activities and is valuable in improving the quality of articulation.

The primary teacher may introduce the after-recess rest period with the following story game. Perhaps she will introduce it at a time when the children are busy with a transportation unit in social studies. The story is about the flat tire on Daddy's car. Daddy is planning to take the children to school on his way to work, but he finds that a tire is almost completely flat. He begins to fill it with air. The class slowly takes a big, big breath as the teacher pantomimes the action of pumping up a tire. Finally bulging cheeks indicate top air pressure. The teacher looks around the room hopefully, but, no, the soft sound of escaping air is heard as the children say, 's-s-s.' The tires in the room are flat as the last of the sounds die away. The children's backs are curved, their arms are dangling, and their heads are resting on the desks, or are simply dropped forward.

Once more the teacher busily fills the tire with air. As she pumps, the children sit taller and taller until their arms are raised high, their backs are straight, and their cheeks are puffed out. Once again the teacher assumes a hopeful, expectant look. Then the soft sound of 's-s-s-s' is heard as the air again escapes from the little hole. The best thing to do, Daddy decides, is to leave the car in the garage and wait for help from the mechanic. All heads sink down for the rest period. This story serves as a breathing exercise, an auditory drill on the *s* sound, and as a re-laxing device.

The music program offers many opportunities to emphasize speech training involving troublesome sounds and sound com-binations. For example, the song 'Little White Duck' found in *Exploring Music* (see in References end of chapter) has the line, 'Little white duck swimming in the water,' which provides good practice on [l], [hw], [sw], and [ð]. Another line is 'Little red snake lying in the water,' which adds the additional sounds of [r] and [sn]. The line 'I'm a little black bug floating on the water' offers good practice on several troublesome l-combina-tions. Another music text, *This Is Music* (see References), in-cludes the old folk song 'I Bought a Rooster,' which contains many examples of [r] plus [l] in several combinations. The song 'Peter's Lion House' also presents examples of [l] in several phonetic combinations, as well as ample illustrations of [s]. Other music texts will offer numberless opportunities for drill and practice on the consonants that many children require some help in perfecting. Work and drill on round full tones and on lip and tongue exercises are given a natural teaching opportunity through the medium of *The Witches Are Calling, What Is March Wind Saying?, Ring the Fire Bell,* and *Clocks and Watches.* A short song entitled *Choo-Choo Train* requires the repeating of the *ch* sound fifteen times, and for additional prac-tice on [tʃ] the song *Chant of the Chipmunk* offers further opportunity for drill. Songs of the bee, such as *Busy Bee* and *Buzz*, through the repeated use of [z], offer a valuable drill. Songs afford the classroom teacher an opportunity to cement and emphasize the correlation of speech education with other parts of the curriculum.

Every teacher has a repertory of various flexing and stretching exercises that children may do beside their desks in the classroom. These exercises relax and refresh both body and mind by giving the child an opportunity to laugh and stretch for a few minutes. This period is a natural time to introduce exercises of the tongue, lips, and jaw. Children respond to and enjoy these drills when they are presented with a sense of humor. The flexing and rounding of the lips, the up-and-down movement of the jaw, the mad capers of the tongue all delight and challenge children. Simple and direct answers to the children's questions of 'Why?' and 'What for?' will satisfy them. The teacher may reply by explaining that good speech depends on active, mobile, and strong lip muscles. She may also say, 'The tongue is a big muscle that helps us in eating and in talking. Muscles get lazy if we forget to exercise them and use them often.' The children respond if they feel that these exercises are something *special*. They feel a pride in achieving good standards, and no other motivation is necessary.

The following pages describe units in which speech education is correlated with special areas of the curriculum.

Integrating Speech Training with Work in Hygiene

The integration of language arts and speech education with hygiene can prove to be very stimulating and interesting. The following material may be adapted to any grade or age level from the first grade through junior high school. The vocabulary and the method of presentation can easily be adapted by the teacher to suit the age of the children involved in the unit.

The classroom teacher should incorporate in any unit on hygiene the concept that each human being is provided with the physical equipment necessary to meet the demands of living. All parts of the body are useful and necessary to personal well-being. Some parts of the body are the tools used in walking and moving. Other parts are concerned with recording sensory impressions and relaying those images to the brain; still other organs have to do with vital life processes such as respiration, digestion, excretion, and reproduction. This particular hygiene unit concerns those parts of the body having to do with the ability to speak. Goals for this unit will include answers to the following questions: What parts of the body are used as organs of speech? Where are these organs located? What are the characteristics of these organs?

As the children learn the answer to the first of these questions, they will discover that, actually, there are no body parts that have as their primary function the production of voice and speech. The ability to speak is not innate; rather, a person must learn to use the body parts concerned primarily with respiration and the intake of food as his tools in speech.

The children may be guided to answers for the second and third of these questions by an examination of their own speech mechanism. For instance, children are familiar with their teeth as tools for the mastication of food, but they may be surprised to learn that a set of teeth is a very necessary speech organ. The teacher may point out to children who are losing their baby teeth, or remind children who have already had that experience, that the absence of front teeth affects the pronunciation of certain sounds. The teacher and class may experiment to discover the position of the teeth in the formation of the various sounds. Sometimes the teeth act as a gate to impede the expulsion of air from the mouth; sometimes the gate is open.

The teacher may use a pair of classroom scissors to illustrate the hinge-like action of the jaws. Children will develop a clearer concept of this action by placing their fingers on their cheeks just in front of their ear lobes as they open and close their mouths. They can run their fingers all along their own jaws to feel the size and strength of this movable bone.

By exploring with their tongues and using small pocket mirrors, the children will learn about the architecture of their own mouths. They will discover that the gum ridge is the area immediately behind the upper teeth, and that it is actually a part of the hard palate. Using their mirrors, the children will trace with their tongues the area of the hard palate, starting at the gum ridge and proceeding to the tissues of the soft palate.

The teacher may call attention to the seam-like line that extends the length of the hard palate through the soft palate to the uvula. This line where the palatal bones join may be compared to a seam in a girl's dress or a boy's shirt. The children will draw upon their experiences with old clothes in which seams pull apart, or new clothes in which a seam has been left unsewn in the manufacturing process. The children can be told that some babies are born with the seam in the roof of their mouths 'unsewn.' This fissure causes difficulty in speech because the breath that properly should be channeled out through the mouth escapes into the nose. If the children are sufficiently interested to ask questions, the teacher should give them as much information as they are capable of understanding. They should know about the wonderful repair work that doctors are able to do for these children. They should understand that several operations are sometimes required to close up this opening. The class may be taught to admire the courage and patience that the child with a cleft palate must develop during this arduous process. Armed with such knowledge, the children in the class who, in the course of their lives, meet individuals with cleft palates will be able to handle the situation with ease and understanding.

The children may learn about the location and function of the vocal cords by placing their hands on their throats where they can feel the vibrations that certain sounds make. They will say the voiceless sound [s] and then the voiced sound [z]. Next they will try the voiceless *th* [θ] as in *thin* followed by the voiced *th* [ð] as in *this*. Perhaps the interest of the class will indicate to the teacher that it would be profitable to experiment with other pairs of voiced and voiceless sounds.

Guided by these examples, the teacher will be able to work out various other exploratory techniques to familiarize her pupils with the nature and function of such parts of the speech mechanism as the tongue, lips, nasal passages, hard and soft palates, lungs, et cetera. This work on the location and function of the speech organs may very well cover several lessons.

As the children examine their speech mechanisms, they will become aware that some parts are movable and some are immobile. The soft palate and the hard palate illustrate these two types. The hard palate is, of course, a bony plate fixed rigidly between the oral and nasal cavities. The soft palate, by moving up and down, gives proper direction to the air stream in the production of speech. For group demonstration of soft-palate action, the children are instructed to produce first a good wide *ah* [ɑ] and then, with the mouth still open, produce the sound of *ng* [ŋ]. By listening carefully and by feeling the vibrations along the sides of the nose with their fingers, the pupils will be able to tell that *ah* is coming out of their mouths but that *ng* comes through the nose. The teacher will explain that for *ah* the soft palate is raised, closing off the nasal passages, but that it is lowered against the back of the tongue closing off the mouth for *ng*, thus forcing the tone up through the nose. If this experiment is repeated in front of a mirror, most of this activity of the soft palate will be quite plainly visible.

The tongue is extremely mobile. Teacher and pupils may take one of the reading or spelling words for the day to use in analyzing the tongue's activity. For example, going 'slow motion,' the children will find that at least four quite different tongue positions are involved in the pronunciation of the small and commonplace word *strike*.

A rubber band can be used to show how the movable vocal cords change their shape and size. A taut rubber band illustrates the vocal cords on high-frequency sounds; if the band is only slightly stretched, it illustrates the vocal cords on low-frequency sounds. This very simple and elementary demonstration is adequate when a hygiene unit is used with elementary-school children.

In the intermediate grades or in junior high school, children will be able to do individual and group reading and research about the organs connected with speech. They will want to share their knowledge with others through discussion and oral and written reports as well as various art media. Dictionary work will be stimulated and encouraged. Spelling lessons might include the words that pertain to the mechanics of speech, such as *tongue, larynx, palate, uvula, vocal cords, throat,* et cetera.

Primary-grade children, of course, will not be ready to spell these words, but they will enjoy working with their teacher to make a vocabulary chart or reading chart. The chart will contain simpler words such as *nose, teeth, lips,* and *throat.* The children may draw pictures to illustrate these words or they may cut suitable pictures from magazines. Many children will soon learn to read these words through seeing them on the chart and by copying them for sentence building.

The study of hygiene, when it is in keeping with sound educational philosophy, is concerned with preventing ill health and injury. Guiding the children in the assimilation of knowledge is not enough; they must learn how to put that information to use to safeguard their own well-being. Children participating in a unit on the teeth, for example, will learn how to protect these tools which are so necessary in the process of digestion as well as in articulation of speech sounds. The children should know that continued improper use of the voice can be physically damaging to the vocal cords. The simple study of the mechanics of the larynx previously described will be fascinating and challenging to the children. Some of them may be motivated to make an accurate representation of this structure.

Too few parents and teachers know why the adolescent's voice changes, and the frequent reactions of amusement to the peculiarities characteristic of the voice during this period are not helpful to the child. A serious discussion with an adult should reveal real knowledge of why the voice range varies and why the youngster lacks control over it, but few adults are well enough informed on the subject. If a hygiene integrating unit is used for the upper grades, the teacher will wish to develop the study of the vocal mechanism and vocal hygiene to a much greater extent than for a primary grade. The interest with which the upper-grade pupils read, discuss, and do research on the changing voice will not seem strange to those who work with and understand the early adolescent. Nothing interests this age group more than a phenomenon that affects them directly. The teacher need provide little motivation here.

Listings of resource material available for use in teaching this speech-hygiene unit is provided in the earlier chapters of this book. Chapter v on articulatory disorders contains a detailed account of the activities of the tongue, teeth, lips, and soft palate in speech. The exercises for the tongue which are included in this chapter will be welcomed by the teacher as a device to aid the children in learning not only the versatility and mobility of this organ but the location and structure of the various parts of the mouth as well. Suggestions for using the techniques of the tactile, visual, and kinesthetic approaches to speech training will also be found in this chapter. If the teacher feels that an advanced group of children could profit from a study and discussion of such speech handicaps as a partial paralysis or a hearing loss, she will find ample material to implement such a unit in previous sections of this book. Chapter viii will be of value in the direction and guidance of the phase of the unit concerned with the adolescent voice change.

A wealth of other materials is readily available for use in this speech-hygiene unit. Each child should provide himself with a small hand mirror as a necessary tool. Encyclopedias and similar books contain excellent drawings of the head, throat, and chest regions. The visual-aid departments in many school systems have head and mouth models available for classroom use. Many manufacturers of dental products are glad not only to provide valuable pictorial and written material but also to supply assembled units on dental care suitable for various grade levels. The Bell Telephone system has made some excellent films on the mechanics of the human voice available for public education. These films would be suitable for the junior and senior-high-school level.

Correlating Speech Training with Art and with the Language Arts in General

Speech education, art, and the language arts can be effectively correlated if long-range planning is undertaken. Although the teacher in her planning and preparation will outline the program for a term in advance, some modifications and changes will necessarily be made as the year progresses. A bulletin-board display unit centered around various holidays or special events is one way of integrating these three parts of the curriculum.

A small section of the display board should be set aside from the very beginning and designated as the Art and Speech Education Holiday Board. The authors have known several classroom teachers who decided to use a bulletin board outside their door for their speech and art board. The children eagerly respond to such a project because they enjoy sharing with other classes the pleasure their finished board display brings. They are proud of their group contribution to the attractiveness of their school building. They thus have an opportunity to work together as a group, to receive satisfaction from their service to their school, and to talk to others outside the classroom to explain the aims and purposes of their art and speech display. All these activities are good and accepted ways of learning. Although every teacher will have many original and creative ideas for developing these displays, the suggestions included here may prove helpful in stimulating that originality and in giving the teacher a feeling of greater security in the beginning.

September—The Opening of School

A fun possibility for the debut of the display board when school opens in September is a lesson from which the making of pipe-stem figures will grow. This lesson introduces the causes of good speech and of poor speech in such a way that the children are taught to appreciate the importance of developing habits conducive to good speech.

The lesson is introduced when the teacher asks the children, 'What do you do now that you didn't do and couldn't do when you were babies?' Among the answers of, 'Walk,' 'Eat by ourselves,' 'Dress ourselves,' 'Sit up,' and many other enthusiastic indications of present maturity, the teacher will receive the answer, 'Talk.' The teacher will guide the discussion with a question such as this: 'How did we learn to talk?' The conversation which follows this question will bring forth the points that good hearing and a good speech model to imitate are essential to the development of good speech habits. The children will be guided to the realization that speech is a learned activity and that achievement of good speech is a challenge and a worthy goal for each and every child.

The teacher may ask next, 'What tools did we need to learn to talk?' The group discussion which follows will conclude with a summary including the following points: 'We need lungs to contain and expel the air we use in speech. We need vocal cords which, when we speak, vibrate like the strings of a violin or cello. The mouth cavity, the tongue, the lips, the teeth, and the jaw are instruments we use in forming sounds.' In this first lesson the teacher will be satisfied merely to introduce the essential organs used in speech. In the preceding section suggestions were made for a more detailed study of the voice and speech mechanism in connection with a unit on hygiene.

The teacher will ask, 'Does just having these speech tools guarantee us successful and beautiful speech?' She will lead and motivate her group to volunteer certain rules for good speech, and she will write these rules on the board. The rules will be couched in the words of the children, but essentially, they will be the points listed below:

1. We must stand up or sit up tall.
2. We must open our mouths as wide as necessary.
3. We must have active tongues.
4. We must have mobile, free-moving lips.
5. We must have relaxed body muscles for relaxed and easy speech.

A culmination of this discussion designed to promote good oral communication will be the preparation of the art and speech bulletin board. The first display will be the product of an activity project to make stick figures out of pipe cleaners. The little figures will represent the 'do's' and 'don'ts' of good speech. The activity period will go smoothly if materials are prepared in advance. Each child will be given three pipe-stem cleaners. Some of the more enterprising children may require a fourth, so extras should be ready on the art-supply table. The display will be more effective and attractive if each white figure is stapled to a piece of black paper four by six inches in size.

What kinds of figures will the children make? Little figures with curvatures of the spine will illustrate poor posture, but figures with straight backs, legs, and arms will represent the best of postures. The figures can be made to show correct and incorrect positions for sitting down and standing up. Some children, after curling up the pipe-stem cleaner to form a head, will draw in facial details. The figure which represents good speech, for example, will have a wide-open mouth, but the figure which represents poor speech may have no mouth at all! Perhaps some other children will make little figures who are covering their mouths with a hand. These figures are using a screen; they are muffling their words so that their speech is not clear.

The children will discuss, share, enjoy, and evaluate the illustrative figures they have made and they will select those they wish to use on the display board. In the center of the display board, carefully mounted on black or colored paper, will be the caption, OUR RULES FOR GOOD SPEECH. Above each 'do' and 'don't' of good speech will be the appropriate illustrative figure.

Beginning of the New Year

An example will illustrate how—by means of the display board —art and speech education can be integrated with an observance of the beginning of a new year. Discussion will center around an evaluation by the children of their growth during the past year. They will be led to examine not only their physical growth, their height and weight, but their general maturation and educational growth as well. This type of conversation is exciting and stimulating to children, as every teacher knows. After the children have analyzed their growth during the past year, they will be ready to look ahead to formulate individual and group goals for the coming year. The teacher can guide both oral and written discussion toward New Year's resolutions to improve speech habits. The group will want to pool their ideas and select four or five of the most important resolutions relating to speech.

Big letters may be cut out of paper and placed in an arch at the top of the board. These letters will announce, 'Our Speech Resolutions for the New Year,' and the resolutions decided on will be listed underneath this heading. This might perhaps be a first grade's list of resolutions:

1. A round full voice.
2. A sweet tone.
3. An open mouth.
4. Raggedy Ann muscles.
5. We shall think about how we speak every day.

A sixth-grade class might make the following resolutions:

1. We shall help to maintain a high standard of speech in our classroom.
2. We shall use to best advantage all our organs of speech.

3. We shall not abuse speech by allowing careless habits to develop.
4. We realize that a high standard of speech means practice and drill.
5. We will listen carefully to what we hear.

At this point the teacher may want to elaborate somewhat on these resolutions, or such as the class may have chosen, and to explore speech standards in general with the children, especially the older child. She may wish to bring out that one's style of speech should be appropriate to the occasion in which it is used. When the child is talking to the principal, for example, or speaking in the classroom, he will want to use the best speech of which he is capable and take more care than he would if he were with his pals or playing on the playground. The child should be aware also that effective oral communication involves more than just voice and the formation of speech sounds. It includes adequate vocabulary, effective phrasing and sentence structure, good grammar and clear organization, some degree of interest and earnestness, and a generally pleasing personal appearance. The teacher can illustrate these points as she sees fit and present them in such a way that they will be meaningful to the age group she is dealing with.

Special Day—George Washington's Birthday

As in previous examples, the observance of George Washington's birthday provides another opportunity to stimulate activity centering around the speech and art display board. Every child must be guided to understand and appreciate George Washington's role in our nation's history. Discussion, research, dramatizations, and art activities will center on the qualities which the class considers to be characteristic of the great man. Dictionary work will come into the planning for the children in the intermediate and upper grades.

Most children associate two incidents with the life of Washington—they remember at once that he was the first President of the United States and then they recall the charming cherry-tree legend. In the course of the discussion of the cherry-tree incident, the teacher writes on the board, 'Little George Washington chopped down the cherry tree.' She underlines the *ch* in *chopped* and *cherry*. The teacher suggests that the class make a tree characterizing Washington and his times. The tree will be covered with red cherries, and on each cherry will be a descriptive word beginning with *ch*. Now an opportunity presents itself for a review of the mechanics involved in the formation of the *ch* [tʃ] sound.

Children will do individual reading and research to compile words to hang on the cherry tree. They will have group discussions and they will present written work based on this theme. The primary grade teacher will first read short stories and articles about Washington to the class, then discuss Washington with the children. In the course of the conversation, the group will discover appropriate descriptive words beginning with *ch*. The teacher will list these words on the board.

The culmination of this activity will be the making and mounting of a large green cherry tree for the display board. The children will make large red cherries with one word written on each cherry. The cherries will be pasted or pinned to the tree. A sample of the words that will adorn the tree might include charm, charter, chores, church, Charleston, chance, charitable, cheerful, charged, chosen, chary, chase, challenge, and chop. There will be no limit to the possibilities.

The sound [l] is a troublesome one and therefore often needs special drill and attention. This sound may also be made the basis for the selection of words to be used on the cherries. An appropriate heading for this unit is, 'Key Words, Places, and People in the Life of George Washington.' Words that could grow out of this study are Delaware, Philadelphia, Williamsburg, Valley Force, Laurence, Lord Fairfax, Lexington, and such key words as election, revolution, colonies, life, liberty, leadership, and self-reliance. After words have been selected for the cherries, two teams may be chosen to participate in a summary game for reviewing facts and for drill in speech. The members of each team will take turns selecting a cherry from the tree and then using the word on the cherry in a short report. The teacher will judge each player's report on the basis of correct speech as well as accurate subject matter, and she will assign points to each player. The side that has been able to amass the greater number of points wins the game.

A plan for individual work on sounds that might well be an out-growth of this integrated unit on the life and times of George Washington would be to have each youngster make his own tree and cherries. The selection of words for the cherries would be determined by the sound the youngster needed to practice and drill on. However this unit is handled, it will, first of all, center attention on one or more of the important speech sounds. It will also provide an opportunity for the study of word meaning, including practice in dictionary use. It will motivate oral and written expression of ideas, and its culmination will be a summarizing art display.

Easter

Easter is a special day that affords another opportunity for activity culminating in a bulletin-board display. The teacher will undoubtedly wish to present the serious and impressive aspects of Easter first. Individual and group reading will result in discussion and in written compositions about this holiday and its history. If the class is studying a foreign country for social studies, the children will be interested in investigating the traditional Easter celebration of that country. Primary children, especially, like to hear about the Easter Bunny. Santa Claus and Easter Bunny, the two festive symbols of our great religious holidays, may be compared and discussed by the older children. The pupils will make a large Easter Bunny for the display board. The legs, arms, and ears can be made separately and hinged to the bunny. A large, pocket-like basket is hung from the bunny's paw. Each youngster will cut several Easter eggs from colored paper to put in the basket. The teacher will prepare letters of uniform size, one letter to be pasted on each egg.

Several speech games may be played with this bunny and his basket of eggs. Two to four children may be included on each of two opposing teams. Another child, called the 'hunter,' takes an egg from the bunny's basket and shows it to the players. The first player who pronounces a word starting with the sound represented by the letter on the egg gets that egg. At the end of a predesignated playing time, the two sides count up their eggs. The side that has the most eggs is, of course, the winner. In intermediate and upper grades, children can be asked to supply a word that ends with the sound designated, or a word that has the sound within it.

A boy may oppose a girl in another variation of the game. This time the 'hunter' gives the egg to the first person who can make the sound the letter represents. Each child is given three trials before he yields his place to another child. The teacher or the children might draw several eggs from the basket and write the letters on the blackboard. The children will make a list of words, each of which contains one of the sounds designated. These words must pertain in some way to Easter.

The teacher will realize that the lesson plans included in this section to illustrate how art, language, and speech training may be effectively correlated are merely suggestions and nothing more. They should serve, however, to stimulate the imagination and ingenuity of the teacher and help her develop additional activities.

Integrating Speech Training with Primary Reading in the Language Arts Program

The reading program affords the teacher an excellent opportunity for speech integration, since reading ability and speech maturation are closely related; slowness in speech very often correlates with slowness in reading. Attention is again called to the Jones study, referred to in an earlier chapter, which demonstrated that training in speech materially improved reading ability. The implication is clear—if training in speech and reading can be combined, speech will not only be improved thereby, but the reading program will profit as well. Many of the suggestions included in Chapter IV about the role of the school and the home in promoting the speech and language development of the child are equally effective in preparing the child for reading. The present section will explain a number of practical devices whereby the classroom teacher can effectively combine training in speech with training in reading within the framework of a typical reading program in the lower grades.

A reading program which includes grouping the children according to the readiness and the developmental level of each child affords the teacher with an excellent opportunity for drills to build up correct patterns of speech. Since these daily groups are small, individual speech problems can be dealt with effectively, usually to the benefit of all the children in the group.

Concrete examples will reveal some of the opportunities that present themselves in the reading circle for direct-approach drills to establish good speech patterns. Substitutions commonly found in the child's speech are [θ] for [s], [f] or [v] for [θ] or [ð], [w] or [j] for [l], [w] for [r], and sometimes [t] for [k] and [d] for [g]. In almost any pre-primer the teacher may encounter the sentence, 'We look and see.' The two important words here contain sounds frequently substituted by children. A child may read, pronouncing 'wook' and 'thee.' Since these words are probably repeated many times throughout the book, the child unfortunately is provided with ample opportunity to perpetuate his pattern of infantile speech. On another page the child may come upon the word *run* and pronounces it 'wun.' It is almost a certainty that the words *mother* and *father* will be added to the child's reading vocabulary at this early stage. He pronounces them as 'muvver' and 'fahver,' or perhaps as 'mudder' and 'fadder.' He learns to read *something*, but he says 'somefing.' When the child encounters the word *three*, he says 'free,' or more likely, 'fwee.' The child who is left to his own faulty pattern of speech and is not given adequate visual or auditory training will now start to build an incorrect pattern of reading as well. This situation is familiar to every primary teacher, but those teachers who integrate speech education with the curriculum can effectively handle the problem. The approach to be described is used within the context of the reading program and it meets the need of the child when that need is felt.

A practical example best illustrates the procedure the classroom teacher may adopt. It is Anne's turn to read orally, and in the first pre-primer she encounters the words, *look, look.* Anne reads, 'wook, wook.' The teacher writes the word on the board just as the child read it, but underneath 'wook' she writes *look.* The child, with the teacher's guidance, realizes that she has not read the word correctly, that is, she has not pronounced it correctly. As the emphasis is put on correct reading, nothing need or should be said about incorrect or infantile speech. The child examines and says both words and then compares the word in the book with the words on the board. She points out the word on the board that matches the one in her book. All the members of the reading group participate in examining the word, saying it, and listening to it. The teacher utilizes this natural opportunity to show them how to say *look.* She demonstrates how the tongue goes up to touch the ridge back of the upper teeth for the first sound in *look,* and the children imitate her by raising their tongues and lowering them several times. They join the teacher with 'la-la-la' in a little song rhythm; 'la' is printed on the board close to the two words. Then they all say, *look, look, look.*

'What am I?' is a sound game to review and reinforce previous work in sounds. This speech game is used as a variation to other drills during the reading and spelling periods. Its purposes are to train the ear, to emphasize the individual sounds which a word contains, and to reinforce the learning of letters. As continual bombardment of the auditory senses is a major principle in speech education, the value of this game is obvious. The game atmosphere removes the tensions and anxieties that words produce in some children.

The teacher will start the game with a twinkle in her eye and a challenging air. 'I am a little voice. I say "s-s-s-s." What am I?' The children might answer that they hear the voice of the teakettle or the little green garden snake. The teacher would write *s* on the board. The sound 'z-z-z-z' represents the voice of the bee. The teacher writes *z* on the board. The sound 'sh-sh-sh' [ʃ] is the voice mother uses when she speaks to a noisy child. The teacher or a member of the class writes on the board the letters that represent this sound. The leader makes the voiceless *th* [θ] and the children respond, 'That is the voice of the gray goose.' The sound 'r-r-r-r' is the voice of the airplane or playful puppy; 't-t-t-t' is the sound of the little clock; 'b-b-b-b-b' is the sound of the little motorboat; 'f-f-f-f-f' is what the kitten says to warn the puppy not to chase her; 'm-m-m-m' is the sound that boys and girls make to show how good a warm cookie tastes. The teacher or a child writes each letter on the board as it is used in the game. As the children become more familiar with the game, they will think of sounds they would like the class to guess. Each will want the chance to ask the riddle, and each questioner will be replaced by the child who correctly answers his question, 'What am I?'

This game can also be carried over into art and penmanship. The children are given a piece of black art paper and a white pencil. Each child selects a sound. Some children select the *s* sound, some select the *ch* sound, and others choose the *sh* or *r* or *t* or *w* sounds. As the child writes the letter or letters representing his sound, he softly pronounces the sound. Each child varies the size and placement of the letters to suit himself. The concentration with which the children apply themselves to the sounding and writing of the letter guarantees immunity from distraction. Children who have a tendency to be tense and cramped in their writing show a new relaxation and freedom in this activity. The designs the children produce will have individual artistic appeal to a surprising degree.

The children will not be satisfied with the creation of only one design. They will want to try again using a different letter.

A repetition of the activity should be postponed for at least a week in order to allow time for evaluation by the teacher and the children. The evaluation should include an examination of the formation and shape of the letters as well as the production of the sound itself. This activity combines auditory, visual, and kinesthetic experiences in an effective manner.

At this point the teacher's attention is again called to the discussion in Chapter II in which the distinction between a speech sound and an alphabet letter is clearly explained. While for speech purposes it is the sound that is important, the teacher who is integrating speech and reading will be concerned with letter symbols as well, and the relationship between the two may very well need to be explained if the children are to get the greatest benefit from these experiences.

The techniques presented in this section can be adapted for use in every instance of a sound substitution or similar speech disorder disclosed in the reading lesson. The teacher must maintain a standard that will give impetus to the integration of speech training with the other subject-matter fields. To condone such speech deficiencies on the part of the child as the substitution of 'thee' for *see*, for example, will not only defeat the purpose of the integrated speech program but will jeopardize progress in reading as well.

As was pointed out earlier, there is more to effective oral communication than merely articulating all of the speech sounds correctly, and the relationship of speech to reading is deeper and more far-reaching than has been implied thus far in this section. As an example, this relationship is exploited very advantageously in a pre-primer reading text appropriately called *Sounds of Home* (see References at end of chapter) in which, as the author states, 'Children are talking their way to reading.' Thus, if talking is defective, reading will be also. The material consists of a number of colorful pictures for illustrations and for conversation, and several short poems incorporating words that children should have heard around the house, but often only in limited contexts. The poems are to be read and re-read to the children until they are memorized and then the oral word, actually the phrase, is matched to the printed word and phrase on the page, and the child eventually is reading it. Thus vocabulary, both oral and written, is expanded and enriched, and phrasing and sentence structure are made more effective by suggested alternative words and phrases that may be substituted for portions of the poems. Note, for example, how the meaning or concept of the word *round* is broadened and intensified in the following selection:

Round is a pancake, round is a plum,
Round is a doughnut, round is a drum.
Round is a puppy curled up on a rug.
Round are the spots on a wee lady bug.
Look all around, on the ground, in the air,
You will find round things everywhere.

Besides the built-in practice on several troublesome sounds—[r], [dr], [gr], [l], [pl], [sp], et cetera—there are other more basic aspects of language involved that can carry over to enrich the child's oral communication as well as contribute to his development in reading. Thus, speaking leads into reading, and the two come to reinforce each other.

Integrating Speech Training with Spelling in the Language Arts Program

Suggestions have been made in this book for the use of the phonetic approach in speech education. A speech clinician works to familiarize the child with the sounds represented by alphabet letters and with how those sounds are made. The classroom teacher can use this approach even more effectively to further training in speech education. She has an opportunity to include speech-sound analysis in a live classroom situation when her groups are studying words in spelling or in reading. This brief, daily study of sounds and how they are made is facilitated if the children have learned about the organs of speech in a previous speech-hygiene unit. The technique for the study of sounds recommended here involves the auditory, the visual, and the kinesthetic senses.

If the letter *s* occurs in the words under discussion in spelling or reading, for example, the teacher makes the sound of [s]. Then she writes *s* on the board. The class and teacher together make the sound of [s] as they trace the shape of the letter in the air with their fingers. The teacher makes the sound of [ʃ] next, and the same procedure is followed. Other sounds will be analyzed by the same method from day to day.

There is value in pairing certain sounds for purposes of comparison and contrast. When the frequently confused sounds of [θ] and [s] are analyzed, for example, the important differences between them, both in the way they sound and in the way they are produced, become apparent. On the other hand, [k] and [g] have a relationship to each other because they are both made similarly in the back of the mouth. The tongue first presses the gum ridge and then drops explosively to form both [t] and [d]. The sounds [n] and [l] resemble [t] and [d] in important ways, but each is different from the other two. Can the children explain the difference?

Children can become fascinated by the study of letters and the sounds they represent, of the way they are made, and of the changes that take place when they are coupled with or influenced by certain other sounds. The teacher need take only a few minutes in her daily spelling or reading groups for this speech activity. Each of these periods should include a brief review. In this preliminary review the teacher makes only the sound of the letter. The children echo the sound as they trace the shape of the letter in the air with their fingers. If this is done correctly by the group, the teacher will then introduce a new pair of sounds in a similar manner.

At the conclusion of a four-week period of spelling, the teacher will undertake a review of the new words learned. A speech game called 'Toboggan,' which uses the review words, may be introduced. (If the children are unfamiliar with snow, the game may be called 'Slide.') From the accumulated spelling lists, the teacher may select words containing the *r* sound. For instance, a third-grade list, based on the first nine lessons, would be likely to contain these *r* words; *fairy, river, ground, drag, dry, drop, race, orange, rag,* and *grade.* A child needing special training in the [r] will have the first chance to earn a toboggan ride. The teacher gives the first word from the list, *fairy,* to the child. The child says the word after her. The word repeated correctly with a good *r* sound makes him eligible to write the word on the bottom step of the ladder which leads up to the 'slide' that has been drawn on the board by the teacher. After writing the word, he says it a second time. If the pronunciation and the spelling are both correct, the player is given a second word. If the child achieves correct pronunciation and spelling of all the words he needs to reach the top, he gets to slide down figuratively, thereby earning a point for himself or his team. The game may be played among individuals in the group or the group may be divided into teams.

The next child may be having difficulty with the correct pronunciation of *s.* The teacher has grouped on her card all review spelling words containing this sound. The first nine lessons in the third-grade spelling book would likely contain these words: *basket, inside, send, sea, sand, still, mouse, dust, supper, sick, cost,* and *sled.* This game, integrating speech and spelling, has been used successfully in grades two through six. This technique requires some advance planning and preparation on the part of the teacher and it takes, too, a firm belief in the value of the correlation between spoken and written English.

Integrating Speech Training with Word Study in the Language Arts Program

The unit described below may be used in any elementary-school grade to integrate speech education with word study. This unit is also designed to show children that words, as such, can be interesting. Children should be taught that different words create different feelings. Some words bring pleasure, some bring joy, some bring sadness, and some, by their sound alone, create a desire to laugh. Occasionally teachers, under pressure to teach words for the purpose of achieving certain goals in reading, spelling, and composition, lose sight of the possibility of teaching words simply for the pleasure they bring to children and adults.

The unit is entitled 'What a Difference a Sound Makes.' A comparison of words is made on the basis of spelling and meaning. For instance, a picture of a tiger and a picture of a flower are mounted side by side on a tagboard chart. The word *tiger* is printed under the first picture and the words *tiger lily* are printed under the second. A second addition to the chart might be the words *pot* and *spot*. The word *spot* is illustrated by a white piece of paper bearing a big ink spot. A flower pot or kettle is drawn for the word *pot*. *Three* and *free* may be paired. *Three* may be illustrated by a big number 3 or a picture of three objects. *Free* may be illustrated by the picture of a bird flying from its cage. This illustrated word chart may grow indefinitely as the children discover additional pairs of words from their spelling and reading lessons. Some children will come from home with examples and illustrations such as coat-goat, filly-lily, and bass-bath as a result of interested family discussions. The teacher has the opportunity to include spelling, reading, and speech education in this word study.

'What makes *spot* different from *pot?*' the teacher may ask. The children must respond with the sound of the letter rather than the letter name. 'How do we make the sound that changes *pot* to *spot?*' The children experiment, then answer that the sound is made with the edges of the teeth together, the air escaping over the raised tongue tip and through the teeth. The teacher calls upon a child to go to the board and write what he hears as the other children make the sound.

The children may experiment by using the paired words interchangeably in sentences, and they will be delighted with the ridiculous results. Children's laughter, so often misdirected, challenges a wise teacher to supply situations where humor will further learning. Purposeful misuse of words in this unit will amuse children and increase their realization of the importance of correct pronunciation and spelling. The class will be delighted to experiment with such sentences as 'Mother put the "spot" on the stove' and 'Daddy has a "pot" on his shirt.'

As was mentioned earlier in this book, speech training can be —and should be—fun. The pleasure and motivation inherent in speech education or re-education properly administered can be made to pay dividends through its 'halo' effect upon all other activities with which it is associated. Effective oral communication is vitally important to the child in learning situations because in most of them speech and listening play such a significant role, especially in the lower grades of the elementary school. This natural involvement of speech in so many of the activities that make up the school curriculum provides the teacher with the only justification she needs for making speech education a part of the daily routines of the classroom. Such integration of speech improvement with the regular school curriculum accomplishes two desirable objectives: it makes speech training functional and meaningful to the child because it becomes a part of a situation in which speech is naturally used; and such integration also makes speech training and retraining possible in an already crowded curriculum without requiring additional valuable time from either teacher or pupils.

References

Anderson, Virgil A., *Speech Improvement in the Classroom*, Houghton Mifflin, Boston, 1968.

Blake, James N., *Speech Education Activities for Children*, Charles C. Thomas, Springfield, Ill., 1970.

Boardman, Eunice, and Beth Landis, *Exploring Music*, Holt, Rinehart and Winston, New York, 1966.

Brisbane, M. H., *Speech Therapy: Teacher's Guide*, T. S. Dennison, Minneapolis, 1967.

Burns, Paul C., and Leo M. Schell, eds., *Elementary School Language Arts: Selected Readings*, Rand McNally, Chicago, 1969, Part III.

Johnson, Wendell, et al., *Speech Handicapped School Children*, Harper and Row, New York, 3rd ed., 1967, Chap. 9.

Los Angeles City Schools, Division of Instructional Services, *Language Arts in the Elementary School*, Part I, 1961, Chaps. I, II.

McCall, Adeline, *This Is Music*, California State Department of Education, Sacramento, 1968.

Martin, Bill, Jr., *Sounds of Home*, Holt, Rinehart and Winston, New York, 1966.

Michael, A., and Lloyd L. Michael, *Speech Fun for Everyone*, Prentice-Hall, Englewood Cliffs, N. J., 1958.

Pronovost, Wilbert, and Louise Kingman, *The Teaching of Speaking and Listening in the Elementary School*, Longmans, Green, New York, 1957.

Rasmussen, Carrie, *Speech Methods in the Elementary School*, Ronald Press, New York, 1962.

Scott, Louise Binder, *Developing Communication Skills, A Guide for the Teacher*, McGraw-Hill Book Company, Novato, Calif., 1971.

Shine, Richard E., and J. Joseph Freilinger, *Practical Methods of Speech Correction for the Classroom Teacher*, Teaching Aids Company, Davenport, Iowa, 1963.

Strickland, Ruth G., *The Language Arts in the Elementary School*, D. C. Heath, Lexington, Mass., 3rd ed., 1969.

Van Riper, Charles, and Katherine Butler, *Speech in the Elementary Classroom*, Harper and Row, New York, 1955.

General References

Alpiner, Jerome G., *Speech and Hearing Disorders in Children*, Houghton Mifflin, Boston, 1970.

Black, Martha, *Speech Correction in the Schools*, Prentice-Hall, Englewood Cliffs, N. J., 1964.

Chicago Board of Education, *Speech Correction Techniques and Materials*, Board of Education, Division of Speech Correction, 1968.

Ecroyd, Donald H., *Speech in the Classroom*, Prentice-Hall, Englewood Cliffs, N. J., 2nd ed., 1969.

Egland, George, *Speech and Language Problems, A Guide for the Classroom Teacher*, Prentice-Hall, Englewood Cliffs, N. J., 1970.

Eisenson, Jon, and Mardel Ogilvie, *Speech Correction in the Schools*, Macmillan, New York, 3rd ed., 1971.

Hopkins, Lee B., *Let Them Be Themselves*, Citation, New York, 1969.

Hopper, Robert, and Rita C. Naremore, *Children's Speech: A Practical Introduction to Communicative Development*, Harper and Row, New York, 1973.

Huckleberry, Alan W., and Edward S. Strother, *Speech Education for the Elementary Teacher*, Allyn and Bacon, Boston, 1966.

Irwin, Ruth B., A *Speech Pathologist Talks to Parents and Teachers*, Stanwix House, Pittsburgh, 1962.

Johnson, Wendell, et al., *Speech Handicapped School Children,* Harper and Row, New York, 3rd ed., 1967.

Jones, Merritt, and Mary Pettas, *Speech Improvement: A Practical Program,* Wadsworth Publishing Company, Belmont, Calif., 1969.

Karlin, Isaac W., et al., *Development and Disorders of Speech in Childhood,* Charles C. Thomas, Springfield, Ill., 1965.

Marquardt, Eileen, *Talking Magic,* The Interstate, Danville, Ill., 1966.

Morley, Muriel, *Development and Disorders of Speech in Childhood,* Williams and Wilkins, Baltimore, 2nd ed., 1965.

Palmer, Charles E., and John W. Kidd, *Speech and Hearing Problems: A Guide for Teachers and Parents,* Charles C. Thomas, Springfield, Ill., 1961.

Perritt, Margaret Floyd, *Hear, See and Tell Stories.* The American Southern Publishing Company, Northport, Ala., 1964. For children 4 to 7.

Phillips, Gerald M., et al., *The Development of Oral Communication in the Classroom,* Bobbs-Merrill, Indianapolis, 1970.

Pollock, M. P., and M. S. Pollock, *The Clown Family Speech Book,* Prentice-Hall, Englewood Cliffs, N. J., 1960.

Sayre, Joan M., *Helping the Child to Listen and Talk,* The Interstate, Danville, Ill., 1966.

Scott, Louise Binder, *Learning Time with Language Experiences,* McGraw-Hill Book Company, Novato, Calif., 1968. For young children.

Scott, Louise Binder, and J. J. Thompson, *Rhymes for Fingers and Flannelboards,* McGraw-Hill Book Company, Novato, Calif., 1964.

————, *Talking Time,* McGraw-Hill Book Company, Novato, Calif., 2nd ed., 1966.

Smith, Donald E. P., *Listening,* Ann Arbor Publishers, Ann Arbor, Mich., 1967.

Tomm, Martin, *Animal Adventures, Tell-a-Story Series,* T. S. Dennison and Company, Minneapolis, 1962.

Van Hattum, Rolland, J., ed., *Clinical Speech in the Schools,* Charles C. Thomas, Springfield, Ill., 1969.

Van Riper, Charles, *Your Child's Speech Problems,* Harper and Row, New York, 1961.

Warkomski, Robert C., and Ruth Beckey Irwin, *Play and Say*, Stanwix House, Pittsburgh, 1970.

Weston, Alan J., *Communicative Disorders: An Appraisal*, Charles C. Thomas, Springfield, Ill., 1972.

Appendix

Test for Speech-Sound Discrimination—
High Frequency Sounds

Instructions   Select only one word from each group of three according to a predetermined pattern. Pronounce the word easily and naturally, without undue emphasis or exaggeration, standing or sitting where the pupil cannot see your face. The pupil has this test before him and indicates, by pointing or otherwise, the word from each group that he thinks he has heard you pronounce. As soon as the pupil has indicated his response, proceed to the next group. If the pupil makes more than three or four errors on the test, some deficiency in his ability to discriminate between speech sounds is indicated, provided, of course, he can read the words without difficulty.

1. boat	goat	dote
2. rid	rig	rib
3. bay	day	gay
4. rode	robe	rogue
5. deer	gear	beer
6. ten	Ken	pen
7. tick	kick	pick
8. pad	Tad	cad
9. sap	sack	sat
10. zee	thee	V
11. shoe	Sue	foo
12. thin	fin	sin
13. sought	fought	thought
14. mass	math	mash
15. roughed	rushed	rust
16. sung	sun	sum
17. thread	Fred	shred
18. rung	lung	young

Test for Speech-Sound Discrimination—
Middle Frequency Sounds

Instructions Use the same procedure as recommended for the previous test.

1. pig	peg	pug
2. cat	cot	cut
3. sin	sun	seen
4. like	lake	lack
5. back	buck	beck
6. moon	moan	main
7. dog	dug	dig
8. not	net	nut
9. tan	tin	ton
10. caught	coat	cat
11. luck	lock	lick
12. bug	beg	big
13. deem	dam	dumb
14. gone	gun	goon
15. rock	rack	wreck
16. shirt	shot	shut
17. wood	wad	wide
18. head	had	hood

C.I.D. Auditory Test W-22 (PB Word Lists)*

LIST 1A

1. an	18. high	35. isle (aisle)
2. yard	19. there (their)	36. or (oar)
3. carve	20. earn (urn)	37. law
4. us	21. twins	38. me
5. day	22. could	39. none (nun)
6. toe	23. what	40. jam
7. felt	24. bathe	41. poor
8. stove	25. ace	42. him
9. hunt	26. you (ewe)	43. skin
10. ran	27. as	44. east
11. knees	28. wet	45. thing
12. not (knot)	29. chew	46. dad
13. mew	30. see (sea)	47. up
14. low	31. deaf	48. bells
15. owl	32. them	49. wire
16. it	33. give	50. ache
17. she	34. true	

* These word lists, developed at Central Institute for the Deaf under a V.A. contract, are reproduced with the permission of the Veterans Administration.

LIST 2A

1. yore (your)	18. send	35. own
2. bin (been)	19. else	36. key
3. way (weigh)	20. tare (tear)	37. oak
4. chest	21. does	38. new (knew)
5. then	22. too (two, to)	39. live (verb)
6. ease	23. cap	40. off
7. smart	24. with	41. ill
8. gave	25. air (heir)	42. rooms
9. pew	26. and	43. ham
10. ice	27. young	44. star
11. odd	28. cars	45. eat
12. knee	29. tree	46. thin
13. move	30. dumb	47. flat
14. now	31. that	48. well
15. jaw	32. die (dye)	49. by (buy)
16. one (won)	33. show	50. ail (ale)
17. hit	34. hurt	

LIST 3A

1. bill	18. smooth	35. owes
2. add (ad)	19. farm	36. jar
3. west	20. this	37. no (know)
4. cute	21. done (dun)	38. may
5. start	22. use (yews)	39. knit
6. ears	23. camp	40. on
7. tan	24. wool	41. if
8. nest	25. are	42. raw
9. say	26. aim	43. glove
10. is	27. when	44. ten
11. out	28. book	45. dull
12. lie (lye)	29. tie	46. though
13. three	30. do	47. chair
14. oil	31. hand	48. we
15. king	32. end	49. ate (eight)
16. pie	33. shove	50. year
17. he	34. have	

LIST 4A

1. all (awl)	18. ear	35. his
2. wood (would)	19. tea (tee)	36. our (hour)
3. at	20. cook	37. men
4. where	21. tin	38. near
5. chin	22. bread (bred)	39. few
6. they	23. why	40. jump
7. dolls	24. arm	41. pale (pail)
8. so (sew)	25. yet	42. go
9. nuts	26. darn	43. stiff
10. ought (aught)	27. art	44. can
11. in (inn)	28. will	45. through (thru)
12. net	29. dust	46. clothes
13. my	30. toy	47. who
14. leave	31. aid	48. bee (be)
15. of	32. than	49. yes
16. hang	33. eyes (ayes)	50. am
17. save	34. shoe	

Index of Names

Index of Subjects